THE LYING STONES
OF DR. BERINGER
being his
LITHOGRAPHIÆ WIRCEBURGENSIS

The

LYING STONES

of

DR. JOHANN BARTHOLOMEW
ADAM BERINGER

being his

LITHOGRAPHIÆ
WIRCEBURGENSIS

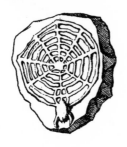

Translated and annotated by
MELVIN E. JAHN *and* DANIEL J. WOOLF

1963
UNIVERSITY OF CALIFORNIA PRESS
Berkeley and Los Angeles

UNIVERSITY OF CALIFORNIA PRESS
BERKELEY AND LOS ANGELES, CALIFORNIA

CAMBRIDGE UNIVERSITY PRESS
LONDON, ENGLAND

© 1963 BY THE REGENTS OF THE UNIVERSITY OF CALIFORNIA

LIBRARY OF CONGRESS CATALOG CARD NUMBER: 63-8585

DESIGNED BY ADRIAN WILSON

PRINTED IN THE UNITED STATES OF AMERICA

Happy the man whose lot it is to know
The secrets of the earth. He hastens not
To work his fellows' hurt by unjust deeds
But with rapt admiration contemplates
Immortal Nature's ageless harmony,
And how and when her order came to be,
Such spirits have no place for thoughts of shame.

EURIPIDES

ADMODUM PRAECLARO
DOCTORI CHARLES L. CAMP,
QUI SUMMAE SCIENTIAE
SINGULAREM HUMANITATEM
IN SEIPSO FELICISSIME CONJUNCTAM
LUCULENTER OMNIBUS PRAEBET,
HUMILE HOC OPUS
LIBENTER DICANT AUCTORES.

Acknowledgments

THE UNDERTAKING of a vernacular presentation of the Beringer romance inevitably owes a great deal to many helpful individuals. The translation and researching might have ground to a halt on sundry occasions save for timely and friendly assistance.

Special thanks are accorded to Warren Howell of John Howell Books for his diligent and successful search for a copy of the original text of the *Lithographiae Wirceburgensis*. Scarcely less important, and not infrequently more difficult to obtain, were the scores of books requisite for an adequate and intelligible edition of the work. In meeting these needs, which were often quite exacting, the editors were generously aided by many members of the library staff of the University of California, Berkeley. Most notable are the following: Kenneth J. Carpenter, Miss Geraldine Clayton, Mrs. Beatrice Germano, Miss Jeannot Nyles, Miss Eliza Pietsch, and Mrs. Margaret Uridge.

The quest for seventeenth- and eighteenth-century texts extended to many book dealers, and here business was permeated with invaluable friendly coöperation. The following have the unbounded gratitude of the editors for their tireless searches: the staff of B. H. Blackwell Ltd., Warren Howell and John Swingle of John Howell Books, Harry Levinson of H. A. Levinson Rare Books, the staff of Bernard Quaritch Ltd., H. K. Swann of Wheldon and Wesley Ltd., and Jacob Zeitlin of Zeitlin and Ver Brugge.

Priceless material most pertinent to the text, including the photographs of Beringer's "Lügensteine" and the various manuscript materials concerning the trials described in Appendix B, was supplied by L. J. Hofman of the Universitätsbibliothek, Würzburg; Professor Georg Knetsch of the Geologisch-Paläontologisches In-

ix

stitut der Universität Würzburg; Gustav Beck, Staff Photographer to the Universität Würzburg; Professor Kolb of the Naturwissenschaftliches Museum, Bamberg; Professor Bruno von Freyberg of the Geologisches Institut der Universität Erlangen; and Dr. Scherzer of the Staatsarchiv Würzburg. These gentlemen augmented our data by dint of incredible personal inconvenience, surpassing our boldest hopes and requests.

Lhwyd's letter to John Ray came to us on microfilm produced by Mr. Vivian Ridler, Printer to Oxford University.

It is with the kind permission of the Oxford University Press and A. E. Gunther that we are allowed to quote from the works of the late Dr. R. T. Gunther.

The task of typing the manuscript devolved on Miss Edith Morrison, who volunteered for this ordeal with a generosity bordering on the heroic. We humbly tender Miss Morrison thanks for a prodigious job handsomely accomplished. We must also thank Miss Sheila Gordon for the donation of her time in typing the final draft of the Appendixes. Not dissimilar in exaction on nerves, time, and convenience are those hundred and one nondescript necessities, which in this case were unfailingly and magnificently fulfilled by Mr. and Mrs. Harvey D. Sandstone, Jr.

Thanks are to be accorded to Donald R. Fleming, who read the manuscript at all stages of completion. William B. Coit, Miss Margaret Yarwood, and Rudolf Saenger generously prepared German translations for the editors. Frank M. Boardman assisted with the research on the ecclestical synods. Michael E. Boardman critically read the first typescript, and made invaluable suggestions. The editors are indebted to Richard Hagelberger for his very knowledgeable assistance at all stages of progress.

The arduous detail of reading the final typescript fell to a number of professors at the University of California, who gave the editors the benefit of their comments and criticisms. The editors will remember with gratitude the following: Charles L. Camp, J. Wyatt Durham, Joseph T. Gregory, and Ruben A. Stirton, all of the Department of Paleontology; Thomas S. Kuhn, of the Department of History; and Herbert McLean Evans, of the Department

ACKNOWLEDGMENTS

of Anatomy. Ernest Callenbach, who edited the manuscript for the University of California Press, displayed great patience and perseverance.

Thanks of a special sort are due Douglas Cargille.

Mr. Woolf wishes to thank his wife, Shirley, who more than once chained herself to the typewriter in furtherance of the project.

To the many others who have not been mentioned, but who, through conversations and encouragement, contributed assorted quisquilia, the editors extend their warmest thanks.

Contents

CONTENTS
xiv

Introduction to This Edition

In entering upon any scientific pursuit one of the student's first endeavours ought to be to prepare his mind for the reception of truth, by dismissing, or at least loosening, his hold on all such crude and hastily adopted notions respecting the objects and relations he is about to examine, as may tend to embarrass or mislead him; and to strengthen himself by something of an effort and a resolve, for the unprejudiced admission of any conclusion which shall appear supported by careful observation and logical argument, even should it prove of a nature adverse to notions he may have previously formed for himself, or taken up, without examination, on the credit of others.

SIR JOHN HERSCHEL [1]

THE HISTORY OF IDEAS has time and again shown the significance of Sir John's sage observation. That a single preconception which finds expression can eclipse a scientist's life work has been demonstrated many times in the history of science. An outstanding example of this is Dr. Johann Jacob Scheuchzer's determination to find the remains of the Noachian flood-man, which led him to label a Tertiary batrachian *Homo diluvii testis*. Yet another learned physician of the eighteenth century has been castigated along the lines suggested by Herschel.

Dr. Johann Bartholomew Adam Beringer (1667–1740), son of Professor Johann Ludwig Beringer (Behringer), was an eighteenth-century savant, and like a great majority of the physicians and divines of his day was a virtuoso—a unique term roughly equivalent to "learned dilettante." [2] Not being content with his reputation as physician—a reputation which must have been considerable—he plunged himself into the study of oryctics, or "things dug from the earth." It was this study that became his undoing.

Figured stones particularly attracted Beringer, as did the study of disquisitions which sought to reveal their origin. He began to assemble a cabinet of natural rarities sometimes before 1725—a cabinet which included not only local specimens but specimens "gathered on nearly all the shores of Europe" as well. We can infer from Beringer's introduction that the cabinet was not remarkable until 1725. Up to May of that year it doubtless resembled any number of private collections of natural and artificial rarities which were assembled by ingenious persons.

The story of Beringer and the *Lithographiae Wirceburgensis* begins on May 31, 1725. The initial steps in a conspiracy to ruin the career of the learned doctor had already been taken. The first of innumerable hand-carved stones had been "dug up" on a hill near Würzburg, Germany and three of them were delivered that day, or shortly after, to the worthy physician and virtuoso: one bearing the figure of the sun and its rays, the others having the likenesses of worms.

Subsequent discoveries in the field continued to provide such patently unique stones that Beringer was compelled to seek a new explanation to account for their origin. There is evidence in Beringer's introduction that up to this time he was inclined toward the diluvial theory, this being one of several theories much favored by scholars before the organic origin and historical significance of fossils had become generally recognized. "It is true that in vine-covered and rugged mountains and in quarries there has been gathered so prodigious a collection of ammonites, of petrified shells from the sea and the rivers, that entire walls constructed of rocks densely encrusted with shells turned to stone take the place of the customary hedges surrounding the vineyards." [3] The *lapides figurati* of Mount Eivelstadt, however, necessitated an examination of the abundant literature which had endeavored to account for the phenomenon of figured stones.

Beringer studied his stones in terms of theories which extended from the *vis plastica* to the *aura seminalis*—even the possibility of human artifice was touched upon. The results of this inquiry were published in 1726.

History tells us that his glory was short-lived, and that not long after the publication of his learned treatise, *Lithographiae Wirceburgensis*, the hapless Beringer found his own name among the rocks. The source of his wonderful stones was not nature or any of her miraculous processes, but some sons of Belial among his students. Whereupon Beringer attempted to buy back all the copies of his recently published book, ruined himself financially, and shortly died of chagrin and mortification. The prank of his heartless students had succeeded too well.

This is the story bequeathed to us by popular history.

In 1935, in the Würzburg State Archives, Dr. Heinrich Kirchner came upon the transcript of a series of judicial proceedings which took place in Würzburg in 1726. These were the only documents to come to light in more than two centuries which gave a detailed account of Beringer and his "Lügensteine" (literally, lying stones). Kirchner's paper [4] was generally overlooked until 1954, when Carl Christoph Beringer edited it for inclusion in his *Geschichte der Geologie und des Geologischen Weltbildes*.[5] These same transcripts have been photocopied and transcribed for the present edition, and are translated in their entirety in Appendix B: An Account of the Beringer Hoax, and of the Subsequent Trials.

The transcripts have destroyed the traditional misconceptions of the Beringer hoax. They show the hoax in an academic setting, motivated by envy. In place of students' pranks we see the clandestine scheming of two colleagues of Beringer's: J. Ignatz Roderick, Professor of Geography, Algebra, and Analysis at the University of Würzburg, and the Honorable Georg von Eckhart, Privy Councillor and Librarian to the Court and the University.

Rather than go into laborious detail on the veracity of historical treatment of Beringer here, we have set this aside for treatment in Appendix B. In that appendix we have endeavored to reconstruct the episode of the hoax from the manuscript materials which exist in Würzburg today, and at the same time to note several contemporary and near-contemporary reactions to the treatise.

Present attitudes toward the hoax and surmises as to the contents of the *Lithographiae Wirceburgensis* are not remarkable. The legend which engulfed Beringer and this his third published work has largely eclipsed the value of the work's contents and prevented a reasonable treatment in terms of intellectual and scientific history. What, then, is the significance and value of the *Lithographiae Wirceburgensis?*

Appraisals of past scientific works are too often exclusively in terms of the work's "greatness," its "awakening influence," and whether it was a "forerunner" of something—in short whether the work has become a classic.

There are few classics in the history of science, yet these few admittedly monumental books have come to dominate the minds of scholars. We speak of Agricola, of Steno, of Cuvier, of Darwin. We are also acquainted with the near-greats, if only through the legendary rarity of their works: Olao Worm, Athanasius Kircher, Edward Lhwyd. But what do we know of third-rank figures such as Mercati, Lang, Büttner? By concentrating on the great and near-great we still leave vast gaps in our *apparatus criticus* of the history of science. It is not reasonable to judge the progress of any phase of the natural sciences from a few extraordinary works, yet this is what has too often happened.

What *is* the significance of this third group of scholars? What *was* their part in the development and progression of science? These authors and their largely unexplored "minor" works constitute a nebulous realm and backwash of science where there are only names to contend with. They were virtuosi: part of an "age" in thought, or members of a "movement"; as such they contributed to the characteristic literature of that "age" or "movement." These "minor" works set the background against which—and in fact by way of which—the classics are established. They are in essence a medium in which a given classic of science can develop—an ancestral form in the dynamic evolution of ideas. Few indeed, if any, are the concepts which have sprung full-blown from the mind of man, without established precedent or prototype.

The study of any subject necessarily transcends the mere contemporary understanding of that subject. For does not the proper study of a given concept include the study of its history? And is not the study of the history of a concept an inquiry into the failings and near-accuracies of the past?

Now Beringer is clearly one of the third group: the virtuosi or learned dilettantes. The name Beringer is well known, as is his book: not really a monumental book but a great curiosity. To point to Beringer as a highlight in the progress of paleontology would be wrong. To say that his book had a positive effect on science by destroying outdated theories on the origin and nature of fossils would be dangerous, although James Parkinson remarks: "It is worthy of being mentioned, on another account: the quantity of censure and ridicule, to which its author was exposed, served, not only to render his contemporaries less liable to imposition; but also more cautious in indulging in unsupported hypotheses." [6]

The *Lithographiae Wirceburgensis* was published in an extremely dynamic period in the history of paleontology. The twenty-five years preceding and the twenty-five following were times of great change in the study of fossils. Theories which were by then "classical" began to come under close scrutiny. New methods of accounting for figured stones and petrifacts were being propounded daily. It is not surprising, therefore, that Beringer hedged his opinion on the origin and nature of his "earthy treasures." Too much controversy was attached to them—an observation which is often found in the prefaces of treatises concerned with figured stones, as the following from Lang's *De Origine Lapidum Figuratorum*: "What commotions in the realm of letters have been stirred up by the question of the origin of figured stones, will be already a familiar matter to you, kind reader." [7] Rather, Beringer felt it advisable to publish an examination of theories propounded to account for figured stones like those unearthed near Würzburg. In this his treatise is in a category with Lhwyd's letter to John Ray (included as Appendix C).

It would be no difficult matter to make a case for the "overlooked significance" of Beringer's work—no more so than to propose similar arguments for Woodward's *An Essay toward a Natural History of the Earth*. Neither work is great, but both are important in understanding the times and now-outdated theories. Both are part of the intellectual background providing the foundations upon which modern science was to be built.

For many readers the importance of the *Lithographiae Wirceburgensis* will lie in its examination of paleontological theory. Others may see it as a link with the intellectual atmosphere of an era in flux—an era which largely saw the end of the virtuosi and which would see the dawning of the new science. There is obvious justification for both these views.

The *Lithographiae Wirceburgensis* exists in two editions: a first edition of 1726, and a spurious second edition (actually a title-page edition) of 1767. The original edition consists of a lengthy dedication, the text of the discourse, and fifty medical corollaries by Georg Ludwig Hueberg, whose name was abridged to Hueber. The spurious second edition has a new title page, omitting Hueber's name; it omits the lengthy dedication and the medical corollaries. The text of the discourse evidently came from copies of the book recalled from booksellers; the pages bear "Specimen Primum" as a caption title, and the several printing errors are still present.

The title page of the first edition of the *Lithographiae Wirceburgensis* presents an interesting problem in itself: the work is signed (as is the dedication) by Georg Ludwig Hueber. The second-edition title page is signed only by Beringer. A plausible case might be made for the supposition that the work was a joint effort, Beringer being the senior author. The evidence presented in Appendix B, however, nullifies this argument, as Hueber had no part in the judicial proceedings—it is solely Beringer's reputation which was compromised by the hoax. Appended to the first edition of the *Lithographiae Wirceburgensis* were fifty medical corollaries submitted for the *periculum* (See Appendix D). It seems most likely that, following the established tradition that a candidate could only be promoted after he bore the costs of the scientific publications of his professor, whose opinions he was obliged to uphold,

Hueber published and championed (as his dissertation) Beringer's *Lithographiae Wirceburgensis*.

The Latin style of Beringer makes itself keenly felt even in translation. It is wholly typical of the age. The Latin of contemporary scholars and scientific writers was quite stylized—indeed, it appears to have altered little if at all since the time of Erasmus. Gone are the simplicity and succinctness of the medieval Latinists. Brevity is not at a premium: the very core of a technical disquisition is couched in terms and phrases which assimilate it to the most polished, if pedantic, oratory. Occam's Razor was relegated to rusty disuse by the vogue of speculating from flagrantly arbitrary *a priori* premises in a vacuum of factual substantiation. Lastly, these writers evinced an inordinate fondness for the Latinization of Greek words. Terms such as *paegmosynophilus* (from παιγμοσύνη and φίλος) so abound in their writings as to justify a modest lexicon in their own right.

The present translation attempts to dispel for good the preconceptions surrounding the Beringer "Lügensteine." At the same time it presumes to enlarge upon Beringer's examination of the fossil concept by way of historical notes. Four appendixes have also been included. The first enlarges upon the "bibliographical" citations of Chapter I of the *Lithographiae Wirceburgensis*. The second is a lengthy discussion of the hoax itself, including a transcription of the judicial proceedings held in 1726. The third is the now famous "Epistola VI" from Lhwyd's *Lithophylacii Britannici Ichnographia*, in which Lhwyd undertakes an examination of thencurrent trend of thought on the subject of fossils. This will illuminate many of Beringer's observations. The fourth appendix comprises the fifty medical corollaries of Georg Ludwig Hueber.

ON THE FOLLOWING TWO PAGES:
Title page from the 1726 edition of Beringer's *Lithographiae Wirceburgensis*.
Title page from the so-called second edition (1767).

LITHOGRAPHIÆ
WIRCEBURGENSIS,
DUCENTIS LAPIDUM FIGURATORUM, A POTIORI
INSECTIFORMIUM, PRODIGIOSIS IMAGINIBUS EXORNATÆ
SPECIMEN PRIMUM,
Quod

IN DISSERTATIONE INAUGURALI PHYSICO-HISTORI-
CA, CUM ANNEXIS COROLLARIIS MEDICIS,

AUTHORITATE ET CONSENSU

INCLYTÆ FACULTATIS MEDICÆ,
IN ALMA EOO-FRANCICA WIRCEBURGENSIUM
UNIVERSITATE,
PRÆSIDE
Prænobili, Clariffimo & Expertiffimo Viro ac Domino,

D. JOANNE BARTHOLOMÆO
ADAMO BERINGER,
Philofophiæ & Medicinæ Doctore, Ejusdémque Profeffore
Publ: Ordin: Facult: Medicæ h. t. DECANO & Seniore, REVE-
RENDISSIMI & CELSISSIMI PINCIPIS Wirceburgenfis Confiliario, &
Archiatro, Aulæ, nec non Principalis Seminarii DD. Nobilium
& Clericorum, ac Magni Hofpitalis Julianæi
primo loco Medico,

Exantlatis de more rigidis Examinibus,

PRO SUPREMA DOCTORATUS MEDICI LAUREA,
annexísque Privilegiis rìte confequendis,

PUBLICÆ LITTERATORUM DISQUISITIONI SUBMITTIT

GEORGIUS LUDOVICUS HUEBER
Herbipolenfis, AA. LL. & Philofophiæ Baccalaureus,
Medicinæ Candidatus.

IN CONSUETO AUDITORIO MEDICO.
Anno M.DCCXXVI. Menfe Majo, Die.

Proftat Wirceburgi apud Philippum Wilhelmum Fuggart,
Bibliopolam Aulico-Academicum.
Typis Marci Antonii Engmann, Univerfitatis Toypgraphi.

D. JOANNIS BARTHOLOMÆI ADAMI BERINGER,

PHILOSOPHIÆ ET MEDICINÆ DOCTORIS IN ALMA EOO-FRANCICA WIRCEBURGENSIUM UNIVERSITATE PROFESSORIS PUBL. ORDIN. FACULT. MEDICÆ ASSESSORIS, REVERENDISSIMI ET CELSISSIMI PRINCIPIS WIRCEBURGENSIS CONSILIARII, ET ARCHIATRI, AULÆ, NEC NON PRINCIPALIS SEMINARII DD. NOBILIUM ET CLERICORUM, AC MAGNI HOSPITALIS JULIANAEI PRIMO LOCO MEDICI,

LITHOGRAPHIA WIRCEBURGENSIS,

DUCENTIS LAPIDUM FIGURATORUM,

A

POTIORI, INSECTIFORMIUM,

PRODIGIOSIS IMAGINIBUS

EXORNATA.

EDITIO SECUNDA.

FRANCOFURTI et LIPSIÆ.

Apud TOBIAM GOEBHARDT, Bibliopolam Bambergensem et Wirceburgensem. 1767.

THE
WÜRZBURG
LITHOGRAPHY

(First exemplar)

ILLUSTRATED WITH OVER TWO-HUNDRED EXTRAORDINARY
ENGRAVINGS OF FIGURED AND INSECTIFORM STONES,
SUBMITTED FOR PUBLIC DISQUISITION BY
GEORG LUDWIG HUEBER, A.B., LL.B., PH.B.,
CANDIDATE FOR MEDICINE,
AS AN INAUGURAL DISSERTATION IN PHYSICS AND HISTORY,
WITH MEDICAL COROLLARIES AND ANNOTATIONS,
BY THE CONSENT AND AUTHORITY OF THE
FACULTY OF MEDICINE
OF THE
UNIVERSITY OF WÜRZBURG IN FRANCONIA
UNDER THE DIRECTION OF
THE MOST NOBLE, ILLUSTRIOUS, AND LEARNED

Master JOHANN BARTHOLOMEW
ADAM BERINGER,

Doctor of Philosophy and Medicine, Senior
Professor and Dean of the Faculty of Medicine,
Advisor and Chief Physician to His Most Reverend
Highness, the Prince of Würzburg, Chief Physician
of the Royal Seminary of Nobles and Clerics and of
the Julian Hospital
Having Successfully Negotiated the
Prescribed Rigid Examinations,
For the Supreme Degree of Doctor of Medicine,
with all the Privileges Annexed Thereto.
In the Hall of Medicine
the . . . Day of May, in the year 1726.

On Sale at Würzburg in the Collegiate
Bookshop of Philip Wilhelm Fuggart
Printed by Mark Anthony Engmann,
Printer to the University.

Dedication by Hueber

TO THE IMMORTAL GLORY

OF

THE MOST REVEREND AND MOST HIGH

PRINCE AND LORD OF

THE HOLY ROMAN EMPIRE

CHRISTOPHER FRANZ,

BISHOP OF WÜRZBURG,

DUKE OF FRANCONIA,

OUR MOST CLEMENT PRINCELY

LORD AND MASTER

Most Reverend and Benevolent Highness

WITH GOOD REASON do I call the mountain, which my lord the director has depicted in the frontispiece of his Lithographic dissertation, a new Parnassus of our fatherland. For thereon, amid the silence of the Muses and to the astonishment of Apollo, the eloquent stones proclaim the felicity of Franconia, and above all, your

glory, Most High Prince. Scarcely had you risen as the new sun of
Franconia when this neglected and heretofore barren congeries of
earth and rocks, in a prodigy unheard of by your native subjects
—sensitive to the emanations of your wisdom, clemency, justice,
and other princely virtues and emulating the eloquence of the
Rhodian Colossus—undertook to hail its nascent Phoebus with as
many tongues as the stones which it poured forth, remarkably
graven with exquisite figures representing the threefold realm of
Nature. The learned ones still reserve their judgment. Pondering
the equally weighty reasons of either side, they are undecided
whether the progeny of this aged mountain should be ascribed to
the thaumaturgy of Nature, or to the labors of ancient art. In any
case, all join me, with unanimous consensus and public rejoicing,
in affirming that by these stone treasures the otherwise useless mass
of this uncultivated mountain has sought to adorn the beginnings
of your most auspicious reign, and to immolate to you, as to the
most wise prince of learning and the peerless patron and promoter
of men of letters, a hecatomb of petrified animals, flowers, plants,
and testacea. Were it proper to turn one's gaze upon the workings
of ancient art, I would be tempted to say that Franconia, rivaling
Egypt of old (thanks to the magnificence of her Dukes) had
erected a mighty monument, ornate with hieroglyphics and heroic
symbols, the fragmentary remains of which we are unearthing in
our day—but since Phrygia alone possessed the custom of inscrib-
ing its wondrous pyramidal monuments with hieroglyphics in a
manner foreign to the more westerly nations, I will forego this
conjecture as devoid of any sound basis. Nevertheless, I fear not to
stray from the truth if I assert that in this spacious variety of petrified images your exalted virtues, Most High Prince, are propheti-
cally foreshadowed, and, blazoned upon this mountaintop colossus,
are unfurled before the whole world. One majestic stone bearing
the ineffable name of Jehovah in letters transposed yet most elegantly formed occupies the apex of this obelisk, clearly indicating
under Whose leadership and auspices you wield the keys of the
most noble bishopric and venerable duchy, under Whose patronage

you rule, what sublime and sacred purpose you have determined
for your princely solicitude, namely, the esteem, the exaltation, the
glory of God's name. From the rest of the face of the obelisk
there smile down upon us beauteous images of the sun, the crescent
moon, and the stars, kyriological tokens of your virtues, beaming
forth the salutary efforts of your beneficence, justice, providence,
and tireless vigilance for the public weal, as well as the ancient
splendors of the House of Hutten, ever glorious in your forebears.
The comets, too, are represented, not indeed as lugubrious portents
of war, death, or other calamities (for who will maintain that these
stellar phenomena of the ethereal regions are born and kindled
only to portend terror and catastrophe to the world below, not
prosperous times as well?), which in the broad light of their radiant
tail, draw in their wake the long years of a golden age. The conches
liberally dispersed at the base represent the hearts and souls of your
subjects, whereby they embrace their most amiable prince as the
priceless pearl of their affections, crowning his inestimable merits
with the fronds and foliage, the flowers and fruits of divers plants.
The Oreads of Eivelstadt have, it would seem, grown jealous of
the privileges of the Würzburg flora, and seeing that in the botanical garden, which your princely munificence beautifies and expands,
the rarest plants of Asia, Africa, America, and of our own European
pleasances flourish with incredible copiousness and fecundity, and
are preserved and fostered for the health of the body, the delight of
eyes, and the erudite allurement of medical studies, they in their
turn with no less zealous devotion to your Highness have wrested
from the bosom of a solitary hill and erected into a monumental
pyramid to your glory whatsoever of a prodigious nature the petrificous earth has produced in idiomorphic stones on all the shores of
this wide earth—a pyramid impervious to the scorching sun of the
summer and the blasts of the winter's storms, because fashioned
from flint and marble.

It was, moreover, a familiar usage among the Egyptians to assume into their hieroglyphics not only the species of perfect animals, but the lowliest orders of insects, and thereby to symbolize

the works of the gods, the genii, the stars, and the elements. It was easy, then, to adapt serpents, worms, scarabs, crabs, wasps, fishes, and other ectypes of insectiform stones to the publishing of your praises, were it not that the grandeur and glory of the deeds wrought by Your Highness and those yet to be felicitously wrought claim our eyes by their own clarity. Nor would it be seemly to veil this clarity in recondite Canopican enigmas, more productive of obscurity than of illumination. Now, if the features of these idiomorphic stones, particularly the inscriptions on the lettered tablets, persuaded some viewers that they should be classified with the heathen amulets or the mysterious talismans of the Hebrews, I should not quarrel with them at this juncture. Yet, because enlightened Christian piety and religion has long proscribed such protective charms of superstitious antiquity, I choose to revere you, Most Reverend and Exalted Prince, as the sacred amulet of our land, vouchsafed to Franconia by a singular favor of Divine Providence. So long as you are preserved among us, the lowering tempest of ills and adversities is thrust back from the boundaries of your Duchy; and should some scourge raise its ugly head, it will wither beneath your antidotal efficacy. More, whatever the scholars may opine concerning the origin and nature of these stones upon seeing this first exemplar, your indulgence in suffering us to dedicate this first harvest of the Würzburg Lithography to your Most Exalted Name is our irrefragable testimony and impenetrable shield against all emulous charges of imitation and artificiality. Your princely favor which permits me to tender these as the theme of my inaugural disputation, stirs me profoundly to pursue with like fervor and diligence the singular study of the natural history of Franconia upon which I entered some years ago under the direction of my illustrious Doctor and Master. Turn, then, upon this effort of mine, Most Learned Prince, that gracious regard which it is your wont to deign to all scholars of the fine letters. Long may you live for our fatherland and for the Muses of Franconia, that the cultivation of Lithography, heretofore appreciated by so few and hence neglected by so many, as well as of the other fine arts may, under your favor, your protection, your fostering, receive a new increment. This in most obedient affection is the prayer of

> Your Most Reverend Highness'
> Lowliest and most devoted
> servant
>
> GEORG LUDWIG HUEBER,
> *Candidate for Medicine*
> *at Herbipoli*

EDIDIT INUMERAS SPECIES PARTIMQUE FIGURAS, REDDIDIT ANTIQUAS, PARTIM NOVA MONSTRA CREAVIT. OVID L.1 METAM.

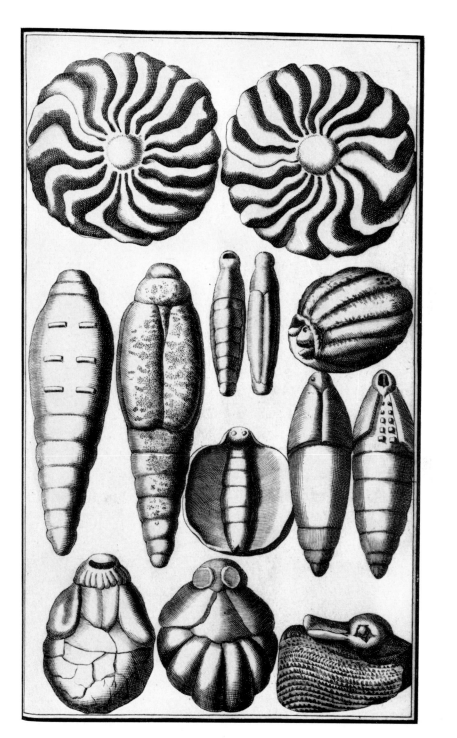

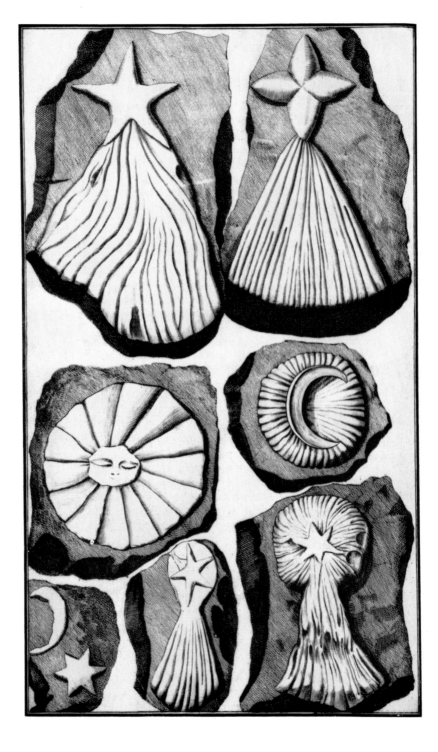

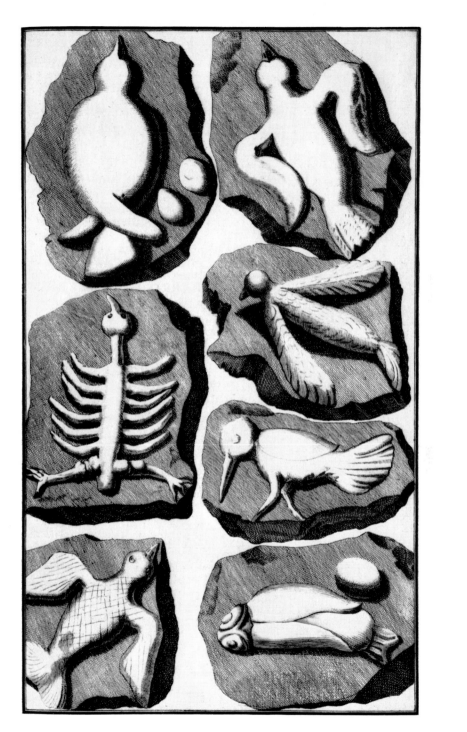

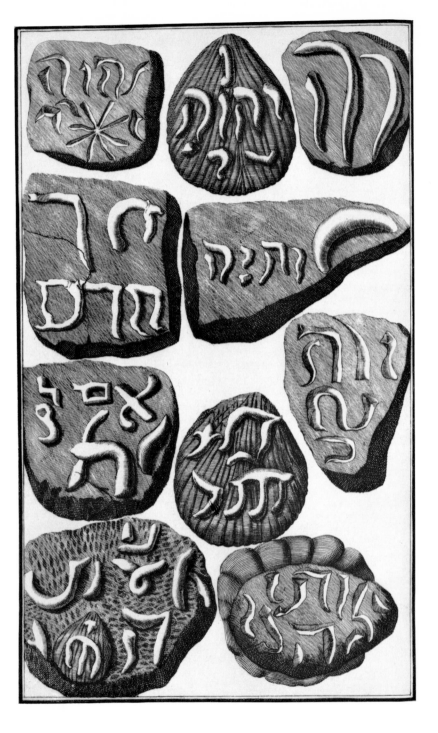

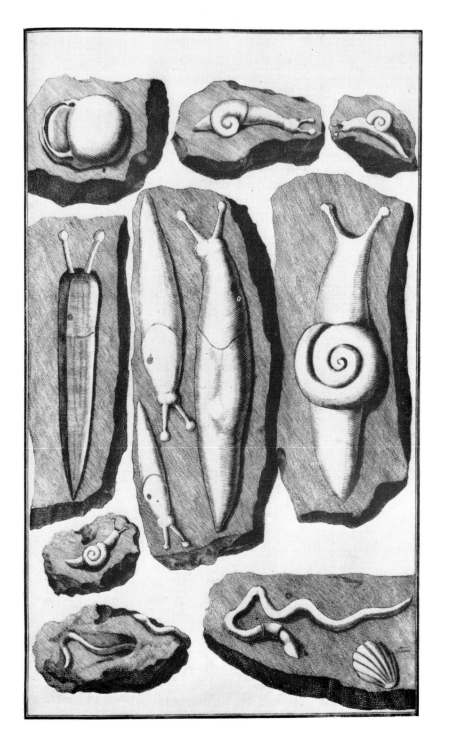

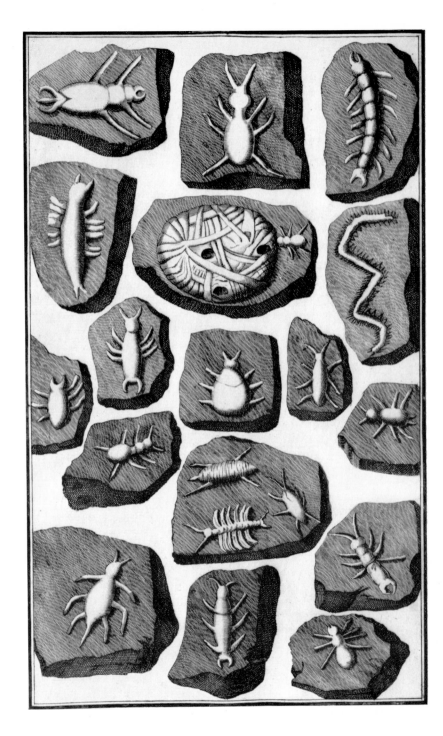

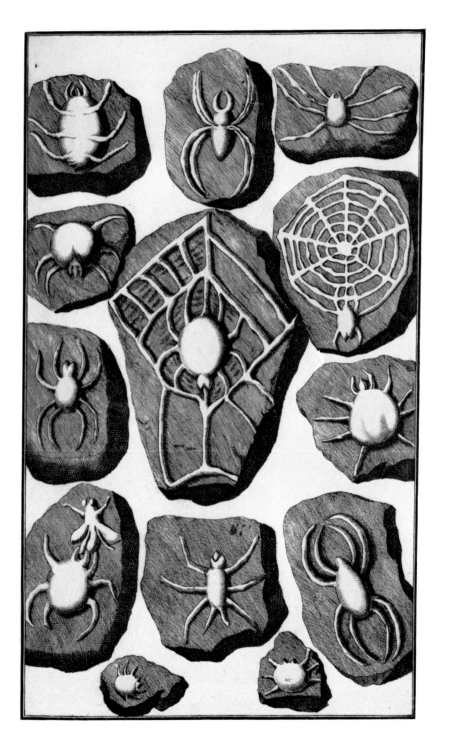

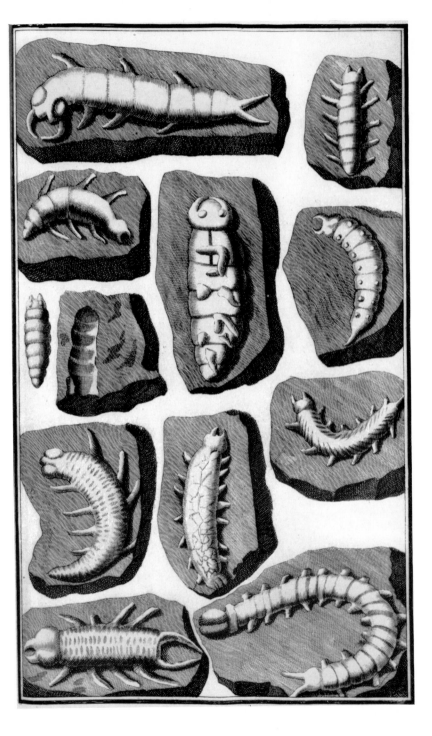

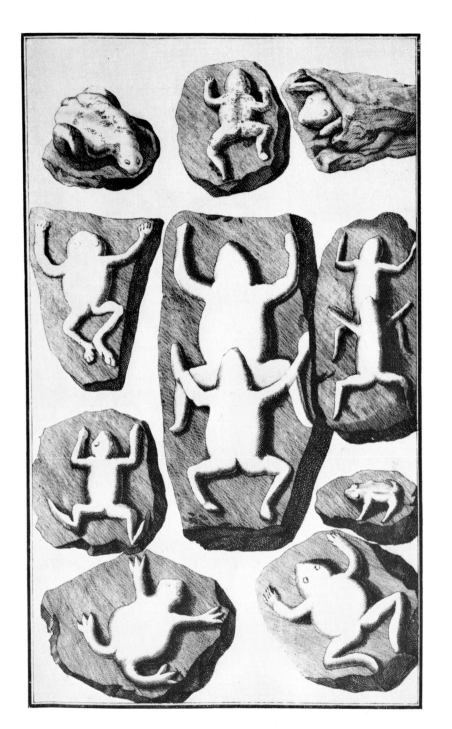

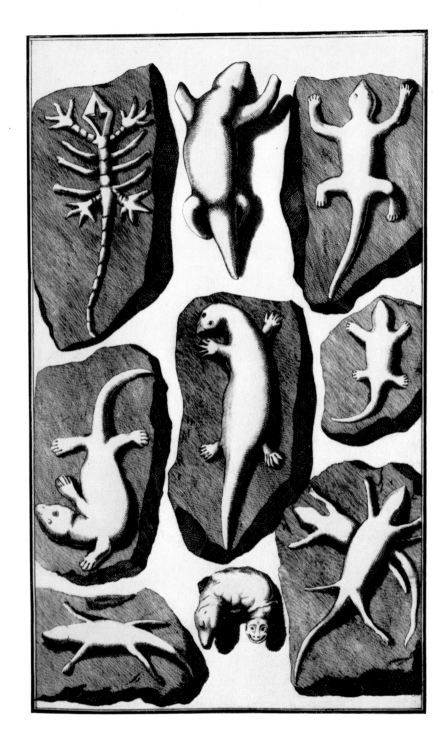

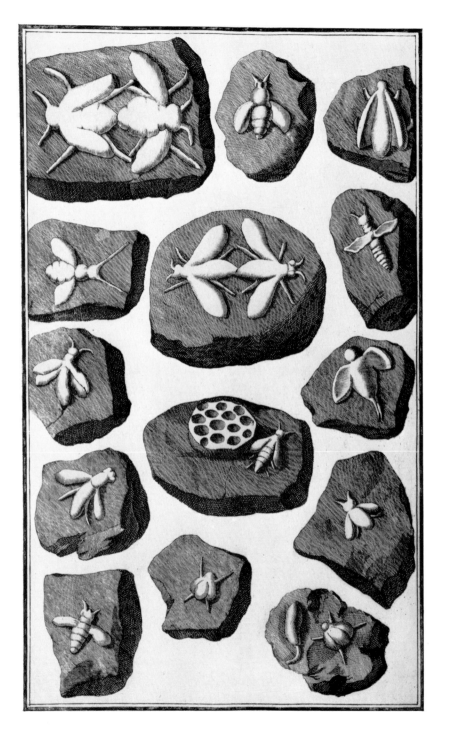

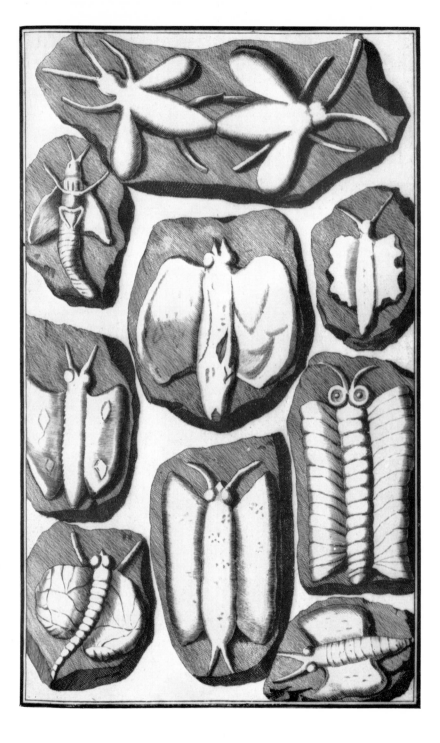

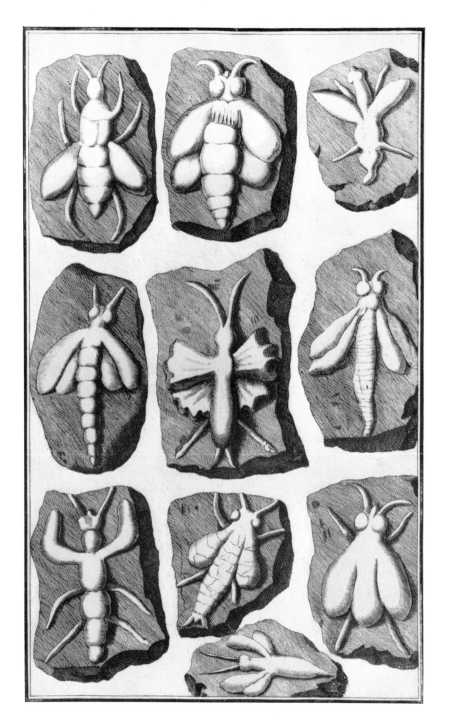

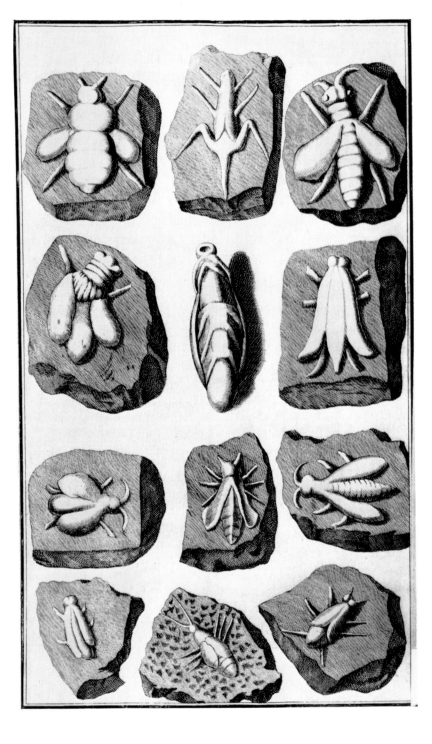

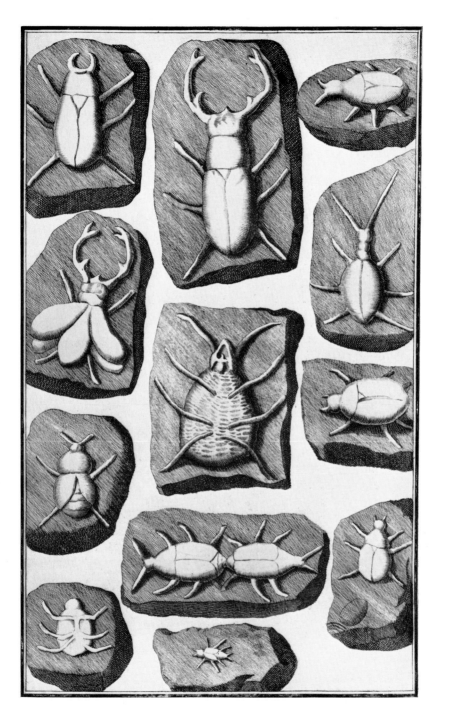

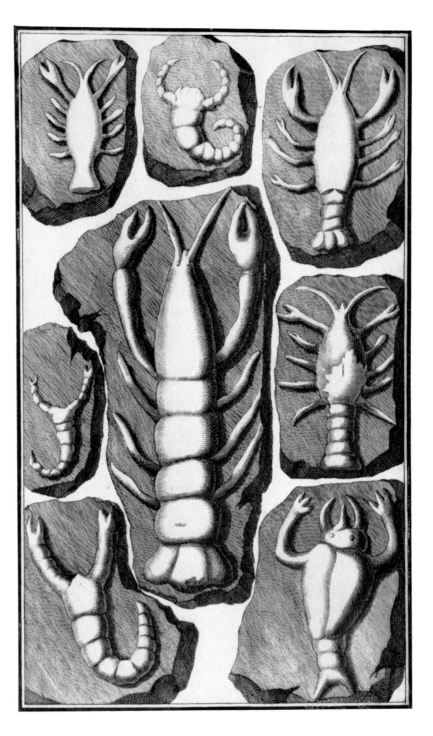

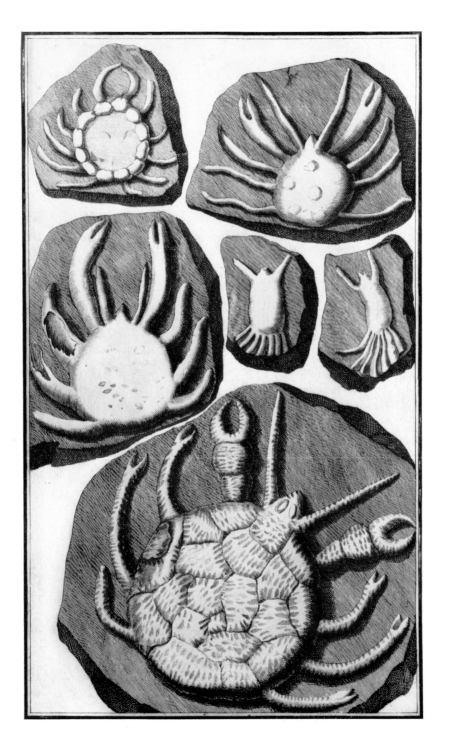

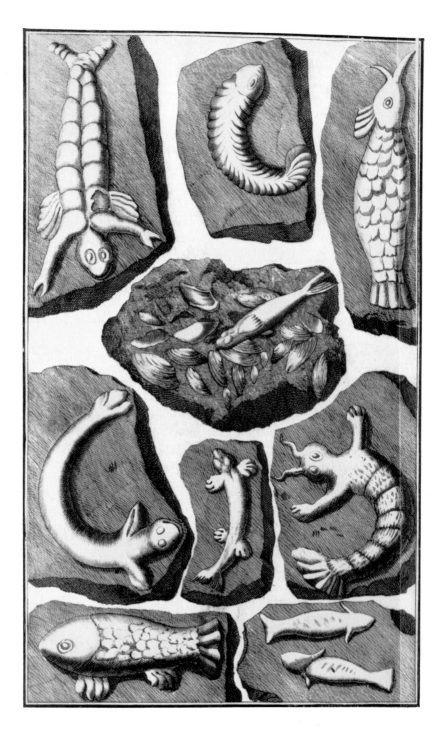

EXTANT STONES

SCALE: Large grid units are centimeters.

Upper left: Plate I	Upper right: Plate III
Middle left: Plate VII	Middle right: Plate VIII
Lower left: Plate XII	Lower right: Plate XIII

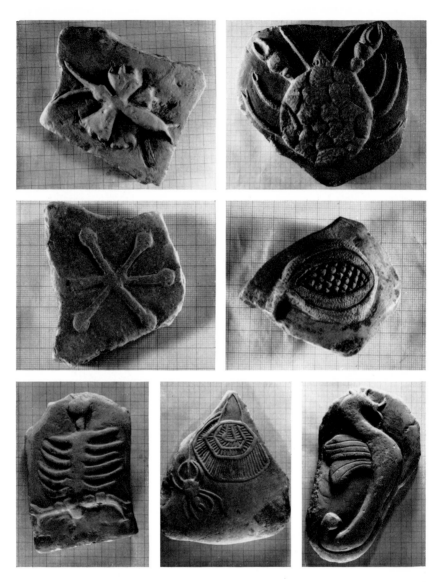

EXTANT STONES

SCALE: Large grid units are centimeters.

Upper left: Plate XVI   Upper right: Plate XX
Lower left: Plate IV

(Stones without plate numbers were not included in
the illustrations of the original edition.)

Introduction by Beringer

SCHOLARLY INVESTIGATORS of the inanimate and insensible objects of the natural world seem to be divisible into two groups. One, being wearied with the visible, inferior world, is caught up with rapt eye and mind in heaven, solely intent on the movements and nature of the stars and other celestial bodies. The other is made up of those who, with their regard fixed on the more proximate earth, find by sedulous investigation so great an abundance of admirable things hidden in the earth and in the sea that they expend themselves in considering these things with no less pleasure and fruit than the astrologers in observing the courses (both in conjunction and in opposition) of the fixed and wandering stars. The outstanding attempts of both, besides the great utility which they bring to the world of letters, as well as to that of the whole commonwealth, merit also this praise before others, that as eloquent Interpreters of the Divine Plan they expound the supreme power and wisdom of the maker of all things, shining more clearly than the sun in such stupendous effects, to be adored and proclaimed by all (which is the principal end of Natural Science).

Now, if one were to compare the merits of both schools, it would be difficult to say whether greater esteem is due the astrologers by reason of their sublime pursuit than that which redounds to those who, exploring the depths of land and sea, bring forth by their sagacity and labor more cogent motives for praising God. For, in the first place, the immense distance of the heavens from the earth, the nebulous phenomena of the intervening air, the elusiveness of stars that never become visible, the feebleness of human sight, render their labors and vigils during sleepless nights in frigid air all but insurmountable, and not infrequently leave all their efforts empty of expected results. But, moreover, there is the ever-present danger that their ardent studies and their scrutiny of the future may lead them to illicit practices of divination, to pry into the hidden counsels of Providence, to subject man's free will to the influence of fate, and to the conjecturing of future events by fortuitous judgments and by prophecies which are often vain. Still, the beauty of the heavens does, by its very nature, surpass all the praises of human words in showing forth the majesty of the Creator in its natural splendors, as though its every ray were a tongue of praise.

On the other hand, those who uncover the hidden things of earth, handle them, peer into them closely and often subject them to inspection not only with the instruments of anatomy and chemistry, but with all the means of experimental philosophy—these, I say, apart from the enlightenment of their scholarly efforts, reveal the greatness of God in little things, the transcendence of God in lowly beings, the preciousness of God in things vile, and in so doing they attract the greater admiration of men as these hidden mysteries were the less known to the unlearned and unscholarly.

Now it is my opinion that Lithologers must be numbered in the ranks of these latter. By Lithologers I do not at all mean only jewellers, who with much trouble and expense search for the colored drops enclosed in shiny stones, more perhaps for the swelling of their coffers than for the advancement of learning. Rather, by Lithologers I mean those who, fired by a more lofty zeal for natural history, without regard for the nobility or disdain for the ignobility of the matter they are handling, dig up from the bowels of the earth or collect from the surface that stupendous deposit of formed stones heretofore neglected. They exhibit these findings, marked with the designs of many divers bodies more excellent than the artifacts of Phidias or Apelles, to a world that is awed by their new-found elegance. On high mountain peaks, in rocky caverns, in stone strata, in the clefts of rugged roads, in the deep recesses of mines, in the furrows of fields, even in the center of Germany so far removed from the ocean, they find, hardened in rock, numerous species of shellfish, bits of coral, the remains of fishes, marine monsters, and even wild animals such as flourish only in Asia or Africa. They bring forth from the solid heart of cleft stones designs of fields, pastures, citadels, cities, flowers, plants, and brute animals, sometimes done in their proper colors. Nor do they uncover only images, but the very bodies of fishes, cattle, and other quadrupeds, even of men and of dense trees, as though these things had met the dreaded head of Medusa or Gorgon and had been transformed into stone. These new wonders of nature, undiscovered by other ages, except as a fiction, are a pure metamorphosis, wherein no Daphne assumes the disguise of the laurel, no Narcissus or Hyacinth that of the flowers, nor any others with the ingenious deception of the Poets hide beneath the forms of other bodies. Rather, whatever of beauty Nature has produced in its threefold realm, has, by a specific glutinate of salt, earth, and moisture been changed into stone.[1] This is indeed a reversal of the fable of Pyrrha and Deucalion, for here no stone thrown over the shoulder turns into man, but the corpse or skeleton of man or beast is solidified into stone.

There is scarcely a province in Germany, not to mention other regions, which the tireless labor of Lithophiles has not ennobled by the discovery of such prodigies of petrification. Austria, Silesia, Carinthia, Swabia, Switzerland, Bavaria, Thuringia, Württemberg, Hessia, Misnia, Saxony, Noricum, Westphalia, and many of the coves, mountains, and fields in these provinces are rich mines of figured stones, and open up abundant fields in our day wherein the learned may exercise to satiety their ingenuity in investigating this class of relics. In Franconia alone, or at least in the field of Herbipoli, except for the extraordinary fertility of the soil, this happy quality seemed to be lacking to the present day, while in other respects a generous Nature, or more correctly God, the Maker of Nature, poured out His riches upon it with a more lavish hand. In this place wines flow in so great an abundance from the hills that if the Main River were suddenly to dry up, Bacchus could inundate its dry bed with his sweet and copious nectar. Here and in the fields of Oxaria and Schweinfurt the blessed crops fill the granaries not only of our country, but of other regions as well. Rich pastures nourish vast flocks of cattle. Streams and rivers, descending through the valleys with placid current, almost match their waves with fishes. Our grazing lands are crowded with beasts. Salt sources gush forth. Healthful and medicinal pools boil. In other parts of our meadows and woods there flourishes a rich and rare harvest of botanical treasures. But, though the mild climate and the fertility of the soil have lavishly supplied the inhabitants of our land with these and other necessities for a standard of living that approaches the opulent and luxurious, there have been lacking those nutriments so vital to men of letters and the students of the noble disciplines of physical science, such as they might test with their own eyes and minds, and share in gratifying exchange with the learned men of other lands. Hence, while praising Nature for its largesse toward Franconia in other respects, they have reproached its niggardliness in the matter of fossil deposits.

It is true that in vine-covered and rugged mountains and in quarries there has been gathered so prodigious a collection of ammonites, of petrified shells from the sea and the rivers, that entire walls constructed of rocks densely encrusted with shells turned to stone take the place of the customary hedges surrounding the vineyards. However, since these are common to many lands and have been amply publicized at the expense and by the efforts of many writers who have had easy access to them, I have considered them unworthy of further research and study. Meanwhile, since I did not find the more rare and precious stones in Franconia, I have filled my cabinet with specimens gathered on nearly all the shores of Europe, thanks to the generosity of friends and benefactors who augmented my own efforts and expenses. Thus I battened on the treasures of other lands while awaiting the time when my own country would serve me with a wealth of its own—and I had a distinct prescience that this would eventuate sooner or later. Nor was I deceived. For by a singular stroke of Divine Providence, which I thank and adore on my knees, a mountain which I had frequented and examined in the past but had never scrutinized very closely, revealed a treasure, at first scattered sparsely on the surface, then when excavation had been resorted to, yielded even more in its interior, as though in that one bountiful horn of plenty were contained all those things which Nature had begotten in the pits and caverns and various receptacles of other Provinces. Here, representing all the kingdoms of Nature, but especially those of animals and plants, are small birds with wings either spread or folded, butterflies, pearls and small coins, beetles in flight and at rest, bees and wasps (some clinging to flowers, others in their nests), hornets, flies, tortoises from sea and stream, fishes of all sorts, worms, snakes, leeches from the sea and swamp, lice, oysters, marine crabs, pungers,[2] frogs, toads, lizards, cankerworms, scorpions, spiders, crickets, ants, locusts, snails, shell-bearing fishes, and countless rare and exotic figures of insects obviously from other regions. Here are nautili, ammonites, starfish of very different and very delightful species,[3] shells, spiral snails, winding shells, scallops, and other heretofore unknown species. Here were leaves, flowers, plants, and whole herbs, some with and some without roots and flowers. Here were clear depictions of the sun and the moon, of stars, and of comets with their fiery tails. And lastly, as the supreme prodigy commanding the reverent admiration of myself and of my fellow examiners, were magnificent tablets engraved in Latin, Arabic, and Hebrew characters with the ineffable name of Jehovah. These wondrous exhibits reveal the most bountiful treasury of stones in all of Germany, buried for so many centuries, and at last, thanks to my persevering efforts and investigation under a benign Providence, discovered and unearthed at no small cost and labor.

I doubt that any more heart-warming spectacle can come to the eye of a scholar of natural science. For all these figures are not merely outlined or sketched, but stand out so boldly after the manner of sculptured relief, that many erudite scholars and illustrious men of letters could not refrain from suspecting that some imposture lay hidden beneath these extraordinary mysteries—that the stones were fictitious and were fabricated in secret for purposes of fraudulent avarice, and, as frequently happens in coinage, were exposed to the wiles of forgers.[4] To dispel these misgivings from their minds, I led some companions on the pleasant jaunt to the site, where they partook of the joyful and curiosity-inspired labor of climbing the hill—no difficult task in this soft mass of earth—and where they dug out these portentous symbols of natural things with their own hands. What felicitations this elicited! How universal was their assent and approval, I leave to the surmise of the reader. Suffice it to say that the exhilaration which filled me at the first finding of this treasure was increased a hundredfold by the added consolation of the presence of those most authoritative witnesses. So this late date has ended the long vigil of many centuries. These earthly treasures that have lain hidden, covered, and buried beneath the muddy, slimy, sandy squalor of this uncultivated mountain have (considering the rarity of this deposit) compensated with interest my expenses and my ceaseless efforts which for so many years had been ill-rewarded with success.

Wherefore I reckoned to render a most important service to the realm of letters if I should liberate from the walls of our museum and propose to the eyes of the world these things which the goodness of God has entrusted to my hands as no mean reward for my daily research and studious labors, and, rather than proffer my own opinion concerning this new object, previously unknown to the devotees of Natural Science, should await the verdict of wiser heads after they have subjected these stone images to a meticulous examination.

For whatever can or has been said concerning the origin of figured stones: that they derive from relics of the Flood, or from the marvelous force of petrifying moisture and salts of the earth, or from the seminal and plastic influence of some subterranean Archaeus or Panspermia or a generative vapor,[5] or finally from the vagaries of Nature [6]—none of this would seem to be applicable to the harvest of our prodigious mountain. Possibly the parturition of these prodigies has been delayed until this later age, when the hidden objects of Lithology have been considered so thoroughly uncovered and so exhaustively exposed in numerous commentaries that nothing new can be obtruded upon the delicate palate of the mind without being distasteful. Now here is a new method of learning and teaching, a new course of argumentation in thorny questions which have not been completely resolved. We have known that art is the ape of nature; now we shall attempt to determine whether our present stones are the work of art or, as some say, of the imitator of nature. For whatever power has fashioned and animated the plants, the animals, the testacea, etc., the agent, in this case in Phrygian style and with sculptural skill, seems to have formed in clay and stone beautiful ideas (albeit inanimate) and ectypes of living prototypes. Indeed, he has surpassed his limits by employing the art of writing, and has traced the characters of several languages, but especially those of the sacred tongue, so exactly in accordance with the rules of Hebrew orthography that they were adjudged in the opinion of experts to extol in eloquent titles the most holy name, power, and wisdom of God, and thus perhaps manifest the one and only author of these wondrous stones.

Behold these tablets, which I was inspired to edit, not only by my tireless zeal for public service, and by your wishes and those of my many friends, but by my strong filial love of Franconia, to which, from these figured fruits of this previously obscure mountain, no less glory will accrue than from the delicious wines of its vine-covered hills; and to the field of Herbipoli as well shall new fame be added by this rock in all its dryness.

To these is added the indulgent approval of our most reverend and high prince, which has for me the force of supreme command. For how could I tarry in bringing to publication those things which our most learned leader in the sacred and profane sciences has, as the supreme arbiter, decided and, by indications of his most indulgent will, approved that I should edit?

During all these centuries our Franconia, chafing at the delay, yet restrained to await so illustrious a prince and leader, has concealed these stupendous miracles in its stones, until recently, at the very time when his most reverend highness was receiving due homage from his devoted subjects of Herbipoli amidst the unrelenting joy and congratulations of the entire kingdom. By a singular favor, Heaven, as if it were placing in my hands the key to the stone treasury of Franconia, has uncovered these wonders, and by this precious gift has, with the other inhabitants, presented to our great and munificent princely patron of letters, a fitting pledge of sworn fidelity. By these inscriptions it has signaled the first year of this auspicious reign more happily than ancient Rome adorned the consular tablets with letters of gleaming gold. Herein indeed is fashioned and circulated to the ends of the earth a monument more lasting than bronze, to the glory of our Prince. Moreover, this is an effective incentive to students of medicine to pursue the mysteries of nature, as with equal constancy and zeal, so with equal hope of desired success.

Without fear of envy I must confess this noble and praiseworthy prerogative of the illustrious Faculty of Medicine, that by reason of the form of its institution and studies it trains and designates the principal teachers, administrators, and interpreters of nature for the entire world of public learning. Nor will you readily find among the students of the other disciplines any who cultivate nature with more reverence, and who from their persevering and industrious examination, shed upon it the light of more prolific writing. So the man of medicine is, as it were, antonomastically dignified by the honorable title of physician. And so I say to all you candidates of medicine who have made your profession before the altar of this deity, in this new pit a new shrine has been thrown open to you, and vestiges from on high are impressed upon its earth. Prior ages have taken much; the present has uncovered yet more, but it still reserves for you in the future no small deposit of the inexhaustible riches of nature. Be true to your calling and imitate the energetic devotion of your elders. Love or fortune or the generosity of the Mecoenates will supply your needs. And God, for the spreading of the glory of His Name in these wonderful works of His hands, will bless you with that felicitous success for which I devoutly thank His Supreme Majesty, and which I pray may be yours.

CHAPTER I

*Wherein the opinion of those who oppose Lithology
as a vain and useless pursuit is refuted both by reason and
by the example of the celebrated authors, ancient and
modern, who have treated this part of Natural Science
and have elucidated it by their writing.*

IT IS THE JUST COMPLAINT of serious men in this age of ours,
which is so much more refined in letters and manners than the
coarse ages of the past, that men are to be found who so heartily
detest all fine literature that they would have only those arts and
sciences endowed and accepted in our centers of learning which
contribute to gainful employment, while they would have all others
perpetually banished as vain and useless. Among the first of the latter they number the knowledge of natural things, and its most noble
part, which we call Lithology; they pursue it with an especially
censorious rod, and condemn it to rejection from the world of
erudition as one of the wanton futilities of intellectual idlers. To
what purpose, they ask, do we stare fixedly with eye and mind at
small stones and figured rocks, at little images of animals or plants,
the rubbish of mountain and stream, found by chance amid the
muck and sand of land and sea? To what purpose do we, at the
cost of much gold and labor, examine these findings, describe them
in vast tomes, commit them to engravings and circulate them about

the world, and fill thick volumes with useless arguments about them? What a waste of time and of the labors of gifted men to dissipate their talents by ensnaring them in this sort of game and vain sport! Does this not amount to neglecting the cares of the realm to catch flies; to sending a mighty army out to collect shells, and then to reward their glorious expedition by building them a triumphal arch or shrine of shells, wherein the high priest is the physician, the idols are stone images of little beasts, the incense and victims are the efforts, the genius, and the expenses of learned men gone mad? To hunt for prodigious pearls, to gather the precious coral from the depths of the sea, to wrest gems and metals and marble from the bowels of mountains, or to transport these things from foreign shores over the immense distances of ocean and foreign lands, through countless storms and perils, these are labors worthy of the expenses of princes, of the care and diligence of great minds. Such things fill the treasury, increase the wealth of private citizens, and contribute to the commonweal. The fruits of such labor are never matters of regret. Thus in defiance of all the rules and precepts of sane philosophy do those souls, bent to the ground and tormented by the pseudosacred and insatiable hunger for gold, esteem the dignity and worth of the sublime sciences in terms of usefulness and gain.

Of old it was the laudable opinion of the wise men among the pagans, an opinion in keeping with right reason and confirmed by the sacred laws of Christianity, that the solicitude and labors of those who rule the hearth as fathers of families or those who, in magisterial or princely positions, rule the community, should be directed primarily and especially to procuring sedulously and with appropriate means all those things which they prudently adjudge necessary for the preservation and protection of the life, the fortunes, and the condition of their subjects. If moreover, God so blessed their labors that their solicitude was rewarded by an exceptionally rich return, and their wealth and treasuries increased, they should not thereby so attach their souls to riches that they would seem the possessed rather than the possessors. The mind of man was made for higher things, not for the fattening of the belly, nor for the luxury and delights of the body, nor for that most inane occupation of all, the custody of a pile of gold or brass—that custody which the mythologists of old committed in their fables to dragons and monsters rather than to strong men. It is miserly cupidity to follow only that which smacks not of use but of usury. It is the scheming of the servant and the mercenary, not the counsel of the free man, it is the backstairs machination of petty business to convert our halls of wisdom into taverns of merchants and workshops of mechanics, to change the lecterns of the learned into tables of moneylenders. Such as these do not have a clear perspective of that Good Truth which joyous honesty and honest joy renders lovable. Hence we do not recognize as scholars of the fine arts those who are the slaves of lucre and mere utility, but rather those noble souls who expend their energies and not infrequently their substance, stimulated by the very dignity of learning and of laudable work, in order to experience the pure joy born of knowledge.

This is the core of Christian ethics, the norm, the soul of all those moral virtues, which, in its absence (either openly or under the specious disguise of simulated virtue) degenerate into vices. What more noble purpose for human actions can be conceived than that whereby from the marvelous effects of nature we ascend as by so many steps to the recognition of the power of the Creator? Mighty indeed are the wonders of the Author of Nature. The sun rises and sets daily, and with the other stars and planets, circles the earth in a completely orderly and unswerving course.[1] The earth, from a wide variety of tiny seeds produces the herbs, the plants, the flowers, the fruits, and the vast forests, all with unfailing fertility. The seasons come and go, alternating in an orderly fashion. The rivers abound endlessly in water. On land, in the sea, and in the air innumerable species of animals are preserved and propagated. Myriad other wonders there are which, because they are objects of daily familiarity, are so little esteemed, not only by the ungrateful common populace, but by learned men—alas forgetful of God —that they are scarcely reckoned among the wondrous works of the Creator. The wisdom of God, to remedy this execrable folly of mortals, frequently brings to light from the hidden treasures of His power and the unknown deposits of the earth, through the labor of honorable and zealous men, wonders and portents of the great architect, Nature. Human curiosity, fed by these morsels while it examines each of them, and stupified by their novelty, while contemplating them with astonishment, is gradually raised above itself, and at last is fired by sincere and holy devotion to supplicate and adore the marvelous power of the Creator, the working of Whose hand it is compelled to acknowledge in such phenomena. In the course of this dissertation we shall demonstrate that among these wonders are to be reckoned many, if not all, figured stones [*lapides figurati*], and particularly those which our Franconia and the field of Herbipoli has borne, and that this is the more obvious, as their origin is more difficult to explain and surpasses human reason.

If you would know the good offices of Lithological studies, consider for a moment the worthy arts of depiction and sculpture. By the graces of these arts, things dead and past are restored in image and are endowed with something very like immortality. The visages of great men, of parents, friends, and loved ones are rescued from oblivion and preserved from dust and corruption. Memorials and statues are erected to virtue and service. Gardens, palaces, and public gates and roads are adorned with exceeding beauty. Nature in its work uses a similar artistry, and though it may not open to you a group of great statues or a pantheon, still it does offer a most delightful and unexpected collection of iconoliths of an all but extinct art, such as you will not find among the inspired works of bygone ages nor in the earthen chambers of graven crypts, nor amid the hieroglyphic sculptures of the Egyptian pyramids. Herein the marvelous form renders the rude stones so precious that they are installed in the art treasuries even of kings and princes as painstakingly as gems and priceless pearls are set in crowns and rings. With painstaking care and exacting scholarship learned men devote the unfettered capacity of their minds to the study of these things, classify them according to their divers species, arrange them in display cases, and exhibit to all eyes the whole realm of Nature more pleasingly than newly discovered regions are depicted on the charts of the geographers. These are delicacies which nourish erudition. And if they fail to tempt the palate of the mediocre it is not the fault of Natural Science which, as we have said, is most honorable and attractive, but of paltry talent, inept at scrutinizing the mysteries of Nature.

Very different is the mind of the foremost men throughout Europe—men who flourish in the halls of royalty, in the courts and magistracies of the great republics, in the high seats of learning in the most famous academies, men who enjoy the greatest distinction and wealth, yet so love and prize not only physical science in general, but the study of Lithology, that they undertake long, laborious, and expensive journeys with incredible zest and perseverance, in order to explore the hidden recesses not only of their own regions, but of others that have been recommended to them, there to unearth the secret stone miracles of Nature, publicize them, and write vast and enlightening commentaries on them. Passing over Pliny and other ancients whose efforts cannot be compared to the diligence of more recent scientists,[2] it may be worth while to draw up a brief alphabetical synopsis of Lithographers, to whom I have access among the other works of the Doctors in our library. The very names of such illustrious men should suffice to brand the idleness of that avaricious and crude pack of academicians who attack Lithology as a useless pursuit.[3]

Agricola, Georgius. *de re metallica, de Natura eorum, quae e terra profluunt, & de fossilibus.*
Aldrovandus, Ulysses. *de Simia in lapide.*
Assaltus, Petrus. *in notis ad Metallo-thecam Vaticanam Mercati.*
Bajerus, Joannes Jacobus. *de Orychtographia Norica.*
Balbinus, Boheslaus. *in Miscellaneis Regni Bohemiae.*
Bauhinus, Joannes. *de Fonte & Balneo admirabili Bollensi.*
Bauschius, Carolus. *de unicornu fossile.*
Becanus, Goropius. *in originibus Antwerpiae.*
Behr, Hennigius. *in Hercinia curiosa.*
Bel, Mathias. *in Hungaria antiqua & nova.*

Boccone, Paulus. *Recherches & observations Naturelles.*

Büttnerus, Daniel Sigismundus. *in Tractatu, cui titulus, Rudera Diluvii testes, & in Dissertatione de Corallis fossilibus.*

Columna, Fabius. *de Purpura.*

Coringius. *de antiquo statu Helmstadii.*

Crollius. *de Signaturis.*

Erhard, Balthasar. *in Dissertatione de Belemnitis Suevicis.*

Fabricius, Georgius. *de metallicis rebus ac nominibus in Georgium Agricolam.*

Gesnerus, Conradus. *de omni rerum fossilium genere, gemmis, earumque figuris.*

Guericke, Otto. *de Quedlinburgensibus.*

Helwingus, Georgius Andreas. *in parte prima & secunda Lithographiae Angerburgicae.*

Heraeus, C. G. *in Dissertatiuncula oblata Illustriss: Gall: Scientiarum Academiae.*

Hiemerus, Eberhardus Fridericus. *de capite Medusae.*

Kentmanus, Ber. Jo. *de Calculis, qui in homine ac membris nascuntur.*

Kircherus, Athanasius. *in Mundo subterraneo.*

Lachmundus, Fridericus. *in Orychtographia Hildesheimensi.*

Lambecius. *in appendice Bibliothecae Vindobonensis.*

Lancisius. *in Notis ad Metallo-thecam Vaticanam.*

Langius, Carolus Nicolaus. *in historia lapidum figuratorum Helvetiae, & de origine lapidum figuratorum.*

Leibnitius, Godefridus Guilielmus. *in Dissert: de figuris Animalium, quae in lapidibus observantur, & Lithozoorum nomine venire possunt.*

Leigh, Carolus. *in Historia naturali Langastriae.*

Luidius, Eduardus. *in Ichnographia Lithophylacii Britan.*

Major, Joh. Daniel. *in Dissert: Epist: de Cancris & Serpentibus petrefactis.*

Mascardus. *in suo Musaeo de fungorum petricosorum matricibus lapidescentibus.*

Mercatus, Michaël. *in Metallo-theca Vaticana.*

Monti, Joan. *de Monumentis diluvianis Agri Bononiensis.*

Mylius, Godefridus. *in memorabilibus Saxoniae subterraneae.*

Rueius, Francisc. *de Gemmis.*

Sachs, Philip. Jacob. *a Löwenheimb Gammaralogia.*

Scheuchzer, Jacob. Joannes. *Orychtographia Helvetica, Specimen Lithographiae Helveticae, Herbarium Diluvianum, Piscium querelae & vindiciae.*

Scilla, Augustinus. *al vana speculatione dissingannata del senso.*

Spenerus, Christ. Maximil. *Disquisitio de Crocodilo in lapide scissili expresso, aliisque Lithozois in Miscellaneis Berolinensibus Anno M. DCCX.*

Sponius, Jacobus. *in Itinerario Hispanico de Regno Valentiae.*

Steno. *in Prodromo de solido intra solidum.*

Tenzelius. *in Colloquiis menstruis.*

Valentini, Bernardus. *in Musaeo Musaeorum.*

Volckmannus, Georg. Anton. *in Silesia subterranea.*

Welschius. Hecatost: *in observatione XLIV. pag: 60. & 62. de variis Astroitae nec non Cometitae, sive lapidis Cometen caudatum referentis, effigiem praesentantibus.*

Winckelmannus. *in Descriptione Hassiae.*

Wodwardus, Joannes. *in specimine Geographiae physicae.*

Wolfardus, Petrus. *in Descriptione Hassiae inferioris.*

Wormii. *Musaeum.*

Zahn, Joannes. *in Mundi mirabili Oeconomia.*

Now, were I to add to this list the names of those writers who are cited by the above-mentioned authors, but whose works I have not yet obtained, I should set forth the entire host of Lithographers, any one of whom, like David of old, would be able with one flawless stone picked from the bosom of Nature, to prostrate, by one blow on the forehead, the gigantic mass of objections and satires and to vindicate the honor of this sublime science from all its calumniators.[4]

For such is the working of the human mind: those things it perceives to be pursued and cultivated by men of great repute in virtue and learning, with the universal consent and approval of the wise, it prudently esteems that it too should treat with a similar interest and approval, notwithstanding the contrary mutterings of a few obscure adversaries. And although the reward of such labor is not obvious at first sight, the mind is convinced that that discipline must be numbered among the best and most useful, since the very flower of the doctoral ranks has brought the full force of its genius to bear upon it, the mighty patronize it, its own dignity renders it estimable, its beauty makes its pleasing, and its usefulness augurs a full harvest from it. Examples and experience indeed demonstrate that all this is true of our science of Lithography. For as its prestige began to be more widely acclaimed, literary exchanges between academies increased, conventions of erudite societies became more frequent, more accurate descriptions of vastly different regions were obtained, the nature of the earth was more thoroughly studied and understood in the light of this highly diversified mass of material, the petrifying quality of earthborne salts and of mineral springs was shown, the alteration of vegetable or testaceous bodies into rocks and stones was demonstrated, the treasures of museums and scientific collections were augmented, the abundance of natural wonders was endowed with new beauty, and far excelling all these, the wisdom and power of God were more clearly perceived, and consequently, the praise and glory of His infinite majesty more widely propagated.[5] Further, the truth of Sacred Scripture and the account of the Universal Flood which God inspired the sacred writer to relate, are established in contradiction to the impiety of atheists, the vacillating doubts of skeptics, and the quips of the facetious, with arguments as solid as the rocks from which they derive. It is fitting, therefore, that we, though only recently arrived, should yield to the example of so many wise men, that we should subscribe to their opinion and considered judgment of Lithography, and exhibit in the following chapters and plates the new specimens of research produced by our land.

CHAPTER II

Wherein are described the situation of the mountain, and the nature and composition of the stones that were dug out of it.

THE REGION OF THE DUCHY of Franconia, nurtured by the placid current of the Main, ascends in a long range of mountains separated by modest valleys. The banks of the river, entrenched in these mountains, retain within a deep hollow the rising waters of spring and autumn and prevent them from flooding and damaging the fields and meadows of the inhabitants. Running its long and winding course between the close walls of the mountains, the river turns aside from the level fields. These mountains are not steep or extremely lofty, yet neither are they so low that they can be climbed without difficulty. For Nature has graciously disposed these mountains to allow the approach and cultivation of the vintners, though at the cost of a slightly bent back and of arduous labor. By virtue of their height they enjoy closer contact with the sun's rays, which they absorb freely and expend in maturing the vines and grapes. This they do the better since these rays are reflected from the Main and are retained longer and with more concentration in the deep valley of the mountains. Thus the mountains, planted to the peak on every side with vines decorously trimmed by the vintner's shears, form a verdant circlet or a diadem of grapes to crown the shores of the onrushing Main.

Among the mountains there is one, lying a mile or so outside the city of Würzburg, wholly uncultivated, adaptable to no uses, rugged and difficult to ascend, because instead of being covered with a more or less consistent rock formation it bristles with fragments of rocks protruding from it in wild disorder. It has no clusters of trees, only mere scrubs. It is stark, bald, and sterile. Dwarfed as it is by the surrounding mountains, the rains pour down upon it with greater force; and the waters that gather on neighboring peaks to disperse in numerous torrents, hack out of it a multitude of crevices, fissures, ditches, and troughs, till they hurl themselves down into the nearby valley in a stream so swollen that at times it could float a merchant vessel. Moreover, due to the violence of the storms, great landslides block the roads of the valley and menace travelers. This probably explains the unrelieved barrenness of the locale, as well as the quantity of slimy, earthy, muddy, and sandy lumps adhering to and between rocks both large and small. This may also account for the preservation of the mountain and even its increase by the influx of tons of sand, for on the right side it touches vine-bearing but muddy mountains higher than itself, while on the left it drops off into the valley. Its top is leveled to a wide plain abounding in sand and dirt which, with the aid of a copious overflow, replaces whatever is lost to the valley or washed away by the torrential rains. This rugged and chaotic mass, muddy on top, has in its middle no solid strata, but disparate rocks clinging to muddy and sandy earth. The foot of the mountain is of the same formation, so that it resembles not so much a mountain as the bulk of a mountain that has been overturned, or has been piled up haphazardly in the course of time. Only the unbroken height of this tract bordering the Main Valley would appear to retain this place in the ranks of mountains.

The stones that are found in this mountain vary according to location as to color, quality, and firmness. Those that were taken from the peak are of a yellowish tinge, and exhibit the qualities of mud, though weaker in adhesive force, on their rough and unpolished surface. Those found in the middle, confected of mixed slime and sand, are white and resemble gypsum in their chalky hue and their soft fragility. Those extracted from the base approximate the hardness and density of stone and flint, because their greater exposure to the rays of the sun promote their hardening. When properly cleansed of the soil coating which covers them to perhaps a finger's thickness, and allowed to dry, they change in color from a baked brown to a dull white.

Thus I have seen fit to divide these rocks into three or four classes, according to the diversity of their matter: sand, clay, mud, and lime. Now, all these, because of their deficiency in size, or solidity, or other qualities, are unsuitable for building purposes or for the manufacturing of mortar. Nevertheless, they possess certain singular properties which distinguish them entirely from all other petrified fossils and figured stones, and which richly deserve to be noted. They are as follows.

First: When our stones have been thoroughly cleansed of coagulated dirt by the water in which they lay immersed, they exhibit a smooth surface on top, as though they had been highly polished with pumice. This polished smoothness is characteristic of both the figured and unfigured stones of our mountains, though not all of them. On the bottom side which is imbedded in the earth they are coarse, and covered with rough protruberences, and resemble what we call the water-stone [*Wasser-Stein*].

Second: In digging out the gypsum, or chalklike stones, the greatest care must be exercised. Many of them, particularly those which more closely resemble clay or chalk, are so soft and flexible, as though newly formed by the skill of Nature, that if they are clumsily handled or struck with a shovel they shatter. They do indeed harden when they are exposed to the air, but so poorly that if they are subjected to an excessive washing they boil and crumble like quicklime. Now this pliant softness of our stones can scarcely be called decay, as some insist, nor ascribed to an inherent putredinous disposition. For in the place which Nature has allotted to their preservation, there is no perceptible source of such a disposition.

Third: The figures expressed on these stones, especially those of insects, are so exactly fitted to the dimensions of the stones, that one would swear that they are the work of a very meticulous sculptor. For there is scarcely one in which the dimensions of the figure are not perfectly commensurate to the length and breadth of the tablet.

Fourth: Though the diggers were sufficiently instructed in this matter, and were quite alert, they seldom discovered any tiny animals or insects (representing numerous species of the same genus) which correspond precisely to the proportions and other elements of the figures. In all specimens there was a partial conformity, but never total.

Fifth: Very few of the figures in our stones appear to have been affected by impression or, as it were, by forming a matrix of incumbent bodies, after the manner of the examples adduced by Scheuchzer. Rather, they are raised on the tablets in a kind of carved and polished relief, but so obviously a continuation of the rest of the stone that they cannot possibly be said to be affixed or superimposed by an extrinsic agent.

Sixth: A number of images of insects, shellfish, and ammonites are to be noted, complete in their members and chambers on both sides, though their furrows are not always equal or regular. Further, they are not in relief upon a stone base or tablet, as are those just mentioned; instead the entire stone is one integral figure, complete in itself without any further matter.

Seventh: The animal and plant figures, whether solitary or set on stones, whether intact or broken or cracked, or inspected and examined by any other method of experiment are found to contain nothing of the natural color, matter, covering, or armor which might be described as congenital to them, nor have they transferred these things to the stone. Rather, they bear the exact consistency, material, and color of the stones in which they lie and to which they owe their origin.

Eighth: All the small beasts and insects are found in that proper posture which Mistress Nature desires for them, very rarely on their back or side. The order with which their members are disposed is so striking (though in some it does not extend proportionately to the other dimensions of the body), and their parts so perfectly formed that they elicit the most enthusiastic admiration of all who see them.

Ninth: In many of the figures one notes no disjunction of parts, no distortion, curvature, or flaw, no declivity or deformative cracks or chinks. There is no slightest indication of any violence, but only splendid grace and elegance over all.

Since words and pen scarcely suffice to describe these and other remarkable properties of our stones, we have enlisted the skilled artistry of the designer and engraver, and herein present to the eyes of the benevolent reader more than two hundred engraved pictures, faithfully reproducing the originals, in twenty-two plates. Several others are being withheld until the first exemplar of the Würzburg Lithography has been examined and approved by the learned censors.[1] Our mine is not yet exhausted. There is one spacious section, fortunately uncovered by the rains of last summer's storms, which holds our stones in still greater abundance within its fertile bosom—what treasures the heavy downpours, scooping out the overlaid mass, have opened up to us. The willingness of competent laborers has been sharpened by generous wages: high prices have rendered the labor tolerable, and expected remuneration is presently having the same effect. My presence and that of men of honored positions whom I have at times invited is a considerable incentive. It has been my pleasure to array these men as witnesses against possible doubts and suspicions of fraudulent artificiality and imposture.[2] Their signed affirmation will, if necessary, confirm the truth of this matter. Meanwhile, it has been deemed prudent to conceal the name of the place until our museum is properly prepared to receive the first installment of this find. My stone treasury will in time be opened to visitors, the mountain itself will be pointed out, so that all may see at first hand in Nature what we are showing now in pictures. This will be a pleasant task, both by reason of the delightful journey among the vine-laden valleys of the Main, and of the satiating of curiosity by a strolling inspection of this mountain's wealth of portentous yields.

CHAPTER III

Wherein are set forth succinctly divers famous opinions of the authoritative writers concerning the origin and genesis of figured stones.

TO EXPLAIN THE ORIGIN and genesis of petrified and figured fossils in the light of the principles by which Nature operates, and to do so in such a way as to command the unqualified assent of judicious men, this indeed is a work that has been undertaken by many, and moreover has proven successful in accounting for the origin of various iconoliths. However, it has not yet been so lucidly and convincingly accomplished as to escape entirely the opposition of solid arguments. In fact, if I may make bold to suggest the heart of the matter, the power of wonder-working Nature or of any operative cause, or again sportive dalliance or sheer error, has led many into such a diversity of opinions that when they endeavor to elucidate the subject, the variety simply further obscures this subject, which is already essentially misty and elusive.[1] At this point I shall briefly outline the more famous ideas of the Doctors, with the eminent respect befitting such celebrated writers. Nor am I one to detract from the respect which their very wise assertions have merited by force of evident demonstrations and experiments. This only I contend, that not one of all these opinions is so general or so universally true that it can be applied, without encountering the doubts of other thinkers, to all the species of figured fossils, much less to the Würzburg stones which we have produced.

First place among the Genealogist-Lithographers belongs to the

ancient philosophers of the Aristotelian era who, eschewing necessary experimentation, were all too prone to ascribe the mysteries
of nature, such as magnetism, attraction, and repulsion between
beings both animate and inanimate, the ebb and flow of the sea, the
cross-currents of alternating winds from the various parts of the
world, and numerous other phenomena, to occult qualities. If you
press your inquiry further, you are accused of begging the question, for, so they say, it is the very essence of these things to be
occult.[2] Now, since they assign the origin of figured stones to these
impenetrable causes, your investigation is as vain as the striking of
a flint against an oak. Where you anticipated light and sparks, they
shroud you in vapors and shadows.

Not dissimilar to these are the thinkers who turn to the influence
of the stars, or to the silent intercourse between things celestial and
things terrestrial.[3] They would seem to imply that Hydrus, Scorpio,
Cavela, Taurus, etc. are in stone, or even are stone, because some
poet-astrologer has assigned these names to the constellations. This
is the pitiful attempt of a scientist to circumvent his ignorance by
seeking his answers in the stars which are so far removed that they
place him beyond the challenge of the untutored. The most learned
Lang[4] aims a well-deserved rebuke at this Phaëthontean subter-
fuge: "Since the influence of the stars is universal and, for the most
part, has a simultaneous effect on all sublunary bodies, it should follow that all bodies originating under the dominance of a particular
celestial body should, by force of this same influence, be worked
with the same figures. This would hold more true for animals and
plants than for minerals and subterranean bodies, since the matter
of the former is more fluid, and is more exposed to solar influences
than are the fossils buried in the earth." (*De Origine Lapidum*
Book I).[5] Perish such majestic inanities which flit about the heavens
—seeking, by impossible trails among the stars and even in the
curvature of the moon, the answers to the new and wondrous things
of the earth.

Much more rationally, Plot in his *Oxford Natural History* [6]
sought (and considered that he had found) the beginning of earthy
things in the earth itself, designating as the efficient cause of figured

stones a certain formative property of the salts secreted in the earth.[7] With some slight modifications this same explanation is proposed by the learned Helwing in his *Angerburg Lithography*,[8] wherein he would seem to attribute an exaggerated graphic and plastic force to the salts.[9] Now at this point the Aristotelian will demand, with just indignation, "What, pray, more certainly and evidently, is this plastic power [*vis plastica*] of the earth's salts than the occult quality [*occulta qualitas*] postulated by the Peripatetics?" The very learned Ray, in his oppositional efforts, recruits an adversary more formidable even than himself in Lhwyd's letter on page 130 of his *Lithographia Britannica:* "On the Origin of Marine Fossils and Mineral Leaves," [10] wherein the latter derides as incredible the notion that "any salts, as though perpetually marshalling to one plan of one mind, should conspire consistently to represent in some cases a blade of *glossopetra*, others the root or fragments of a jaw, yet others the convex and polished side of a pepperwort." [11] To this I might add, against Helwing: could they even arise out of the stones in the form of perfectly accurate letters?

Lhwyd, *loc. cit.*, page 139, finding the salts of Plot not at all to his taste, has recourse to another, and indeed most spacious source: the sea. From its depths he draws forth the first principles of figured fossils. "I strongly incline to the opinion," he says, "that the vapors rising from the sea and penetrating at sufficient altitude the upper stratosphere in the form of rain or mist, are frequently impregnated with the seed of testacea and of many other fishes, and that thence, depending upon the perfection of seed and the propensities of the matrix, they are formed, some into whole fish, others into their outlines only, others into the teeth, jaws, vertebrae, or other small bones, and among the crustacea, sometimes into whole animals, at others, only into their members; among the testacea, at times into univalves, but frequently into bivalves, etc." [12] Thus this illustrious Englishman, sequestered from the rest of the world and not finding on his native isle the cause of petrified animals, swims and gazes into the surrounding sea, and opines that they are transported thence to the land by the rains and mists. I would refer the indulgent reader to Scheuchzer, who in his *Herbarium Diluvianum*, page

29,[13] explodes this opinion with no less erudition than salty wit.[14]

Charles Nicolaus Lang in his *Tractatu de Lapidum Figuratorum Origine*, Book 2, Chapter 8, seems only to have introduced a few changes and additions into the conjectures of Lhwyd. He proposes that figured stones bearing the bodies of sea animals are generated by seeds dispersed about the earth.[15] "Since the seed of marine life is tiny and light, even when perceptible and formed—although sometimes imperceptible and unformed as when it remains in the parts of dead bodies or persists in the mucosity of the limbs—it is wafted about the earth by the movements of air, vapors, and water.[16] Subsequently it is decanted into the pores of the earth. Once descended into the subterranean layers, through the agency of the underground heat and of the steams and vapors boiling up from the sea and from other places, it is distributed among the open passages of the nether world, the fissures of rocks, and the apertures of the different strata. Thus it often reaches the surface of the earth, where it is deposited in a fitting matrix within the earth or upon its surface. To this matrix it clings firmly by reason of innate magnetism until, with the coming of the subterranean heat, its latent plastic force is stirred to action; whereupon, through the medium of the rock-forming current or (what is virtually the same thing) the seminal breeze [*aura seminalis*], it shapes and molds the disposed fluid matter into the same kind of body as that which it produced from testaceous matter in the sea." [17]

Besides Scheuchzer, Büttner and others, Pietro Assalti, renowned professor of Botany at the Arch-Lyceum of Rome, my cherished friend and patron, has attacked and refuted this verbosely expressed system in his very erudite notations to Michael Mercati's *Metallotheca Vaticana*, Armarium Nonum, page 220,[18] and simultaneously the aggregate of all systems which similarly explain the generation and formation of bodies.

Woodward, Scheuchzer, Wolfard, Büttner, Mylius, Volckmann, and a number of other very sagacious men of letters, labor not wholly in vain to show by incontrovertible evidence that many if not all petrifications are relics of the Universal Deluge [*Diluvii Universalis Reliquias*].[19] For when, with the opening of the cataracts, the unlocking of the abyss, and the gushing forth of the springs, the sea and the rivers, swollen by the unrelieved downpour of torrential rains, leapt their bounds and submerged the entire earth in a terrible inundation, to the accompaniment of wild blasts of winds, there ensued an enormous confusion and mingling of all things, so that vast quantities of things which heretofore had been contained by the earth were hurled into the sea, while those which the ocean had guarded in its bosom were scattered about the earth. Thus it came about that after the tumultuous recession of the waters, the animals, testacea, crustacea, and plants ensconced in the soil or buried in the strata of mountain or rocks were, over a period of centuries, permeated by the proper quantity and quality of petrificous salt and moisture [*sale succoque lapidifico*], and then altered into a stony substance. Finally they were unearthed, as well in other ages as in our days of flourishing natural studies.

Now, although we heartily embrace this theory, so consistent with the truth of natural history, with the Christian religion, and with the texts of Sacred Scripture, as regards petrified exotica, we cannot possibly apply it to the origin of our stones, since not all of these are of the petrified variety.

Friderick Lachmund in his *Orychtographia Hildesheimensi*,[20] and Johann Bauhin, *De Fontibus et Balneo Admirabili Bollensi*, Book IV,[21] with their followers who are variously called Ludions or Archaeists according to the opinion which they favor, ascribe whatever marvels they find in iconoliths to felicitous errors of Nature or to Archaeus dispersed among the lower regions of the earth from its very beginning. Against these Büttner in his *Coralliographia Subterranea*, pages 3, 4, 5, paragraph 7 in particular, inveighs in this scathing outburst: "As though the most high Majesty of the Giver of all being would ever play with the proper direction of the natural order! Indeed, this order, whether you call it Archaeus, and the World Spirit, or *Natura naturata* or *Natura naturans*, depends solely upon the infinitely operative Mind and Will of the all-wise and all-just Godhead. Of itself, it intends nothing, nor, being mindless [ἄνοος] can it intend, propose, or effect anything. Therefore let those who make these statements realize with decent fear, especially such as glory in the name of Christian, that whatever wantonness is charged to Nature is, by that fact, imputed to the most wise Ruler of Nature." [22] Thus does this erudite man expostulate. Nevertheless, I must agree with Baier in his *Orychtographiae Noricae*, Chapter 5, page 31,[23] that in a wide sense of the term a certain playfulness of Nature [*lusus naturae*] is not altogether to be excluded from the ranks of the Genearchs—without, however, postulating any other extraordinary agent distinct from God, the Author of Nature. There are found stones which, whether they exhibit a figure that is *sui generis* or imitate the forms of other bodies, yet accomplish this imperfectly, being defective in mass or extension or other characteristics, so that their origin from the things they resemble is not demonstrable. To what other principle than to Nature playing artistically can one ascribe the texture and design of these things?

To these celebrated theories, long familiar to the learned Lithographers, I now append a quite new opinion, one that is very distinctive, and, it would seem, singularly adapted to the Würzburg stones. It was drawn from historical monuments by a man who is by far the best versed in the various fields of letters, particularly in the area of history, and who was an eyewitness to the unearthing of our stones. Having brought to bear upon our fossils careful and mature consideration, he rightly perceived that they were reducible to no class of common petrifacts, nor could any of the suggested causes, which we have outlined in the various theories, be applied to them. Therefore, he declared that they were not the works of Nature but of Art, and of an impious and superstitious art indeed. For it was customary among the Germans in their pagan state to fashion crude images of plants, trees, and most revolting animals, and to keep these with them as a sort of sacred shrine. Further, they were so pertinaciously addicted to this ungodly superstition, that even after sacred baptism they relinquished it only with the greatest reluctance. Thus in the Synod of Germany of 742,[24] convened under Duke Caroloman, it is decreed in Canon 5, that all bishops, with the help and authority of the Count, who is the defender of the Church, should exercise the utmost care "that God's people not fashion pagan symbols, but reject and eschew all uncleanness." It was again stated in the Synod of Estinnes [*Synodo Liptinensi*] [25] held the following year [743]: "We decree, as our fathers before us commanded, that anyone who practices pagan observances in any matter, be arrested and fined fifteen soldi" (Canon 4). The bishops, therefore, sought to persuade the faithful with pastoral solicitude, or urged them with fines authorized by the Counts Defenders, to remove the relics of pagan superstition, and all images and sortileges from their society and to banish them to desert places, there to be buried in eternal oblivion. Such a place is our mountain: a mound of stones once employed in pagan rites, an infamous receptacle whence these evident vestiges of abolished superstition are being dug today. This is the judgment of this excellent man to which I make rejoiner with another imaginative explanation of the Würzburg stones, proposed by a friend in light conversation, more as a diverting pleasantry than as a serious argument.

Light is assumed to be a flow of minute solar bodies, which, being of a fiery nature, permeate, heat, and illuminate the quasi-liquid and diaphanous body of the air. Thus light is a corporeal substance, possibly not distinct from that primordial light which God created before the sun and the stars, and from which He fashioned the latter. This light takes on the forms and figures of all the things on which it shines, and this is the source of those visible species which we receive in the *camera obscura*, in magic lanterns, in still and limpid water, in mirrors, and in the pupil of the eye. Now, since it is admitted that light possesses the very marvelous faculty of painting, representing, and forming such corporeal images as it acquires in its diffusion, is it not further possible that it is endowed with a kind of active plastic power of impressing these images on properly disposed matter? We know the force of solar rays acting upon the earth. We know that the atmosphere is impregnated with the dregs of countless elemental atoms having a certain efficacy. These atoms, operating in conjunction with the forces of light, would have impressed upon soft mud, or clay, or sandy stones the figures of insects, plants, and even of stars (their light shining at night during the full or crescent moon).[26] After all, the visible image of an object, suddenly falling on the eyes of a pregnant woman, can instantly impress upon the fetus the forms of flowers or fruits, sometimes even the members and parts of animals—and this notwithstanding the resistance of the unpleasantly surprised mother. If you object that these strange markings are made on the delicate fetus not only by the action of ocular images, but of the phantasy and internal sense as well, I will remind you that this operation of the internal sense [*sensus interni*] originates in the impressed species [*species impressa*].[27] Why then does the contrary and resistant effort of the mother not thwart the action of the internal sense? Can we deny the analogy between the womb of the mother and the womb of the earth, that common parent of all, which, albeit inanimate, is apt for the conception and generation of offspring? Why could not the substance of airy light, thus modified, combined with the activity of the fertile earth, and supplemented by the directive force of salts and seeds, even of *Panspermia*,[28] be a determining and fostering agent in the formation of plant or insect figures either in stone or in malleable clay which later hardens into stone?

This could explain why the strange images in some stones, and the composites in ours and in those of other places are unnaturally thick and extended; why the spider webs, which are usually very tenuous, appear so gross. All this would be caused by the refraction, distortion, and confusion of the image-producing light, as we see happen to reflections which fall upon polygonal, cylindrical, convex, or concave mirrors. If, by way of an objection, you point to the stones bearing Hebrew characters, I take argumentative refuge in the ancient Jewish cemetery situated a stone's throw from our prodigious mountain, and uprooted during the expulsion of the Jews from neighboring towns not many years ago. Here the brooding light could come to absorb letters and even entire words, then transfer them elsewhere as it expanded. This is how my friend related his philosophical dreams, as he was pleased to call them. I have deemed it worth repeating here, if only to illustrate how the great minds torment themselves in their quest for some plausible explanation of our figured rocks. I hold all these theories in the highest regard, and to some I give unqualified assent as explanations of other species of petrification. This only will I attempt to demonstrate in the following chapters: that the nature of our stones is so unusual that its very novelty eludes the afore-mentioned opinions, however well established by documentation and searching experimentation.

CHAPTER IV

The figured stones of Würzburg are not relics and vestiges of paganism, and therefore cannot be ascribed to the superstitious art of the heathen Germans.

I AM AT A LOSS to say on what grounds the above-mentioned learned gentleman is persuaded and would persuade others that our stones are superstitious relics of paganism. For whatever was legislated in the Synod of Estinnes or in the Synod of Germany, celebrated the preceding year, anent the wresting of pagan objects from the hands of neophytes and the destruction of all such objects, does not convince us in the least that the figures of our stones are to be numbered among those images which the piety of Caroloman and the zeal of apostolic men desired to confiscate and to withdraw from the eyes and souls of the faithful. Let us peruse the canons of each synod here accurately transcribed. Canon V of the Synod of Germany is as follows: "We have also decreed that, in accordance with the canons, each bishop, abetted by the Gravio who is the defender of his church, should exercise solicitous care that in his diocese the people of God not make pagan objects, but that they reject and abhor all uncleannesses, whether they be the profane sacrifices of the dead, or soothsayers and seers, or amulets and auguries, or incantations, or immolatory victims, which stupid men practice in the shadow of the church with pagan ritual in the name of the Holy Martyrs and Confessors, thereby incurring the wrath of God and His Saints, or those sacrilegious fires known as *nodfyr*

47

or *nodfeyer*, and that they prohibit all such pagan observances." [1]
These are the words of Canon IV of the Synod of Estinnes: "We
have decreed, as my father previously commanded, that anyone
who practices pagan observances be arrested and fined fifteen
soldi." [2] To these is added an index, extracted from the Paderborn
texts, prohibiting thirty pagan superstitions.[3] If these are carefully
studied in conjunction with the canons just quoted, it is evident
that our stones cannot be reduced to any class of these things. Not
to immolatory victims or sacrifices, since they have not done duty
either as idols or as victims used in the worship of idols. Who has
ever seen or heard of stones being offered for sacrificial purposes,
or the images of living things being immolated instead of victims?
Not to auguries, divinations, sortileges or incantations. The opponent of Van Dale and of his defender, Fontenelle, has extracted
very different rites of prophecy, augury, and divination from the
earliest writers, both pagan and Christian, described in a book entitled, *De Silentio Oraculorum*,[4] wherein no mention is made of
similar stones of superstition. Not to amulets or to ligatures [sic].
Who can believe that head-coverings and waistbands were filled
with a pile of such crude stones, or adorned with them in place of
jewels? Things therein forbidden with reference to the weather
goddess, or horns or shells, likewise have nothing in common with
the great variety of insects which we have represented in the attached plate and in others on further pages. On the subject of
heathen amulets, both the synods and the catalogue of pagan objects maintain a stolid silence. Besides, these very heavy and awk-
ward stones could hardly have been hung about the necks of children to ward off spells and witchcraft, unless the cruel parents
intended to suffocate or prostrate their little ones with ponderous
stones hung on rings or chains—and of these the rough form of the
stones shows no evidence. If you contend that these were idols of
a barbaric and uncivilized people, I must indeed admit that not
only barbaric and uncultured nations, but the Greeks and the
Egyptians and (those imitators of all superstitions) the Romans
deified and worshipped monsters and fierce beasts. But who can

recall crickets, spiders, worms, tortoises, and similar castoffs of Nature being raised to an altar and endowed with divinity?

Truly, the complete silence of the Franconian writers on the subject of pagan objects buried in one mountain is, in our opinion, eloquent testimony that no such burial took place as the result of the synodal prescriptions, contrary to what the author of this latest opinion wishes to establish. The *Herbipoli Chronicle MS* does indeed mention certain relics of paganism in the form of statues of Pallas and Mars sculptured in the Greek style, set on the steps to the portico of the cathedral (in the spot now called *Zur Greden*) as antique ornaments, but later cast into the Main as a symbol of the washing away of all former impiety. It makes no allusion, however, to the preservation or confiscation of any other heathen sculptures.

Even in the days of St. Boniface, St. Burchard, and the other prelates and apostles of our Franconia, the Main River bathed Würzburg with its deep stream. These obnoxious relics of heathenism, wrested from the Christian inhabitants by the zeal of the bishops and the fear inspired by the ducal proscriptions, could have been buried in its depths or consigned to the flames. Why would they instead be piled up on a mountain, easily accessible to all and almost touching the royal road on the bank of the Main? These condemned abominations should have been relegated to some desert spot, to uncharted recesses of the dense forests which still surround our country, to the inhospitable rocks of northern Franconia, or to underground caverns, if the bishops in their zeal were truly solicitous for the purity of the faith—not decanted on a mountain spot visible to all, whence they could be furtively reclaimed by a people still prone to relapse into their ancestral superstitions, and thus preserved more perilously because more secretively and cautiously.

Moreover, at that time not only Herbipoli, or Würzburg, was inhabited. Franconia contained numerous villages and towns wherein dwelt people of sound Christian piety and life. Yet nowhere—in the course of all these centuries and despite the continuous cultivation of fields and vineyards, and the wide deforestations—does there occur even a single vestige of uprooted superstition. The same is true of Bavaria, Thuringia, Hessia, and Saxony, all extensive provinces which presented a wide field of apostolic labor to St. Boniface and his companions. The groves were cut down, the shrines and temples of the idols were put to the torch, everything possible was done to withdraw the reminders of primitive superstition from the eyes and minds of men. The efforts of the holy prelates were augmented by those of the most Christian princes who, emulating the zeal of Constantine and Theodosius the Great in the Orient, sought everywhere to deliver and cleanse eastern France from the abominable errors of the heathens. Is it possible that to this late date no cache of pagan paraphernalia, taken from the neophytes and dumped on a mound, has ever been encountered in any of these provinces? Of all the learned men who scrutinized minutely and to its depths the land of all these provinces, brought to light many petrified miracles of nature, and edited them with scholarly commentaries, not one of them considered for a moment classifying his finds with the superstitious objects of extirpated paganism. Glance, if you please, at the list of eminent Lithographers given in Chapter I; consider their theses and commentaries. You will not find one who ascribes these exotic figures to an extinct paganism. Now no author, whom I or other Lithophiles have seen or read, has come upon any stones similar to ours, even after sedulous investigation. Are we to suppose that the Thuringians, the Bavarians, the Hessians, the Saxons were exempt from those decrees and laws of the Frankish synods and princes concerning forbidden uncleannesses which obliged the Franconians? Did these latter hold more tenaciously than all the other German peoples to these condemned rites? Did Franconia alone with its modest little tract, the field of Herbipoli, dig a grave wherein to bury the collected images of ancient impiety, there to be preserved unbeknownst to other ages, until our own day?

If you examine carefully the quality of engraving in these figures, you will observe that it is so diverse in one and the same tablet, that while you admire the art of a truly fine sculptor in one small animal, you see in another figure of the same stone the primitive crudeness of a people but little advanced in the arts. Why would the art of these pagans execute the form of one insect so skillfully, and another so defectively? More pointedly, why are the figures of extraneous and marine animals frequently more elegantly and perfectly executed than those of domestic creatures which were objects of daily familiarity? What wind or current bore foreign and marine animals from the ocean and from distant lands into the interior of Germany and placed them in the hands of the pagan barbarians, to be used in effigy for the superstitious cult of idolatry? Why would the artists or priests, undertaking a work intended for the veneration of the gods or, as they falsely supposed, for supernatural effects, select fragments of the ugliest stones, even of limestone or clay, in preference to the better stones or marble which abound in the neighboring mountains?

The very nature of these stones, which we treated in Chapter II,[5] militates against this opinion. We have shown very many of these to be so soft and malleable that they disintegrate when handled roughly. We have found the figures impressed on them as fresh as if they were turned out by the hand and wheel of a potter—or of Nature (if we may speak of her as the artisan here)—intent upon ceramics. Many of them, when immersed in water, boiled and dissolved after the manner of limestone. Several specimens of this sort may be seen in the accompanying Plate I. How have they been preserved intact for ten long centuries in a mountain exposed to continual rain wash, rent and perforated by innumerable fissures and clefts? Why, in these rain basins under a thin covering of earth, or out in the open through hundreds of storms, rained upon and soaked by the torrential showers that penetrate the seams of the mountain, why have they not been resolved into dust or their original sand?

Finally, to the definitive refutation of the suspicion that these are pagan relics, we have found not a few stones, in the same place as the rest, inscribed with Hebrew characters (omitting for the

moment those bearing Arabic, Latin, and Teutonic inscriptions).
On these stones the ineffable Names of God—Jehovah, Strength
of the Lord, Mercy of the Lord, Power of the Lord, and other
divine perfections expressed in most eloquent terms (as seen in the
next to the last chapter)—proclaim His praises as the true and
supreme Godhead. Thus they clearly have no pertinence to the
gods and goddesses of the heathens, nor can they ever be linked
with the superstitious ceremonies of error, and with unholy magic.
Now you may argue that the Jewish cemetery is not far distant
from this mountain, and that the gravestones, inscribed quite ex-
pectedly with Hebrew phrases, were transported here at the time
when the Jews were dispersed from the neighboring town, and
their cemetery overturned and destroyed. In this case, you would
more accurately designate our stones as Jewish headstones, than as
pagan monuments. Even this, however, cannot be maintained.
There are still living more than a few townspeople who, in their
day, saw the Jewish inhabitants outlawed and banished. Yet none
of them recalls these stones being floated on rain wash across the
deep and precipitous valley to the other mountain, or transported
there by the vintners. The stones which the Hebrews use for their
monuments are very large, and are inscribed with the names and
deeds of their deceased and intimates. Our stones scarcely exceeded
by an inch the size of the very accurate engravings included in this
text. They are no more than large pebbles or formless fragments of
rocks by comparison. Furthermore, specialists in the sacred tongue,
as well as very learned rabbis, who were consulted, have observed
no proper names, no mention of personal facts, no chronological
data, nothing except the references to God. How vehemently the
Jews, after the fall of Jerusalem, abhor the least shadow of idolatry,
and shrink from all images, painted or graven, of creatures, is a
matter of common knowledge. Nevertheless, there are to be found
in our collection, ammonites, scallops, small animals both known
and unknown, inscribed with Hebrew characters and the sacred
names of God, along with the hodgepodge of scores of insects,
which we have touched upon. Is it credible that such things are
the artifacts of the Jewish sect, intended to adorn the sepulchers of

their dead and to perpetuate their memory in posterity with this immortal mark of superstition in defiance of their ancestral law and its just threat of execration?

May we, then, beg the kind indulgence of the historians, with all due and habitual respect to their erudition, to decline this theory, and to ascribe the origin of our stones, neither to the relics of paganism, nor to those of Judaism partially remnant in a cemetery.

CHAPTER V

On an ingenious fabrication, setting forth certain surmises concerning the plastic force of light that may have formed our stones, as expounded by someone in a friendly conversation.

I DERIVE THE TERM "fabrication" here from the very words of my dear friend, since what he expressed [in Chapter III] is not so much an opinion as a nice blend of philosophical and poetic reverie. Why, he contends, in such an obscure argument so controverted among the men of letters, is it not permissible to conjure up an idea, if not from the well of truth, at least not from the belly or the mountains of the moon or from the brain of Plato but from the wellsprings of Nature? Libavius in his Book I, *On Bitumens*,[1] refers to certain authorities who identified the artisans of figured stones with the underground genii [*genii subterranei*] who fashioned these objects in order to propagate superstition in the minds of credulous men. Others maintain that the caverns which yielded up this universal variety of petrified animals were once inhabited by holy hermits, men absorbed in divine contemplation and withdrawn from the society of men. Evil demons sought to dislodge these men from their holy idleness, to overcome them by vain frights, and, by onslaughts of repulsive and poisonous insects, to drive them out of their holy retreats and back into the world to their former association with men. But these men of God, shielded by divine protection with the sign of the Cross alone, confounded these wretched enemies, and changed into solid rocks the little animals produced by their infernal arts. These rocks, a perpetual memorial of this miracle, are finally in our day brought forth from these recesses. Thus the pious philosophers invoke heaven and hell in order to avoid the appearance of saying nothing in so enigmatic a problem. My friend, on the other hand, has favored the light and defied the darkness. I would indeed be deeply obliged to him, should he happily succeed in establishing parturitions among the serene and golden effects of the radiant and illuminating sun, thus raising up children of light from the stones. Light assumes transient images of all visible things and reproduces them on living eyes, or reflects them through optical glass or the *camera obscura* onto a white screen or wall in such a manner that they vanish as rapidly as they appear. When, pray, did this new artist learn to employ his skill in indelible colors so well as to leave even a trace on this deeply buried material? Everywhere there would be an enormous multitude of iconoliths, not only of insects but of the more noble bodies of Nature, of cities and citadels, of pastures and vineyards, in a word, reproductions of everything under the sun, were light so versatile that its reflection made effigies of all the forms it encountered. Who has captured in stone comets which are rarely seen, perhaps only at intervals of a century, while neglecting the forms of stars that shine daily in our hemisphere? Expose wax to the noonday sun, and it will melt, but will remain unformed. What could be more tractable, or more adaptable to impressions than snow? Yet, though it receives light, both directly and reflected from every angle, it bears no graphic impressions. Has this hill in our Franconia alone brought forth a mound unparalleled in all the land of Europe? And is it alone exclusively disposed to receive these prodigious effects? What a novel and unusual wedding this thinker has schemed between light and elemental atoms dispersed in the air, their conjoined forces generating these marvelous offspring in its formed hardness! What fertility does light obtain from the elements, or the earth from both, that it can generate a cricket, a lizard, a fly, or any other insect in a stone, or can transform the rocky matter of this muddy, sandy mound into any of these creatures? Is he inclining, without admitting it, to the opinion of Lhwyd, mingling seeds with light (as Lhwyd did with the vapors) and by this medium transporting them to the land, there to take on their natural forms? More than most comparisons, the analogy between the maternal womb and the bosom of the earth, limps. Will you attribute the same active force to an inanimate mound of dirt which the physicians correctly predicate of the vital principle in a pregnant woman, though they have not yet explained beyond all dispute those unexpected modalities of operation which spoil the proper symmetry of the natural body? Monstrosities are begotten, blemishes appear on an otherwise well-formed fetus, not only from the perception of visible images, from frightening and unusual objects, but by touch, hearing, and even at times by taste. What has light in common with hearing and touch, or lifeless earth with the senses? Light penetrates only diaphanous and transparent bodies; it merely grazes the surface of dense and opaque bodies such as the earth. It does not permeate or encompass or flood such as these, especially when they lie embedded in another solid body. How, then, would light penetrate piles of earth to a depth of three, or four, or even more cubits, where, in the opinion of many, even the heat of the sun hardly reaches, there to diffuse various species, and, casting them accidentally upon a tablet of soft earth, affix them in picture form? Even more: could this light leave not merely an impression, but a fully formed shell, perfectly wrought in all details, not imbedded in crude clay, but displaying consistent and elegant artistry on every side? Refer to Plate II, wherein both sides of each stone are reproduced.

On this consideration alone, all fabrications about the confusion, mixture, diverted reflection of species, analogous to the unnatural cause of defective images, fall to the ground. In vain, too, does one summon the Hebrew characters from the tombstones of the Jews, and spirit them on the wings of light onto our stones. If the eloquent praises of the Divine Majesty, of the Messiah, and of the Spirit of God are borrowed from the inscriptions of the Jewish tombs (which we have shown in the preceding chapter to be impossible) why is it that the vines, the hedges, the trees, the memorials and columns of the Saints erected in the vineyards, are not reproduced on our stones, particularly when one realizes that they enjoyed even greater exposure to the light? How is Judaism more noble, that its vestiges should be left engraved in stone, while supposedly the light blithely skipped over and airily neglected many other objects?

Finally, with the rays of the sun, light can be collected in a bowl of encaustic glass, and, by the Archimedean process, can be so focused as to set fire to an enemy fleet. Now, if the same can be demonstrated by irrefutable experimentation concerning the propagation and impression of images by the graphic force of light, we will heartily applaud this as the lustrous origin of our stones.

CHAPTER VI

A mingling of the seeds of testacea and marine animals with the vapors rising from the ocean, subsequently to be dispersed on the earth by the rains, is not the origin of our Würzburg stones.

EDWARD LHWYD, a most learned man of indefatigable labors, as Büttner justly praises him in his *Coralliographia Subterranea*, Chapter I, section 17,[1] diffidently proposes his theory on the origin of marine fossils in his sixth letter to John Ray—the theory on which we have touched in Chapter III.[2] But he raises so many and so weighty objections to his own system, and answers his opposition so lightly and perfunctorily, if at all, that I can think of no better weapon than the author's own to pierce this paradoxical opinion.

For who could believe that seeds, borne through the air for so long a distance, would finally be deposited in a matrix exactly conditioned and proportioned to their genesis and natural growth? By what guidance, by what path, by what force are they infused into solid stones? By what skill do they find ready ingress into the tiny pores of dense rocks? Or, assuming that they are imbibed and received by the force of some magnetic attraction, whence, I should like to know, do they obtain the growth to realize the full figure intended for them by the Author of Nature? Whence such velocity and density that they are transported, not only to Britain, which is completely surrounded by the sea, but to the land-bound districts of interior Germany, far removed from the ocean? Why are these offspring of sea life not found readily everywhere, since the vapors impregnated with these seeds and resolved into rain are dispersed in all directions? Why, in some places, are animals found whole and entire, while in others only particles and fragments and incomplete rudimentaries are dug up? To borrow from the argument of Assalti, if Lhwyd suggests that these seeds, dropped into the depths of earth and stone, can be so sustained there that they bring forth little animals, which in this confinement are nourished, grow, live, and mature, is it not obvious that all this is totally averse and foreign to the constant order of nature established by the Maker of the world? "Who has ever observed rising from the sea a bird similar to those that use the air or quadrupeds resembling horses or lions? Conversely, has anyone seen fishes flying in the air, or perfect birds or fishes or quadrupeds spring from plants?" [3] These and like things could not possibly happen without the overthrow of the immutable order of Nature, which is an absurd idea. It is much more ridiculous to believe that seeds carried by the rains into the inner recesses of earth and stone could generate stone fishes, testacea, and virtually all the species of aquatic animals, so similar to the real animals and their parts that they differ only by the absence of movement and life. "For since the structure of internal organs and the mixture of humors differs [4] in the various types of plants and animals, not only are they not all nourished, matured, and sustained by the same things, but very often what is eminently healthful to one is harmful, even fatal, to another. Thus plants which flourish on the mountains waste away on the sea shore; and conversely, those which grow in marshy soil wither in the dry and open spaces. The same can be observed in the animal kingdom. Various of them thrive on various foods, places, climes, and other circumstances." [5]

Hence this perspicacious man concluded that if fishes, testacea, crustacea, and other organisms born in the sea were to be transferred elsewhere in seminal form, they would necessarily corrupt and perish, since they could not possibly obtain sustenance and growth-inducing food, in a manner coinciding with the design everywhere established by the Author of Nature. Rather, it is most probable that such seeds, if they fell into rock depressions or similar places, would be eroded and dissolved by corrosive mineral salts, or at least would be so stifled by stony or metal matter that growth and expansion would be impossible.

The same observations are, as the celebrated author points out, applicable to such parts as may be found separate from the whole animals, since in this case likewise the contrary would be a violation of the natural order, and tantamount to flying in the face of manifest evidence. "For who," he asks, "has ever observed the wings of birds, or the mane of a lion, or an elephant's trunk, or the dewlaps of an ox, or the tusks of a boar generated separately from these animals? [6] Has anyone seen the growth of fruits, seeds, bark, or leaves removed from the plants themselves?" [7]

I forego any further critique of this fable (as Büttner labels the Lhwydian theory). Suffice it to say that whatever truth one may imagine in our learned British confrere's ingenious cerebrations concerning the origin of imaged ($i\theta\iota o\mu \acute{o}\rho\phi\omega\nu$) stones, the theory fails utterly when applied to our stones.

Besides the likenesses of insects reproduced on the frontispiece and plates thus far, there have been found on our mountain numerous other species of zöoliths and lithophytes, which will appear in the illustrations to follow. That these are true marine life of the same form, texture, solidity, and perfection as those which Scheuchzer and his protagonists classify as diluvial relics, is amply demonstrated by the exact expression of sea fish and testacea, by the remains of their armature, by bits of their members and parts adhering to the mass of petrificous moisture, and by the hardness of the stones, characteristic of diluvial stones, often equaling that of pyrites and exceeding that of flint.

Lhwyd, of course, will ascribe the origin of these to seed dropped into the womb of the earth with vapors and rains. But the other stones now under consideration are very different, though many of these also bear not inexact likenesses of insects and testacea. They are soft, fragile, quite lacking the elegance of the others, and evincing no articulation or well-defined internal structure. Why would the seed of what is plainly the same organism, planted in the same homogeneous mound, in the same locale under the same air and sun, operate with so wide a diversity of effects?

Lhwyd deals, if not exclusively, at least primarily, with the origin of marine and testaceous life, wherefore his attention is focused on the sea. Our image-bearing (ἰθιόφοροι) stones represent worms, lizards, wasps, toads, frogs, flies, crickets, scorpions, birds, and flowering plants, the seeds of which are attributable, not to the sea around Britain, but possibly to the vapors rising from the native land of these animals and plants—vapors that share their ascent with these seeds. This last supposition is essential if the Lhwydian system, which deals only with marine life, is to have any possible application to the genesis of our stones. But why are not the seeds of larger and more perfect animals, cattle and beasts of the forests, or carcasses rotting in caves, caught up in the motion of these same vapors and exhalations of the land, and transplanted in the ground with the rains? Why, if they are subject to the same mode of ascent and descent as the spermatic effluvium of insects, can they nowhere find a suitable matrix and cradle where we might stumble upon a petrified deer, or steer, or boar, as we do a cankerworm, or a crab, or a frog? Why is our mountain alone so fertile that it disgorges animals—not dismembered, or their parts only, but nearly always in their integral state, and more frequently than not having the size which Nature has defined for them? Can it be that the rains, with exceptional generosity, deposit in the place, the seeds not merely of some members or parts but of whole animals, undiminished and undivided? Why do these animals and plants, though intact and mature, not depart from the matrix and exist on their own, but protrude only with their upper surface, while half of their body not only is immersed in the stone, but in broken continuity, constitutes one whole mass, with the rest of the matter forming a base? Did the formative fertility of the seed or the matrix become defective in producing the fetus? The nearby hills covered with vines, and other mountains adjacent to Würzburg, are composed of the same muddy and sandy earth and clay, and are watered by the same rains, supposedly pregnant with fertile seeds. Why then, despite my painstaking searches, have I found no similar offspring on any of them? Granted that all parts of the world do not bear all things, why at least does not the one part, subjected to the same principles and causes, not bring forth the same effects? What sort of vapor could bear to the mountain of Franconia the seed of a sea scallop, then so miraculously mingle it with the seed of a toad, that in one parturition a clay or limestone rock would give birth to a well-formed toad enclosed in a scallop shell?

These and other specific properties of our idiomorphic stones I submit here and in the following chapter. I wish to pose only one more query to the author of the seminal hypothesis: does this fertility extend to the sun, the moon, and the other stars? Are they too propagated by some seed, which perchance, possibly dropping out of the Lhwydian mucous of putrefying stars, falls through the air onto our mountain, loses its igneous character, and finally generates stone stars, comets, sun, and moon? [8] Hold your laughter, my friends! The earth shall bear stars, bred in the same manner as animals and plants, when the heavens are put to the plow. Tell me, moreover, and you will indeed be a mighty Apollo, in what lands are born lettered stones, as the lithographers call them, inscribed with the Names of the Most High Godhead most elegantly traced in the letters of the sacred tongue? Are these the work of art, of Nature at play, operating by means of seeds or of salts twisting themselves into letters?

Here indeed the hypothesis of the illustrious Lhwyd fails utterly, and anyone who casts a judicious eye on the third plate (containing celestial bodies) in this first edition will conclude with us that the origin of the iconoliths herein exhibited is to be sought in other principles.

CHAPTER VII

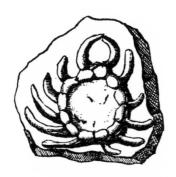

Seed remaining in dead bodies or in the mold of putrefied matter, and distributed through subterranean passages and rock fissures with its plastic force, by a seminal vapor aided by a lapidific current [spiritu lapidifico]*, is not the formative cause of the Würzburg iconoliths.*

As LHWYD RESOLVES the seeds of marine zoöliths and lithophytes into rain by the movement of mists, and thus brings them to the continent, in a similar ratiocination Lang has them driven by water through subterranean passages, distributes them throughout the fissures of rocks and the depths of pits, even wafts them to the earth's surface on the highest mountains. There, with the ministrations (we might say the maieutics) of magnetism, the plastic [*aura plastica*] or seminal mist [*aura seminalis*], or the lapidifical current [1] accounting for the generation of figured stones, he brings to light a stone beast or plant. The same arguments are advanced against this hypothesis, as those which the most eminent and experienced lithographers, such as Scheuchzer and others, leveled against the similar theory of Lhwyd. The principal objections are those already cited from Assalti's notes to *Armarium Nonum Metallotheca Vaticana*, Chapter 2, page 220; [2] the reader will find them there developed at greater length. Yet even at this point I cannot hold in high regard the power of this plastic mist or seminal force [*potentiae seminalis*] which he [Lang] imagines to be in each of the ovules of all living beings, permeating all their parts—stating further that many things, including plants, are born from these ovules, *De Origine Lapidum Figuratorum*, Chapter I, page 42.[3] Assalti, commenting (*loc. cit.*) on Lhwyd and Lang, writes: "They believe that in all bodies there is this [seminal force], which, as though deputed to this function, propels the fluids of the ovules, opens the tiny tubes, selects and admits the proper nourishment from without, and distributes it in proper proportions to all the parts. On the strength of this they deem it possible for the ovules, as well in clay, sand, and rock as in the water of the sea, nourished by the right saline nitrous aliment, supposedly abounding in these places, to grow and mature into the perfect figure of an animal. This they account for by the plastic force disposing all things, by the favorable structure of the ovules, and by the particles of food which adhere readily to the suitable parts." [4] What stupendous power this formative mist [*aurae formatricis*] possesses! Taking the place of the soul, it not only possesses the form of living things in itself, but, in the double role of architect and artisan, it expresses this form in crude matter. This is a new metempsychosis, indeed, more marvelous than the Pythagorean; for while the latter relegated the soul and spirit to a formed body as punishment or reward, this doctrine asserts that a little ethereal soul, innate in the ovule and imprisoned in extremely hard stone or earth, fabricates its dwelling from alien matter.

This plastic seminal vapor is certainly corporeal, and, being divisible, is by no means wholly in the whole of the ovule or corporeal seed and wholly in every part. Are all the parts of this amazing vapor endowed with such power that each one is capable of forming an entire plant or animal? Or is each joint, member, and part of the body that is to be animated, with their differences of figure, position, and quality, the responsibility of a specific part of the plastic mist, its power not extending beyond the structure of this unfamiliar fetus to other structures? If you affirm the first hypothesis, why do we find the teeth of a flat fish or so-called *glossopetra*, several headless ammonites, fishbones or fins, leaves without branches or trunk, trunks without roots, fruits without

tree? Did the slothful artisan, wearying of his work, abandon it un-
finished? Was it for want of a proper matrix and alimentary juice
suitable for the remaining members of this incipient portent? Why
did this formative power [*formatrix potentia*] complete, or select
for the beginning of its construction, a tooth, a tongue, a leaf, or a
fruit, in preference to a head, a jaw, a tree, or roots? As an alterna-
tive you may, with Lang (*loc. cit.*, Chapter 1, page 37), assert the
second theory, as he does in these words: "The seminal vapor is not
the same in every part of the living body, although it is equally
distributed to all the parts. For it is probable that God has inserted
into each part its peculiar seminal vapor which, with its plastic
force, makes it possible for the natural substance and determinate
structure of each part to grow by accretion due to the alimentary
moisture, and by nutrition to be preserved, with the result that in
animals, for example, the alimentary moisture in the fleshy parts is
assimilated into flesh, in bones into bone, in membranes into membrane, in glands into glandular matter, in the blood into blood,
while in plants, it becomes root in the roots, stem in the stem, flower
in the flower, etc., with this inviolable law, that it is produced
exactly in accord with the innate requirements of the specific
nature, in regard to the internal structure and the external form of
each part." [5] Thus, as it were, from the partial forms of the Peripatetics,[6] or the particular ferments of others, he constructs a kind
of metaphor about the seminal vapor exhibiting its heterogeneous
power in each of the parts. But by what accident or chance did it
happen that there fell upon our mountain so many particles of
seminal vapor with their ovules and seed not separated or disjoined
by any violence from the air or the wind or the waters plunging
through the hidden canals of the earth? How did it come about
that in their many and divers matters, sandy, muddy, and lime-
stones, even flint and marble, they found a matrix and cradle so
well stocked with nutritious juice, and preserved by a provident
and considerate Nature against the arrival of exotic colonists and
guests, that insects (with few exceptions), animals, and testacea are
all found intact, and in the exact size determined for them by the
Author of Nature? Why did the errant plastic mist produce in

clay a marine shell, and, in place of the shell's natural inhabitant, a small toad inside the shell (Plate II)? [7] Who deposited the seed of a toad in the ovule of the shell? For what reason were the ovules of birds (shown in Plate IV) borne to this place by mists and rains, or washed by subterranean waters? Why did the egg not turn to stone before it was hatched? Why did the petrifying moisture [*succus petrificus*] exercise its force on a full-grown bird rather than on the proportionate ovule in the shell? Did a mature bird gradually and unwittingly assume the nature of a stone, or did it instantaneously harden entirely into stone? Why did the skeleton petrify, while the feathers and flesh are lacking, as can be observed in Plate IV? Why did the plastic mist, fertile in one ovule, hatch the chick, while in the others it was sterile and turned to stone with the egg?

Truly, these difficulties render the Langian system so ineffectual [ἀδύνατον] with regard to our stones that there is no necessity here to refer to the lettered stones which we will show in Plate VII.

As to the observations of Lang, Book II, Chapter I: on the generation of living things in general; Chapter II, on the generation of testacea, which are most often represented in figured stones; Chapter III, on their nourishment and growth; Chapter V and VI: on living things, wholly alien to the substances of stone, yet born in stone,[8] I answer with the illustrious Assalti: "Much that is expounded concerning fossil flesh or the growing of animal horns in the ground must be discredited as mere fable. For it often happens among writers of things natural, that the truth, and even faith, is very much to seek. The reason is that, giving blind credulity to the assertions of others, or being all too superficial in their own observations, they are frequently led to write errors." [9]

CHAPTER VIII

Wherein it is clearly shown that some of our iconoliths, lithophytes, and testacea, notwithstanding their close similarity to marine fetuses were not transported to our mountain by the waters of the sea, either in the Universal Flood, or through the hidden passages of the earth, and then, over a period of time, turned to stone.

IN CHAPTER VI, I said that there were found on our mountain, besides the controversial stones impressed with the images of insects and small animals, an immense number of petrified ammonites, large and small scallops, mussels, snails, shellfish, strombs,[1] turbinids, and testacea, with and without their armature, some solitary, others enclosed in the matrix (though easily removed with the aid of a hammer), still others solidly compacted and coagulated in one stony mass, variseeded (ποικιλόσπερμον) as they are sometimes referred to in Greek. The polished specimens of this present a marble of magnificent color—the shells are ensconced in marble, polished smooth, and delightfully simulate the veins and flaws of marble. Now all of these, exceeding many thousands in number, we candidly confess that we owe to the universal inundation of the world—tragic yet indisputable witness of the Flood, along with Scheuchzer[2] and his group of Doctors, as listed by Lang (*De Origine Lapidum Figuratorum*, Chapter 9),[3] Tertullian himself claiming membership by reason of a clear text. If, however, the diluvial hypothesis concerning the origin of figured stones is unacceptable to some, we must nevertheless admit with Assalti, that such fruits, never the products of our own springs and streams, are borne to the mountains, crypts, and pits by way of subterranean passages. We transcribe here the discourse in which Assalti departs from the diluvial system. "Though one may freely admit," he says, in refutation of the seminal vapors, "that these animals could not have been left over from the Flood, still we cannot thereby conclude the impossibility of such bodies being uprooted from their native soil and, in some way—known or unknown to us—transported to other lands. As to the islands and other places not far distant from the sea, in which this type of stone has been found, as in Sicily and Malta, which abound in such specimens, it is extremely likely that at one time they were entirely immersed in the sea—as the most respectable writers attest concerning Egypt, and Delos, Rhodes, and other islands—or at least that they were inundated by a particular flood. There is a great deal of evidence favoring this opinion. For in the places where these stones are unearthed, there are to be found testacea, fishes, plants, and other organisms generated only in the sea, even the slimy matter of the sea floor, divers species of sea urchins, conchylia, sea snails, oysters, corals, madrepores, etc., all of them variously combined, some intact, some reduced to fragments yet easily identifiable. For example, here and there one finds the claws of crabs or the diminutive feet of sea urchins, and such things, not far removed from the animals to which they belong. Wherefore it is most probable that this whole mass of things was stirred up by the varying movements of the sea, fused together, and impacted into the earth. It is probable that the transference of these things to lands far distant from the sea and above its level can be explained on these same grounds. The most common opinion has it that the waters of the sea not only occupy the surface of the globe, but that they also penetrate the inner passages of the earth, thence to flow under the most remote and internal regions. This is perforce admitted even by those who assert that the seeds of fishes are borne by the vapors, and, under the influence of the plastic force, grow into idiomorphic stones [*lapides idiomorphi*]. Thus it could have happened that the waters, gradually penetrating the interiors of the mountains, dissolved and buckled the soil, whereupon the mass of earth above the water crumbled with the dissolution of its foundations. Hence the water under the earth would be compressed by the avalanche of earth and flung upward, carrying with it a great mass of testacea and other beings caught up in its sudden motion and fused together. Or it could easily have happened that all these things were dislodged and mixed together, little and great alike, by an earthquake of whatever origin." [4] From which it can be deduced that testacea and other sea life were transported to our mountain by the waters of the sea cutting into the earth through unseen ways (as is unanimously upheld by all who attribute the origin of springs and rivers to the ocean) whether as the result of a universal cataclysm or by a special act of the Author of Nature.

It is quite another matter when we come to our controversial stones, which, as genuine idiomorphi (ἰδιόμορφοι), differ from all other marine petrifications by their peculiar figure, distinct color, matter, solidity, hardness, and other properties. Those which originated and were left either by a universal or particular flood, or by subterranean seepage from the ocean, or those which, due to the action of land moistures and salts turned into stone over a period of time, are so formed that they retain their armature and shells unharmed by petrifying juices, and evident vestiges of their interior structure can be seen when they are broken open. Among these, the ammonites are all very much alike, whether they be striated or undulated, whether with tubercles or with scales, on top and bottom, their whole body being deeply scored with furrows, undulations, and joints, and giving indisputable indications of petrification. By contrast, among the controverted denizens of this same mountain (passing over the lettered stones which are ascribable neither to the sea nor to the Flood), the nonspiny ammonite, seen in Plate V, is smooth on top, furrowed on the bottom, quite different from the anterior part, while inside it has no joints or chambers, being an unformed stony mass. The same condition is noted in all the rest of our zoöliths and lithophytes: on the top half of their bodies they bear the imprinted figure of an animal or plant, but the remaining half is immersed in stone and forms a homogeneous mass with it, as we explained in Chapter II. They cannot, therefore, be classified with the marine petrifications.

Small toads, frogs, wasps, bees, crickets, beetles, scorpions, cankerworms, and similar insects are very easily born, but as readily languish and die. It is difficult to believe that these tiny animals, so susceptible to dissolution and decay, could be preserved undamaged amid the violent turbulence of the sea, either in the Flood or under the earth, and then gradually turned to stone. Or, supposing that the sea is not the natural breeding ground of these creatures, and that therefore they were not brought up from it—who could seriously propose that they were fortuitously caught up by the ocean that somehow spilled over onto the continent, and were cast up somewhere on this native soil where they would turn to stone?

According to the more probable opinion of both theologians and lithographers as related by Scheuchzer in his *Herbarium Diluvianum*, the Flood occurred in the spring, probably in May, at which time flowers and leaves (rather than ripe fruits) flourish.[5] How, then, did the diluvial tempest miraculously deposit on the shores of Franconia a ripe and integral apricot, complete with pit, meat, and skin, and a mature acorn appended to a small branch?[6]

The plants, flowers, and herbs which you see in Plate VI, besides being domestic, rather than exotic or marine organisms, are by nature extremely frail, and under heavy rain or frost, droop to the ground, drop their leaves, and die. Could these have been dashed against rock, and then, over a period of time, have been turned to stone far exceeding their proper density?

Was the mighty turbulence of the waters impotent to dislodge a bee or wasp from the bud of a plant—instead leaving the animal firmly and immovably attached by its proboscis, to be turned to stone along with the flower? The same perplexity arises regarding the cells and nests of wasps, of fragile structure and little more than wax, yet here withstanding the onslaught of salt and water, and turning to solid stone.

Finally, here is a spider web which not only withstands but disperses the rushing waters of flood and sea. The texture is too gross (see Plate X) to excite the envy of Pallas; at one end hangs Arachne poised to trap flies, or otherwise engaged in the weaving of her net. Can we say that this frail thing, which a breeze can destroy, or a fly or butterfly can tear, was not only spared by the force of the waters, but transferred so neatly and exactly to a stone tablet, that it stands as a perpetual monument to Arachnean skill?

But what need to go on? No intelligent person could entertain the slightest suspicion that our iconoliths were petrified by the sea waters—whether in the general flood, or drawn from the ocean by some other channel. However, by reason of the contrast, which we have intimated in this chapter, between our controverted figured stones, and genuine diluvial and maritime specimens found on the same mountain, certain dabblers and other mere amateurs in the field of Lithography have underhandedly and falsely taken occasion to insinuate that, while the others are true relics of the Flood, ours are the supposititious product of recent artificiality. Thanks to their vicious raillery, their false rumors and gossip, they have forced me—though I shrink from the task—to refute and confound them all in good time.

CHAPTER IX

*If our stones are not the work of art but of Nature,
their formation is not the result of playfulness, either
on the part of Nature or of Archaeus dispersed in
the Geocosm.*

ATHANASIUS KIRCHER, S.J., in his admirable work entitled
Mundus Subterraneus, whence not a few modern Lithographers
have borrowed the basis of their theories on the origin of stones,
in Book VIII, Section 1, page 37, describing four ways in which he
considers that these stones might have been effected, gives first
place to fortuitous occurrence. It may interest the reader who has
not ready access to this inestimable opus to read the words of this
sagacious and indefatigable student of Nature. "I would recall to
the reader," he says, "that, as the human phantasy, peering at the
cloud-laden sky, imaginatively reads into the cloud formations a
variety of things—sometimes dragons on the wing, at other times
mountains, cities, or castles, again, crosses, human figures, and
similar phantasmagoria—so too even in spittle on the ground we
sometimes see a figuration of one thing or another. Indeed, in our
travels, gazing at mountain stretches, from a certain perspective
we see a table, as the promontory of Good Hope, at other times a
human face, as the promontory of Scylla in Sicily, again, a reclin-
ing man, as in the Camerino Mountain of the Apennines . . .
Mount Palermo is called Monte de Medaglia by the natives, because the stones, trees, and fragments resemble a human likeness imposed on a coin. Sometimes on the rough surface of burnt bricks we

seem to see the outlines of insects, birds, etc.—not that Nature intended to produce such things, but by reason of a certain resemblance, the mind imagines that these things are there. Reflecting
on these commonplaces, one may not unreasonably ask concerning
the origin of apparitions on stones.[1] I answer that all these were
generated by the flow of saline liquid. When this liquid seeps into
appropriate earthy matter that is still soft, but is beginning to be
riddled with cracks and tortuous ducts under the onslaught of
desiccation, eventually, by the work of lapidific currents, all these
coalesce into one hard and stony mass. Then the liquid, following
the pattern of the cracks and fissures, delineates the forms of beautiful rivers, possibly of fulsome trees, or of birds, or of insects, or
quadrupeds, even a human likeness, or some member of the human
body, all in accord with the dispositions of the matter . . . There
is yet another reason, by no means a light one, supporting the
formation of these apparitions by a fortuitous flow of liquid. It is
that scarcely one of these images simulating animals is perfect.
There is always something lacking to the full figure: an eye or nose
will be missing in a head, an arm will be lacking a hand or fingers,
a leg will have no foot, things which an artist would almost certainly remedy. Wherefore, we must judge, not what, in fact, they
are, but rather what the imaginative faculty pretends they are, as
we said of the clouds, the mountains, the spittle, and the rest." [2]
And there you have the undisguised and candid opinion of this
learned man that the figures in stones are the result of sheer chance,
or that they assume this or that appearance due to the caprices of
the imagination. Büttner's reproach to the Ludions seems to be *a
propos* here (*Coralliographia Subterranea*, Chapter I, Section 9 ff.): [3]
"All these are a fiction of Nature? No, they amend it to a trick of
the imagination deceiving the eyes . . . an imagination bereft of
judgment, confused, inattentive, even gullible or mocking . . .
deceiving as well as being deceived by mere appearances."

What Kircher calls fortuitous occurrence, more recent authors
refer to as the sport of a pleasingly erring Nature [*Naturae
gratiose errantis lusum*]. I can unhesitatingly agree with them
when it comes to marble, agate, roots of nut-trees and other multi-

colored stones and woods, especially when the images are mere sketches, as the Eichstad Dendrites exhibited by Kircher,[4] and very laudably explained by Scheuchzer in his *Herbarium Diluvianum;*[5] but not, however, when they are sculpted in high relief, or are solitary figures adhering to no base. But who would brand as a jest of Nature these stones of ours, in which the forms of bodies of every realm of Nature, even the superlunary, except (to date) a full human figure, are seen clearly and perfectly expressed, so that not only the outlines, but the entire statuettes, either finished on all sides or half raised from their base, seem to bear unmistakable indications of the sculptor's knife?

The freaks of Nature are rarely prominent or raised, being rather smooth, level, and continuous with the surface of the stone. Further, they are found only in the regions, soils, and matters where the diversity of colors, tints, salts, and liquids seeping into the crevices and fissures of the dry earth will permit such handsome aberrations. By contrast, many of our stones—lime, clay, or sand—are of the one texture and color that is proper to such stones. One must conclude then that in this case Nature, wishing to indulge in sportive painting, lacked Kircher's salts and tints.[6] The figures, designs, and colored spots of marble which, as we said in the preceding chapter, we have found here in great quantity, are as our eyes testify the sloughings, remains, and vestiges of conches clinging to the external layer and immersed even in the extremely hard marble or flint.

Idiomorphic stones, in which Nature can be said to have made sport, are altogether of the same type, nor are they unearthed anywhere and everywhere, but exclusively in those places which bear matter similar to that described by Kircher. Würzburg, on the other hand, indeed the whole of Franconia, has but one mountain (no other has been discovered yielding such finds in our land and it is possible that none such has appeared elsewhere) in which, besides marble, there are stones of most diverse species, compacted of sand, mud, and clay, all, without discrimination as to material, impressed with the same forms of animals, vegetables, and letters. How does it happen that here Nature promiscuously, indiscriminately, and with no predisposition makes sport with this new wonder, previously unknown to lithographers?

I again appeal to the plates with their illustrations of the Würzburg iconoliths, as the most eloquent witnesses of my assertions; one of these, number VI, with its exquisite specimens of lithophytes, I have inserted in this chapter. Was Nature jesting when it brought forth an apricot, absolutely perfect and fully ripened, but petrified? Or again, when it fashioned a colt's foot herb in a leaf, a ranunculus and a small plantain, waxing with leaf, stem, and roots? Or when it enticed a wasp to the nectar of a blooming chrysanthemum or white daisy? When it appended acorns to the oak twig? Why did it neglect to color these, while elsewhere in marble, agate, and dendrite it so carefully mixed and applied the colors? Why, in its other jests, as Kircher affirms, did it sketch mere outlines of figures, yet in these and others of our zoöliths and lithophytes, though exceeding the density proper to the plants and leaves, it nonetheless scaled down their size, as though to restore the balance?

But I find myself disinclined to argue further in so obvious a dispute, lest I too appear to squander words and time in mere sport.

CHAPTER X

Wherein are presented ten of our stones impressed with letters, principally Hebrew, along with a succinct interpretation of them by certain scholars.

AMONG FIGURED STONES, greater attention and deeper research is due those which, being marked with the characters of divers languages, are known among lithographers as lettered stones [*lapides litterati*], *grammatiae*, polygrams [*polygrammi*], and grammites [*grammitae*]. Kircher, writing on these in Book 8, Chapter 8 of his *Mundus Subterraneus*,[1] tells of the discovery in the field of Tolfens of a certain species of blue stone wherein Nature had set forth in bright and subtle lines all conceivable figures.[2] "I found," he says, "besides all the letters of both Greek and Latin alphabets, virtually all the groups of simple figures which Euclid sets forth in his *Elements of Geometry*." Assalti in Armarium IX, *locul. octavus* of the Mercati *Metallotheca Vaticana*,[3] describes a long, white, smooth flint, which he classes with the *grammatiae* of Pliny,[4] resembling *smaragdus*,[5] encircled with a white line, and widely circulated in the East as an amulet. To these may be added the sparkling stones mentioned by Lang in Chapter 5 of his *Historia Lapidum Figuratorum Helvetiae*.[6] These are imprinted, not with characters, but with numerous lines of varying size, "which are sometimes distributed separately over the surface of the stones, at other times amassed together from several directions, or yet again, intersect each other in the middle; they are called sparkling because their entire surface is filled with sparkling grains, rivaling the brilliance of gold or silver." Helwing in his *Lithographia Angerburgica*, Part II, Chapter 2,[7] deals at greater length with the question of lettered stones, particularly with the Resavian Stone, bearing the image of the rising moon and the Latin capitals, L.V.R. (see *ibid.*, Book I, Chapter 5, Section 9).[8] He especially notes that between the first two letters there appears a crescent with its horns, while the remainder of the stone is seen to be covered with scallops and small rings immersed in the stone, the branch of a plant rising from the right side. He adduces still other stones bearing the letters I.C.W., E.A.G.V.L., and G.E.U.L., which he decides are the initials of certain very honorable men, whom he names.[9]

The salient difference between all these and the Würzburg polygrams is in this, that while on our stones the letters are, for the most part, prominent, raised, and seemingly sculptured, those seen on other stones are smooth, level with the surface, or even sunken, and appear to be the effect of Nature's handwriting—although Helwing (*loc. cit.*, and Part II, page 46) [10] does mention some Latin and Greek letters standing out from the stones in due proportion.

Let us now turn our attention to Plate VII, and examine each of the stones with its inscriptions in the order of their presentation. Several features are immediately apparent. First: Here and there one finds solitary letters; elsewhere whole words, with or without dots. Second: Some letters are formed exactly according to the rules of orthography, others crudely and imprecisely, so that they are difficult to recognize—whether this is the fault of Nature or of unskilled art, I have not yet determined. Third: The letters in the words are displaced, inverted, and sometimes set at an angle. Fourth: Samaritan, Rabbinical, or, as they are called, Babylonian, letters are interspersed with the Hebrew, while in other lettered stones which are presently in my possession, are Arabic and Latin characters and numerals. Fifth: Various characters and letters are inscribed, not on plain stones, but on scallops, shells, spirals, ammonites, etc.,

not always in relief, but sometimes deeply incised, as seen in Plate
V, and in the present plate [VII]. All these render explanation more
obscure and difficult. Copies of our *grammatiae* were submitted to
expert scholars of Oriental languages, who, though they are not
always in accord concerning the explanation of single letters or of
their unusual displacement, nevertheless were entirely in agreement
on one point: the Most Sacred Name of God and the titles of the
Divine Perfections stood out in practically every stone. We have
determined to publish in this first edition the conclusions of two
of these experts. The first is a Jewish Rabbi of scholarly distinction
who, upon seeing two of these stones, was struck with holy fear,
and after a long silence, avowed that he did reverence to the ineffable Name of God expressed in this wondrous work of Nature.
Pressed for an explanation of the other characters and of their
unusual transposition, he resorted to cabala, which I quite properly
rejected. Nevertheless, through a mutual acquaintance, I delivered
to the Jew several sketches of the lettered stones. His comment on
them, translated from Hebrew, is as follows: "I must confess that
these stones cloak a great prodigy, surpassing human comprehension. In several of them I find the venerable and blessed Name of
God יהוה, though as to the remaining characters, nothing certain
can be stated. They could, of course, be interpreted according to
our doctrine to signify other Divine Names, as the Name of God
contained in the numerals 72, 63, 45, or 52—this with the aid of
other keys and languages, and the inverted alphabet. However, I
do not care to write any further on this subject, for the reason that
it would hardly be discreet to commit to print things which the
Christians could appropriate to their own religion and faith, to the
bitter resentment of their adversaries (the Jews)." So much from
this Rabbi, whom I was delighted to dismiss, since I could expect
from him little more than vain and empty cabalistic contrivances.

Far more honest, clear, and erudite is the opinion of Philip Ernest
Christfels,[11] Prefect of the castle of his illustrious Excellency, Count
von Hohenlohe Schillingsfurt at Wilhelmsdorf. This learned man,
once a Jew, but now incorporated in Christ at the sacred font, care-

fully examined every mark of our stones and wrote a long expository dissertation on them. Some of these I will relate here, omitting solitary or indecipherable characters which can only be explained with the aid of superstitious cabala. In the first, second, and fifth stones, the Most Sacred Name of God, Jehovah, is manifestly expressed, with, however, these peculiarities: that in figure 1, the inverted *vau* is in the place of the *jod*, the *jod* (also inverted) is written under the *vau;* in figure 5, the *vau* occupies the position of the *jod*, and vice versa. He could offer no explanation of his own for this transposition, but fell back upon the interpretations of the Rabbis. These, with their wonted ineptness, teach that the Name of God, Jehovah, dishonored by the sins of the Jews, was split, so that וה *vau* and *he* being disjoined, only יה *jah* remains, which is a common appellation for God both in the Pentateuch and in the Psalms of David. They then infer (taking a line through Verse 12 of Psalm 93) that *Jah* signifies God the Avenging Judge, and that when *He* is appeased by prayers and penance, the Name of Jehovah is reintegrated, revealing the God of Clemency and Mercy. For the rest, the Jews have a superstitious cult of these characters of the Divine Name, hence, since each letter of the alphabet also stands for some number, when they wish to write numerals they scrupulously avoid these letters. Thus, since י equals ten and ה equals five, when they wish to write fifteen, instead of יה, they write טו, that is, nine and six. They do the same for sixteen, and for other numerals, all out of reverence for the characters of the Divine Name. Regarding the representation of the sun in figure 1, and of the moon in figure 5, he believes, after the manner of the Rabbis, that the sun symbolizes the eternity, beauty, beneficence, providence, and eternal splendor of God; the moon he considers a parenetic symbol, warning the Jews not to be vacillating and failing (like the moon) in their worship of the true God.

Figure 2 again reads Jehovah, with an imperfect כ superimposed. Concerning this he draws on the fantastic commentaries of the Rabbis on the Book of Sohar.[12] According to these, *nun* signifies the number fifty, and, in apposition to the Divine Name, indicates the fifty jubilee years of God, the fifty principal gates of heaven, and the like, all of which I pass over, along with his conjectures about the two subscribed characters. The dot under the last *he*, he interprets as a symbol of the indivisible unity of God.

In figure 3 he discerns half of the Name of Jehovah וה: *vau* and *he*. Here too the Rabbis spin their wild fantasies: these are the basic letters of the Divine Name, hence they signify the throne and tribunal of God; they are the insignia of the King of kings; they are the identifying letters inscribed on the *labarum* or standard of the Lord of Hosts, etc.

He extracts no meaning from the distorted and imperfect characters in figure 4. The Rabbi whom we quoted previously, seeing the stone, immediately reverted to the cabala for an explanation. Christfels substitutes another interpretation by interjecting vowels between the consonants, in this manner: סשיחרכניחייללרמנפרותיהו, to read *Maschiach, Raboni chail, Damcha, pedutenu*—that is, "Christ, Our Lord and Master, the power of Thy Blood is our Redemption." All this, however, is entirely arbitrary, and bespeaks neither art nor ingenuity, but more sophistry. This is analogous to the gratuitous interpretation of the letters L.V.R. on the Resavian Stone. Helwing adds a vowel to each of these, then multiplies and repeats them until they spell out the entire dedication of the first book of the *Lithographia Angerburgica* to Ludwig Von Rauter.[13]

In figure 6 he does nothing more than labor the delirious interpretations of the Rabbis. He finds the last character similar to the Babylonian or Rabbinical *aleph*, which, being composed of *jod* (numeral 10) and *vau* (numeral 6), thus: היה, which means *hova*, the ever-existing God, also amounts to sixteen, and is a cabalistic symbol of the Deity. He reasons in the same manner *a propos* the א which has first place on this stone. It is composed, he says, of two *jods* with a transverse *vau*, adding up to the number 26. The same number is contained in Jehovah, therefore *aleph* is the symbol of the Deity. Can one resist laughing at these insipid if charming observances of the Hebrews in the matter of numerals and characters?

The character which in figure 7 is first inverted, then erect, he thinks to be the Rabbinical or Babylonian *schin*. Looked at transversely, it has the form of *daleth*. The accompanying letter is the Samaritan *jod*, thus permitting the reading שׁרי *Schadai*—that is, Omnipotent God, the invocation supposedly employed by the Patriarchs when they blessed their sons.

He simply enumerates the letters in figure 8: *zain*, unformed *vau*, *he*, accent *zarcka*, and *coph*, adding a few cabalistic *jeux de mots* of the Hebrews, which I will spare the benevolent reader.

In figure 9, he names the following characters: *he*, Rabbinical *aleph*, Syriac *theth*, *jod*, and an unidentified Arabic character, *he*, Samaritan *jod*, with one *kamez* being transversely apposited. Making various combinations of these, he again applies them to the Divine Perfections.

I have felt constrained to repeat here in epitome the conjectures and expositions of these men, to whom I am deeply indebted. Should it ever be conclusively demonstrated that these lettered stones are artificial monuments of Jewish superstition, there would be no reason to doubt that the many inverted, varied, distorted, and transposed characters constitute a multitude of expressions of the cabalistic and combinatory art practiced by the Rabbis of this superstitious people. In which case we promise to give an explanation, however imaginative, according to the mind of the Jews. It is a fact, established by a celebrated Jewish Rabbi in his book on the antiquities of the Temple entitled *Schilte Hagiborim*,[14] that in times past, stones intended for such sacred purposes were highly prized by the Jews. There were two reasons for this. First, stones had been used by their ancestors in the Old Law for titles, testaments, and altars, as we read in Genesis 28:11 and 22, and in Joshua 4:3, etc. Secondly, the Law was inscribed on stone tablets, and the twelve tribes were represented by as many small precious stones on the breastplate of the high priest. Thus, as the Rabbi relates, they were wont to sculpt the Names, praises and benedictions of God on stones, which, in time of persecution or war, they disguised with lime or clay and concealed in unsuspected and inaccessible places, to safeguard them from the hands of their enemies.

Still, why should we not attribute our stones to Nature in operation—whatever the mode of this operation? Thus God, the Founder of Nature, would fill our minds with His praises and perfections radiating from these wondrous effects, so that, when forgetful men grow silent, these mute stones might speak with the eloquence of their figures.

CHAPTER XI

*Were our idiomorphic stones fashioned by the hand
of the artist of old, later to be transferred by uncertain
chance to this now famous mountain, or were they
formed and figured by natural causes, as other petrified
fossils? This is the problem.*

As I HAVE FREQUENTLY INTIMATED in the course of this dissertation, the answer to this controversial question is still a matter of
dispute. Weighty arguments favor art; no less impressive are those
which argue for Nature. In this chapter I shall present both con-
tentions, withholding my own opinion, though I shall not hesitate
to declare my stand when, in due time, the diggers will have pene-
trated more deeply into the mountain, and will have uncovered
more lucid evidence to resolve the doubt in one direction or the
other.

That our stones are the product of ingenious and skillful art
seems to be indicated by the extraordinary smoothness of both the
stones themselves and of the forms protruding from the tablets—
a smoothness suggesting the polished effect of applied pumice,
though the lower side retains its natural soiled roughness. One
would swear that he discerned on many of them the strokes of a
knife gone awry, and superfluous gouges in several directions; yet
the figures of plants and animals appear so neat to those who inspect
them, that at first sight one springs, without a moment's considera-

tion of the possibility of natural causes, to the conclusion that they are artifacts. Also, the reproduction of exotic and marine animals in many cases most beautifully imitates the images of the living prototypes, and thus hints at the skill of the artist. By contrast, Nature's art works are for the most part incomplete and defective, offering scarcely more than a shadowy likeness of the objects one fancies portrayed—although among our iconoliths, many fall short of the perfect likeness of the real living creatures, and reveal the unskilled hand of a sculptor whose imitative efforts were but poorly rewarded. Many of the insects found here are not only foreign, but unknown and positively monstrous. No mention of such creatures is made by Jonston,[1] Gesner,[2] Aldrovandus, and the other modern writers of things natural; hence one could reasonably conclude that they were conjured up by the brain that gave birth to the chimera, the centaur, and the hircocervus,[3] then committed to stone in a multitude of little beasts for the edification of those who might gaze upon them. On the other hand, why is it that Nature, recognized throughout the provinces of Europe as the parent of petrifacts, though its mode of operation is in part still a mystery, in part exposed by the researches of the scholars, why, I ask, has it thus far produced nothing elsewhere that resembles the Würzburg finds? Is it, in other soils, utterly destitute of that prodigious faculty of figuring stones which it enjoys only in Franconia? Has it failed to find in other soils than that of Mount Eivelstadt, the same soft earth,[4] terrestrial salts, petrificous liquids, and other aids to petrifaction, wherewith to form this remarkable harvest of zoöliths and lithophytes? Since this is difficult to admit, it is understandable that the cradle of these wonders has been sought among the workshops of artists. The very density of the stones carelessly strewn about the back and foot of the mountain does give rise to the suspicion that this was not the native soil, but the grave of the idiomorphs, where these artifacts were by some obscure chance transported and, over a period of time, immersed and buried. What is to be said of the lettered stones, or *grammati* and *grammatiae*, found to a number in excess of one hundred? On some of these the characters are deeply carved, on others they protrude; at times they are orthographically perfect, in other cases the letters are so distorted, inverted, displaced, or curiously formed, that even the most expert linguists hesitate to identify the language to which they belong— which manifests a decided lack of linguistic skill on the part of the sculptor. Nor are solitary characters alone found on these stones, which, as Kircher, Assalti, Helwing, and others assert, sometimes happens by natural causes, but—what is almost unheard of among Lithographers, and virtually unique among stone collections—one reads entire words and encomia of the Divine Perfections, not only on the plain surface of substratum stone but, more amazingly, on shells, spirals, ammonites, etc., which heighten the prodigiousness of Nature (if work of Nature it be) by deeply carved or slightly raised characters, or (the more likely reaction) draw the viewer's thoughts to art.

But now we are in need of an Oedipus or an Alexander to solve this very thorny riddle and, either by conjecture or by supernatural insight, to inform us as to the purpose of those who at great cost produced these monuments of ancient art. Were they to be adornments of some citadels or military bases or palaces? Once the most noble families of Franconia dwelt on Eivelstadt, and the standard of the Pappenheims is extant today. In the crude ways of the Middle Ages, it was not unusual for architects to adorn the capitals of columns, the arches, vaults, entrances, etc. with miniatures of small dragons, serpents, monkeys, and other monstrosities, as can be seen in the remains of the buildings of those days. In our own day it is customary to incrust the crypts of gardens and fountains with those little aquatic animals in artificial nests, which flourish in lakes, streams, pools, and silvan grottoes. Now, since many of our new-found exhibits are of this sort,[5] does not the thought occur that these few, if more precious, relics of once famous buildings and gardens are found in this mountain precisely because it has remained hitherto untouched and uncultivated, while the neighboring hills have all been planted with vines and cultivated, and from these the carefully working vintners eliminated any stones they might come across, heaping them in hidden spots outside the vineyards? Were one to set eyes upon these piles, the great number of artifacts found to date would be considerably increased, just as, before our observation of the stone treasury of this mountain, the findings that astonished the simple vintners confirmed our theory of antiquity, though we held our peace. But if it is not to our liking to extract the varied deposit of our stones from the ruins of arches and gardens, shall we revert to those relics of paganism which we have already elaborated and rejected? This is, quite candidly, the case for art; and, not to pass over anything that might favor an opinion which I have rejected, I submit here a synopsis of those pagan practices which I referred to in a general way in Chapter IV. Thus anyone who has not access to the Acts of the Councils or the Paderborn records, can draw his own conclusions about the probability of our stones being artifacts. The following is the list of pagan practices and superstitions forbidden to neo-Christians by the synods of Germany and Estinnes.[6]

1. *De sacrilegio ad sepulchra mortuorum.* (Sacrilege at the graves of the dead.)
2. *De sacrilegio super defunctos.* (Sacrilege committed on the dead.)
3. *De spurcalibus in Februario.* (The February pollutions.)
4. *De Casulis, id est Fanis.* (Cottage temples.)
5. *De sacrilegiis per Ecclesias.* (Sacrileges in churches.)
6. *De sacris sylvarum, quae Nimidas vocant.* (The forest rites, which are called Nimidae.)
7. *De his, quae faciunt super petras.* (Rites performed on rocks.)
8. *De sacris Mercurii et Jovis.* (The rites of Mercury and Jupiter.)
9. *De Sacrificio quod alicui Sanctorum.* (Sacrifices to the Saints.)
10. *De Phylacteriis et Ligaturis.* (Amulets and ligatures.)
11. *De fontibus Sacrificiorum.* (Sacrificial fonts.)
12. *De Incantationibus.* (Incantations.)
13. *De Auguriis vel Avium, vel Equorum, vel Boum stercoribus, vel sternutationibus.* (Auguries of the dung or sneezings of birds, horses, or oxen.)
14. *De Divinis et Sortilegis.* (Diviners and soothsayers.)
15. *De Igne fricato de ligno, id est Nodfyr.* (Fire struck from wood, i.e., Nodfyr.)

16. *De Cerebro Animalium.* (The brains of animals.)
17. *De observatione pagana, vel inchoatione rei alicujus.* (Pagan observation or inauguration of any matter.)
18. *De incertis locis, quae colunt pro Sanctis.* (Obscure places cultivated for the Saints.)
19. *De petendo, quod boni vocant, Sanctae Mariae.* (Pagan invocations of Mary.)
20. *De Feriis quae faciunt Jovi et Mercurio.* (Festivals of Jupiter and Mercury.)
21. *De Lunae defectione, quod vocant vince Luna.* (The ceremonies of the waning moon.)
22. *De Tempestatibus, Cornibus et Cochleis.* (The weather god, horns, and shells.)
23. *De sulcis circa villas.* (Trenches surrounding the villages.)
24. *De Pagano cursu, quem Yrias nominant, scissis pannis vel calceis.* (The pagan races, called Yrias, with the tearing of clothes and shoes.)
25. *De eo, quod sibi Sanctos fingunt, quoslibet mortuos.* (The canonization of the dead.)
26. *De simulacro de conspersa farina.* (Images made of scattered meal.)
27. *De simulacro de pannis factis.* (Images made of fabricated cloth.)
28. *De simulacro, quod per campos portant.* (Images carried through the fields.)
29. *De ligneis pedibus.* (Wooden feet.)
30. *De eo, quod credunt, quia foeminae lunam comedant, quod possint corda hominum tollere juxta paganos.* (The belief that women eat the moon, and can extract human hearts.)

Of all these forbidden pagan practices, only those relating to amulets and ligatures, and to horns and shells, could possibly apply to our stones.

That amulets and phylacteries were commonplace among the heathens has been widely divulged by Thomasinus (*De Donariis et Tabellis Votivis,*[7] citing Plutarch and Varro), and other writers. They were hung about the necks of both children and adults, on doorways, litter posts, and the walls of chambers, to ward off witchery, illnesses, incantations, fires, and other evils, by the auspices of the Averrunci gods [8] though they most frequently regarded these deities as distinct from the amulets. Their amulets sometimes represented shameful and obscene objects, sometimes the forms of demigods, birds, fishes, bipeds, quadrupeds, serpents, even of the sacred vessels and other utensils of the sacrifices. Athanasius Kircher in his *Oedipus Aegyptiacus*, especially Volume II, Part 2, Syntagma XIX, Chapter 1, et seq.,[9] writes extensively of the amulets of the Egyptians, and gives numerous illustrations of them, taken from wood or bronze engravings loaned to him from the museums of illustrious scholars. In the fourth chapter [10] he describes four protective scarabs highly venerated by the Egyptians, and worn on the neck, head, or arms with circlets of other amulets. Studying these, I remarked that they were not unlike the several small shell-encased frogs collected on our mountain, one of which I included in Plate II, with only this difference, that the Egyptian scarabs have the belly elaborated to a level surface, and inscribed with gnostic characters or with Egyptian or other hieroglyphic symbols. Our little frogs (though I could call them scarabs, so closely do they resemble the form of those exhibited by Kircher, especially in details of the head) are compeltely surrounded by perfect shell, with the underside of rough and unpolished stone. Kircher also shows that Isis was represented and worshipped in the forms of various animals by the Egyptians. Laurentius Pignorius in his *Expositio Mensae Isiacae*, Chapter 2, page 5 [11] teaches that Isis was the recipient of divine honors and worship, not alone in Egypt, but in Greece, Phoenicia, Libya, Portugal, Italy, and Germany. Noteworthy in connection with this is the assertion in Chapter 1, page 554 of *Anacephalaeosous Oedipus Aegyptiacus*,[12] that the animals which the Egyptians copied in their hieroglyphics were not foreign or esoteric, but local and domestic, objects of everyday familiarity. This he establishes by a variety of proofs. "First, the Egyptians almost never set foot off of their native soil in the interests of philosophy because, as both Strabo and Herodotus testify, they regarded the other nations as loutish barbarians, wholly unworthy of the wisdom of Egypt. Similarly, they were convinced that the true arts and sciences, as well as valid philosophy, were to be found nowhere except in Egypt, which, having primacy as a country, also enjoyed primacy of productivity. Secondly, it appears certain that they had no particular knowledge of animals that throve beyond the boundaries of Egypt, knowing only those which their fertile motherland produced for them. This is supported by strong evidence. For, since the Egyptians were deeply engrossed in scrutinizing the abilities, habits, knowledge, emotions, and other natural endowments of animals, they, as Plutarch asserts, observed to the point of superstition their least movement and action. Indeed, they regarded the knowledge of these matters as the principal part of the more recondite philosophy, and it seems most likely that such observation of animal powers and qualities could have been performed on the beasts that were most obvious and familiar to them. If this is the case, it is clear that they incorporated into their symbols and hieroglyphics only the Egyptian animals, the habits of which were familiar to them by daily experience, because they had no cognizance of foreign animals. As to the host of ancient fragments carved with the figures of deer, elephants, chickens, bears, and the like, these findings must be considered, not Egyptian, but Grecian artifacts." From this it is tempting to suspect that the forms of animals, both domestic and exotic, expressed in our stones are the productions of the superstitious artistry of both peoples—particularly since these things, along with other impious pagan rites, were spread into Germany and Franconia, and used as amulets and phylacteries. Moreover (to continue the case for the hypothesis of superstitious artifacts) I have found on our mountain certain statuettes which have every appearance of being protective charms. They exhibit virtually the same forms as the Egyptian Serapes and the Jewish Theraphim, which, as Kircher brilliantly reveals in his *Oedipus Aegyptiacus*, Volume I, Syntag. IV, page 259 et seq.,[13] were the idols stolen by Rachel from her father Laban, and appropriated by the Jews in imitation of Egyptian superstition.[14] Now the Serapes of the Egyptians were figures "without any members protruding, as though wrapped in winding cloths, made partly from stone, partly from metal, wood, brick." [15] For since the Egyptians, being more superstitious than other races, feared the wrath and outrage of their gods, should their images be damaged, they constructed these images in such a way that they would be safe from all breakage or mutilation, so that, by their wholeness, they would preserve the assistance and influence of the gods, which the sacrifices were considered to have attracted. All this, they feared, would be thwarted, should the least member of a statue be damaged, whether through carelessness or through malice. They were especially anxious about the protective figurines which they carried on their person wherever they went, since it could easily happen that with continual use and movement, an arm, a hand, a foot, or a finger would be broken. To meet this, they formed them in such a manner that only the head, covered with a veil extruded. The rest of the body was swathed, not unlike their infants and mummies. My stone statuettes exhibit, not a swathed infant, but a spiral or oblong shell, sometimes with the head of an idol protruding, while in other figures the corresponding place is inscribed with a character or hieroglyphic symbol, as we shall illustrate later. A figure not dissimilar to these, and bearing a striking resemblance to the Egyptian penates, can be seen in Plate II. The purpose served by the shells is a matter of open conjecture. I hesitate to assert that the term "horns" should be interpreted to mean ammonites, although Lang in his *Historia Lapidum Figuratorum Helvetiae*, Book IV, Chapter 1,[16] refers to a lengthy passage in Pliny [17] to establish that this stone, classed with the most sacred gems of Ethiopia, gave off the likeness of the golden Goat's Horn, and engendered prophetic dreams when laid under the head of sleeping persons, and that it is called ammonite either because it is found in the sandy soil around the temple erected to Jupiter Ammon by Bacchus in gratitude for the discovery of the Libyan fountain, aided by the guidance of the goat which he took to be Jupiter; or because the discoverers of this stone wished to enhance it with a quasi-divine name; or, finally, as an act of devotion to Jupiter [Jovem Ammonem].[18] Could it be, then, that in ancient times this stone was used by the unduly credulous Gentiles, and by the heathen Franks as well, for unholy and superstitious purposes?

Reflecting on our grammites and lettered stones, I am reminded of the talismans in common use among not only the Turks, Arabs, and Egyptians, but even the Hebrews, whose language is principally represented in Plate VII. Kircher, Volume III, Part 1, Class V,[19] may be consulted for the construction and use of the talisman. Its basic form was the Arabic alphabet arranged in the order of the Hebrew letters, from which, by the resulting combinations of pronunciation and equivalent numerals, they formed the various names of God, each of which they converted into their corresponding numerals, assigning each numeral and letter to one of the presiding angels which, they believed, held sway over the elements, the planets, the signs of the zodiac—in a word, all the constituents of the universe. From these intricate and exacting combinations they fashioned their talismans (as can be seen in the charts presented by Kircher [20]), then inscribed them on gems, skins, seals, bands, standards, etc., convinced—and endeavoring impiously to convince others—that these devices possessed miraculous power to fulfill human needs, ward off evils, and even wreak damaging revenge on enemies.

How lamentable that this superstition of fabricating talismans for most improper uses should fester among Christians in our day! No one who examines the preoccupation of the Hebrews with the cabalistic arts will dispute my claim that these people have fashioned and prized the talismans. For what else can one call those protective strips against fever and sickness, fire, storms, and lightning than talismans—damning evidence of the continuation of vain superstition in our own times? They abused the Divine Names and cognomens, variously expressed in the Sacred Books, twisting them by their observances, calculations, and divers modes of writing or painting, in order to obtain these ends. Intimations of this can be seen in the commentaries drawn from the Hebrew authors and applied by Christfels to the stones in Plate VII. It is more penetratingly demonstrated and refuted by that thorough scholar and conscientious critic of Jewish doctrine, Kircher, *op. cit.*, Part 1, Volume III, Class IV.[21] Turn now once again, kind reader, to our stones with the Hebrew letters. Reading thereon the variants of the Most Holy Name of God, can you think for a moment that these are

Jewish amulets, buried in this mountain by the Jews in their anxiety to conceal their superstitions at the approach of their exile from Eivelstadt, or for any similar reason? The obvious errors and transpositions of letters and words, and the unknown or foreign characters present no great difficulty. These you will readily discern as some sort of mystery, or the shortcomings of the artist, or an attempt at the occult by this perfidious people. Some have ventured the opinion that our Judaizing stones (if I may so describe them) were transported to our mountain from the graves of Eivelstadt; but they are more akin to amulets and talismans than to tombstones. On occasion the Jews inscribe on their tombstones the zodiac figure corresponding to the month of birth of the deceased. If he is of the stock of Levi, they depict a laver and hand basin; if they imagine him to be a descendant of Aaron, they engrave a pair of hands, folded in the following manner: Thumb was pressed to thumb, index finger to index finger, middle fingers crossed, with ring and little finger of each hand erect.[22] When the priest blesses the people with this gesture, they believe that the Spirit of God resides in his fingers, and they dare not gaze upon the hands hallowed by the presence of the Deity, lest they be struck blind. Nothing similar has been found to date, except the figures of the stars and the characters which we have mentioned, and the latter are more suggestive of phylacteries and talismans than of gravestones.

So I honestly believe that I have omitted or dissembled nothing that could argue for ancient if artificial origin of our stones. It is now time to speak on behalf of Nature as the maker of our wonderful iconoliths. However, before undertaking this task, I must first set forth a brief defense of my own reputation from the charge of imposture, and of the Würzburg stones from the contemptuous designation of "modern art."

CHAPTER XII

*Our idiomorphic stones are not the handwrought
products of fraudulent recent artistry, as some persons
have shamelessly pretended, and attempted to peddle to
the public by widespread rumor and gossip.*

As I stated in the introduction, the almost unique newness of
the figures in our stones, the like of which has not been seen or
known, either in Herbipoli or (so far as one can learn from the
Lithographers of other nations in their commentaries) in foreign
finds, has led some men of letters to suspect fraud and imposture.
There was one of these men in particular who, after my friends
and I had frequently inspected the mountain and the excavation,
and had diligently examined all relevant circumstances, accompanied me to the fertile source of these prodigies, knowing full well
my thorough conviction regarding their genuineness, and there not
only witnessed and handled more than one of these stones at their
unearthing; but, when asked for an opinion concerning their origin,
stated that he "believed that these iconoliths were artifacts, though
ancient, probably relics of bygone heathenism, confiscated by the
zeal of the German bishops and Duke Caroloman from the Christian people still inclined to the superstitious rites of paganism, and
cast off onto this mountain"; with which opinion I have dealt in
Chapter IV. So with peaceful mind and tranquil pen I pursued the
dissertation which I had begun on this controversy. Then, when I

had all but completed my work, I caught the rumor circulating throughout the city, especially among prominent and learned men, that every one of these stones, which, on the advice of wise men, I proposed to expound in a published treatise, were "recently sculpted by hand, made to look as though at different periods they had been resurrected from a very old burial, and sold to me as to one indifferent to fraud and caught up in the blind greed of curiosity; further, that I, once deceived, in my wretched turn, was deluding the world, and trying to sell new hoaxes as genuine antiques, to the silent laughter of prudent souls." I was shocked beyond words to learn that the authors of this atrocious calumny were two men, perhaps best described as a pair of antagonists, whose names I have reason to protect at present—men with whom I was closely associated in numerous functions, former colleagues in the Academic Society.[1] Why, I could not but wonder, if a reasonable doubt arose in this admittedly uncertain matter, and the genesis of the stones was once more suspect, did they hesitate to face me with it, or, if they felt that I was unduly biased, why did they not lay it before the groups which frequently meet to thrash out intellectual controversies? The arguments for the antiquity of these stones had been publicly expounded. Why, then, did they not cut them down with stronger opposing arguments, and rip off the mask that concealed the fraud? Why did they feign accord for so long, only to launch a bitter strife practically on the eve of the publication of my work? They answer that it is in the interest of my own honor, as well as that of our city and our land, that they stem the course of my vacuous labors at the moment when my reputation is on the brink of destruction. The work, they say, must be suppressed, lest outsiders greet it with derision, and charge the indiscreet author with either supine ignorance or brazen imposture. If this is the case, why are all these negotiations being conducted behind my back? Why, in our frequent familiar conversations, do they fail to admonish, enlighten, and implore me? If, in their eyes, the deceit is so certain and open, why do they scheme and plot in secret, instead of bringing the matter to light in a public declamation? Why do they have recourse to a procedure so unworthy of and foreign to the man of prudence and honor? I beg you, kind reader, to suffer a brief account of the vicious action taken against me. A few weeks ago, when for very good reasons I had closed off the mountain, I nevertheless permitted one of these two men to enter it, obviously in good faith and in a friendly spirit. Unbeknownst to me, he proceeded to throw it open to the public, though he must have, or at least should have, known that I would have objected strenuously. Then with a great hue and cry, he appointed a number of diggers, and, in the presence of the townspeople indulging in drink, he mockingly condemned the unearthed stones as false and supposititious impostures. A short time later, the other of this pair,[2] employing the skill which he possibly learned in his father's shop, and the knife which the Hebrews use for circumcision, carved into some of the more impressionable stones Hebrew characters, the figures of a winged dragon, a mouse, a lion, a pomegranate, etc.[3] Several of these he inserted in various protruberances of the mountain; one or two of them he handed over to a stonecutter's helper, and hired him to sell them to me. The lad subsequently returned to him and exhibited the price he had got for selling me this fraud; whereupon he was roundly applauded and generously rewarded for carrying off the affair so adroitly.

Now then, good reader, I appeal to your justice, I leave it to you to decide. Can these clandestine plots have any other purpose than to bring down to the dust all my sacrifices and labors, my very reputation, with one crafty blow? Moreover, their clever efforts might have succeeded, had not my vigilance, thanks to God, discovered the deceit and throttled it at birth.

But let us concede a little to their invidious minds and wishes. Let us grant that among our stones there are some which are spurious, and that they are found and foisted off on the Lithophiles. Does this mean that every iconolith I have uncovered during the past six months smacks of imposture? There is not an era nor a province that has not suffered from counterfeiters and money spoilers. There are men who can copy the coins of Rome, of Greece, of Egypt, etc., and engrave gems so skillfully as to deceive even the most experienced antiquarians. The same is done in the field of painting and statuary. What, then, must we say of the coins that we use in our daily transactions, of those we find in the fields, villas, vineyards, the rubble of cities and graves, in the abodes of the Greeks and the Romans, of all the gems, pictures, and statues preserved in royal and princely collections? That they are not monuments of ancient art, but the adulterous products of imposters, fraudulent and mendacious imitations of ancient splendor? No one in his right mind would venture such an assertion. No more would he relegate our genuine stones to the limbo of frauds simply because a few had found their way among them from an artistic hand energized by envy, and had been deceitfully sold to the Lithophile. I should like to preface my several demonstrations of this by assuring you, kind reader, that all the figures shown on the plates inserted in this dissertation were drawn and consigned to the engraver long before these two men contemplated stirring up a controversy or challenged the antiquity of the stones. Therefore, I have proffered for your inspection nothing that this modern Praxiteles can claim for his knife and his ingenuity.

There live in the neighboring town certain honorable citizens who testify under oath that many years ago their children brought home from their frolics on this mountain several figured stones. These aroused a mild wonder in the parents who, nevertheless ignorant of the price placed upon such prodigies by men of letters, kept some out of curiosity, letting the rest go to neglect and loss. Who was this artist of years past who secretly played this costly and laborious joke on a group of children? In other words, what never entered the heads of honest natives, is plotted by audacious foreigners and wayfarers, and imposed, not upon mere children, but upon men of the highest orders, even the whole of Franconia. For how can they hope to persuade anyone that an enormous mass of stones was fraudulently manipulated by an unknown counterfeiter, then carried to this wide-open place, under the watchful eyes of the townspeople summer, autumn, spring, and even winter, and this so surreptitiously that no one ever observed the least shadow or trace of the furtive culprit? From June of last year [1725] to November, intermittently, but with almost no cessation, my hired workers delved into the mountain. The rigors of winter and the heavy snows this year suspended operations, until the melting of the ice and more clement weather should render the digging more bearable. In the space of six months some two thousand figured stones have been dug up, not including those which are patently diluvial (and these exist in large numbers), or those which the poorer inhabitants carried off when the mountain was opened, and are attempting to sell. Furthermore, our own sculpture experts testify that many of these zoöliths and lithophytes in extremely solid rocks, of the density of flint or marble, bear the likenesses of plants or animals so exactly and so beautifully, that one or two days' work would hardly suffice to accomplish it—a fact which the amateur artist of the fraudulent stones has possibly learned by experience. Did the worst of Cretan liars ever concoct and decant upon his hearers a more absurd tale? As to my diggers whom I have used exclusively, three are sons of a poor widow, the eldest of them not yet nineteen, and the rest are young lads.[4] All are totally ignorant of the art of sculpture, on the testimony of their pastor and of the town magistrate, both of whom are thoroughly familiar with their education, and their mode of living. Their occupation was to hire out their labor to the stonecutters in the neighboring mountains, and with the meager wages they received for digging out stones or removing mounds and rubble, they supported themselves and their mother as best they could. When I chanced to hire them, with the enticement of better wages, they abandoned their former diggings, and devoted all their energies to the less difficult task of unearthing my stones; and this they did as unostentatiously as possible, so as to avoid attracting fellow laborers who would create an undesirable sharing of the profits. The improbability of these workers being the authors of our idiomorphic stones becomes more apparent when we consider the exact imitation of the natural prototype in many of these, the frequent appearance of exotic plants and foreign animals, seldom seen even by learned men of our land, yet here beautifully depicted, characters and words of various languages, arranged in several orders, and the other unique phenomena of these stones, not to mention the youth, the inexperience, and the simplicity of these workers, qualities scarcely congruous with the more exacting skills. If you counter that the stones were doctored by the hands of another, entrusted to the diggers to be planted on the mountain, then resurrected and sold to me, I ask you: can you really imagine a wealthy and hard-working forger expending a large sum of money and a great deal of work to perpetrate a dubious fraud, which might be exposed by the slip of a youthful tongue, in order to furnish a wide diversity of workers, searching a mountain which they already knew quite well, with a supply of stones to sell to outsiders and foreigners, thereby deluding, however innocently, not only one, but a great many others? Why have these two men shifted their position, now declaring that the stones were sculpted, instead of being the handiwork of potters (as they previously insisted), formed and pressed into molds, then baked to resemble bricks? Why have they proclaimed far, wide, loudly and with much boasting of their historical competence—now that they have been overwhelmed by the unexpectedly great number of the stones? Thus one of this pair altered his opinion from that of the sport of Nature to that of the relics; thence he slipped into the conviction of fraudulence, and finally reverted to the Ludian notion, which he previously denied.

The very condition of this uncultivated mountain, with its covering of grassy blight, gives the lie to this evil raillery. The mountain, as observed in Chapter II, is sterile. It bristles with scrubs of birch and fir, their lower trunks and roots entwined in aged and mosslike grass. The whole surface is cloaked with a netlike protective vest. From time immemorial it has been spared from the spade and the plow (except the peak, which has often been broken open to obtain good earth for the vineyards, but has never yielded any figured stones), and is intact and virgin soil beneath its verdant shield. Thus it is necessary to pierce, slash, and remove this dense and branchy shell of the earth before you penetrate to the clay mass wherein our stones, if they were not generated there, at least lay hidden as very old monuments of unidentified art and labor—so that if newly carved stones were concealed here by the hands of forgers, traces of recent digging would be plain to see, the split surface would be obvious, as would the gaps in the soil and other evidences of work, done even a month ago. Nothing of the sort has been observed by those who, in repeated excursions, have shifted the workers and their assigned spots as they saw fit, and, while penetrating the mountain, have carefully watched the diggers' hands, on the chance (and this was another accusation made) that they might surreptitiously drop into the ground stones which they had brought hidden in their clothes. Were I at this point to divulge the names of these reliable witnesses, as they have graciously allowed me to do, my detractors would burn with shame, and in the murky depths of their remorse they would feel the axe of calumny rebounding to wound the heads of its instigators—the more so that by inquiry and by their own admission they stand guilty and convicted of deceit.

But, so it seems, all others are blind; they alone have more eyes than Argus. In truth, their exclusive vision derives from their exclusive jealousy. All the stones are spurious, because one of this pair, with malicious deceit, manufactured a spurious work of his sculptural art. Not only my words, but a host of unimpeachable witnesses are majestically spurned, because they set not forth the utterances of this restorer of Franconian learning (please God), this Polyhistor, who would have only that believed and given oracular status which he has said—and because he has said it (αὐτὸς ἔφα). I am reminded of Plautus' *Curculio*, wherein one player phrases all the remarks that wise men could ascribe to the man absorbed in excessive self-love:

> Make way for me, friends and strangers too,
> While here I do what from duty I must do!
> Take flight, draw back, and give me ample room,
> Lest in the race my head or limbs spread doom.[5]

But enough of this for now. Our Praxiteles has issued, in an arrogant letter, a declaration of war. He has threatened to write a small treatise exposing my stones as supposititious—I should say, his stones, fashioned and fraudulently made by his hand. Thus does this man, virtually unknown among men of letters, still but a novice in the sciences, make a bid for the dawn of his fame in a shameful calumny and imposture. I am braced for a racy satire, since what less can one anticipate from so bitter a mind and pen? But he and his sponsor and partner in this litigation will have none but themselves to blame if in the future I become so provoked and exasperated by their needling that I broadcast openly to the world the things which I now pass over in silence. However, I cannot resist suggesting a more appropriate symbol than that which he has used to seal his threatening letter. This bold innovator has chosen a flowering and thorny rose with the legend: "I am not handled with impunity." [*Non tangor impune.*] He should indeed have displayed the rose, but with the petals and leaves wilted and dropped, leaving only the bare stem and its armor of thorns, and underneath, the epigraph: "Only the power to harm remains." [*Superest vis sola nocendi.*] Either he will render an account of this legend himself, or I, in a forceful and just defense of truth and innocence, will unfurl it before the whole world.

CHAPTER XIII

Wherein are advanced equally grave reasons for attributing the origin of our figured stones, not to Art, but to Natural Courses.

IN ATTEMPTING TO DEMONSTRATE the impossibility of applying to our idiomorphic stones the natural causes which the more celebrated Lithographers usually designate as the parents of fossils, it may well appear that I have blocked my own path to finding the origin of the Würzburg stones in Nature itself. If, however, you peruse attentively the fourth chapter, where we refuted the theory of the pagan relics, you will appreciate that I hold no more for Art than for Nature as the genearch of these prodigious iconoliths, and that I reserve judgment on both possibilities—the more so since what we theorized concerning amulets and talismans in Chapter XI is easily overcome if one examines the stones themselves in their actual form, rather than in their representations, which are an expedient for those who cannot have physical contact with them. Hence it can readily be conjectured that we need not recur to the stonecutter's knife, nor to the potter's wheel, nor even to the insidious hands of my envious adversaries (to use a mild epithet) in order to discern the origin of figured fossils of animals, plants, stars, and the like. Lithographers are aware of those prodigies which Nature the Thaumaturge has wrought or imitated elsewhere than in Franconia, and if they could or would inspect them at first hand, I would willingly display them, both in the exhibits of my own collection, and in the engravings of the most famous writers. I am here addressing skilled men, taught by actual experience: to such as these the yields of the Würzburg field will appear neither astounding nor unusual, if they are compared to the discoveries made in the mountains, excavations, and caves of Switzerland, Hungary, Austria, Saxony, the Bishopric of Eichstadt, Hessia, Thuringia, etc. In these cases no Lithophile discoverer ever fell under the least suspicion of employing art to elaborate the stones. I could confirm this assertion with numerous instances, but because I am chiefly desirous of brevity, and have no wish to inflate my text, as many do, with footnotes, excerpts, and long digressions, being rather determined to produce a succinct dissertation with bare essentials, with an eye to a wider reading, I will content myself with an appeal to the assent of the learned, to whom such things are neither unusual nor foreign.

Among our suspected stones on Mount Eivelstadt, there has been found, in the same soil, the same spot, an immense number of cockles, scallops, mussels, oysters, conches, snails, spirals, nautilii, ammonites, all in a variety of species, which some regard as diluvial relics, others as ejections of the ocean permeating the earth by the unseen canals of the waves arising from its depths, and others to sundry petrificatory operations of Nature [*Naturae petrificantis operae*]. Why, in analyzing these, do we resort to natural causes for our explanation, while we assign their twins, so to speak, the other figured stones, drawn from the same womb, to the stepmother Art? Who has mingled these offspring of such divergent parentage, one genuine, the other spurious and artificial, in one and the same pit and pile?

There are to be found solitary figures of not a few insects, plants, and fruits, wrapped in their matrices—when extracted from these, as a chick hatched from the egg, they divulge their genus and their habitation. Is it possible that liquified stones were poured into the subterranean fires, either by the sun's rays or by rain wash, as wax is poured into the gypsum mold and metals into those of clay, then took on the embossed likeness of crabs, lizards, snails, etc.? Who formed the apricot, shown in Plate VI, so skillfully out of sheer sandy stone, that he could insert the pit in its membrane and skin, distinct from the rest of the fruit, and without breaking the skin?

In the summer, we found on this mountain certain live insects, obviously exotic and unknown, a sort of spider resembling a fierce human face, analogous to those described by Ulysses Aldrovandi in figure 15 of his treatise on insects,[1] under the heading of the *phalangius* or tarantula. In Plate XXI, can be seen a sucker perfectly formed, colored, etc., in the midst of mussels that are not yet wholly petrified. Wasps' nests, not stone but wax, and many other similar petrifacts have been unearthed. Shall we consign these genuine animals to Art? If so, can it be other than the witch's art, if you rule out the category of natural animals?[2]

In the same spot, we found an abundance of flintlike rocks, to which there clung a mud-colored selenite and crystalline "petricose" flow, hardened into drops, globules, little columns, and rings, extruding from various cavities. The process involved here is the same as that whereby the drops of midwinter snow falling from the roofs, or the petrificous liquid distillating in the subterranean crypt of Homburg near the Main, congeal into icy or stony wedges. And, as further evidence of the work of Nature, this same flow leaves a little toad or a lizard half completed, as though Nature were (in her accustomed fashion) halted by ennui, or impeded by some other obstacle from finishing the work she started. And it is possible that the plastic material of our iconoliths can be accounted the origin and seed of these phenomena. At this point I cannot bypass the observations of Helwing in his *Lithographia Angerburgica*, Part I, page 35,[3] since they are no mean confirmation of my own position. "In England near Harwich I found in approximately one mile of shore an immense number of stones; for this space, instead of sand, displays a very great abundance of petrified bodies, both large and small. I could not sufficiently admire this diversity which the fertile handmaid (Nature) of the Most High God administered. For although all these petrifacts were fashioned from a certain rich mud which took its rotund figure from the motion of the sea, there were, nonetheless, infinite mixtures and nuances of color, size, and

consistency. Some had acquired a perfect hardness, differing not at
all from those that are experienced on the streets of London; others
were in the first stages of the hardening process; still others were so
soft that merely pressing them with a finger left a mark." Next he
explains how he impressed various characters on these lumps, and
inserted needles which after twelve hours could only be withdrawn
by breaking the stones. He continues: "I also observed that some
specimens of this mud were afflicted with small fissures (larger in
the larger specimens) by desiccation from the sun and soil, and that
later a certain flow of salt mixed with petrifying liquid filled these
cracks, leaving in many of the stones an appearance of marvelously
variegated marble." [4] Now, if you will, compare what this eminent
Lithographer has written with what we have noted in Chapter II
concerning the nature and composition of our stones. It is difficult
to discern whether Helwing is describing the shore at Harwich
or the soil from our own mountain. There were found on that
shore of the sea of Britain "various petrified bodies, large and
small," [5] such are also found on our mountain. "The mud is rich,
hardened in some places, in others, beginning to harden, in still
others, very soft" [6]—all of which have their counterpart in our
soil. He found, in the same spot, "a species of wonderfully varied
marble" [7]—to the profound wonderment of all onlookers, the same
was taken at our spot. The polished shell and poecilosperm stones,
when the outer shell was removed, exhibited a marble of red, yellow, and gray color, in which the black, white, and yellow outlines
of conches and scallops underlie the multicolored veins and spots,
surpassing the striated variety of other species of marble. Helwing
recognizes his petrified bodies of the Harwich shore as works of
Nature, notwithstanding that, for the sake of curiosity, he himself
fashioned several figures with his own hand.[8] Surely, then, you will
not eliminate our petrifacts from the ranks of Nature's effects,
simply because the hand of our antagonists formed a number of
likenesses with their knives, not from curiosity, but for purposes of
deception.

Should I, then, have recourse to the opinion of a nameless author
quoted by Spener and referred to (somewhat testily) by Büttner

in his *Coralliographia Subterranea:* [9] that it is of the very nature of these stones to be figured, that they are uniquely formed by the Author of Nature, who, in His omnipotent creative causality, lavishes a no less generous variety upon stones than upon plants and animals?

Seeking a basis for this opinion, which is one of piety and expediency rather than of erudition and the science of physiology, I turn to the conchites and pectinites which are found in such vast numbers even by those who are not expressly looking for them, that they afford a superabundance of material, both precious and solid because it is marble, for the construction of spacious fortresses and palaces. To attempt to construe these as marine births is to run afoul of the same arguments which the very learned Lang and Lhwyd hurl against the protagonists of the diluvial theory. Thousands upon thousands of ammonites have been extracted from the stone sources of Franconia. I myself have in my possession some two hundred of these, most beautifully figured and widely diversified, weighing many, many pounds, both with and without conjunctions, articulations, and chamberings, some acephalous, but many with head, beak, and eyes. Now, I have not heard of or read a single author who extracted from any sea or lake, or exhibited such a variety of testacea, fishes, or insects, living or extinct, whether convoluted in spirals or not. And, pray, why, of all the thousands of ammonites and nautili that have come to light, not only on Mount Eivelstadt, but in every one of the stone sources and vineyards, has not a single one so far been discovered with the armature of crust, testa, cortex, or with vestiges of scales or coating? Why are the pectinites and the host of other petrified shell animals bereft of their natural armature? If these fishes or insects are marine monstrosities, by what wind or storm and from what ocean were they swept into Franconia—hardened as they are in ammonites, which are undulated, but also adorned with divers heads, striations, grooves, and tubercules—a prodigy never before observed, and now in my keeping? What hand wrought in the interior of these scallops (which by nature is smooth) grooves and striations similar to those found on their external surface?

What lithographer, even among the most perspicacious, has revealed the genesis of such diverse ammonites, and has done it so brilliantly and irrefragably as to refute all arguments that would cast doubt and uncertainty upon their diluvial origin? It is still a matter of dispute whether the many maritime and anomalous conches, housed in such generous quantities by our mountain, though described and depicted by neither Lister nor Bonnano,[10] are all of oceanic origin.[11] To date no conches similar to these, either cast up by the sea or brought up by divers, have come to my attention or that of others, although at one time or another I have had several thousands of very fine specimens of testacea, even some from the Indies. Must we not, then, conclude that there are unique types of stones, as there are of gems, marbles, magnates, pyrites, and other prodigies adorning the shelves of stone treasuries? Further, should we not include our singularly figured stones in their number?

But now my case rests. I have willingly submitted my plates to the scrutiny of wise men, desiring to learn their verdict, rather than to proclaim my own in this totally new and much mooted question. I address myself to scholars, hoping to be instructed by their most learned responses in this controversial matter, either from the press or from their own pen. It is my fervent expectation that illustrious lithographers will shed light upon this dispute which is as obscure as it is unusual. I shall add thereto my own humble torch, nor shall I spare any effort to reveal and declare whatever future yields may rise from the Würzburg field under the continuous labors of my workers, and whatever opinion my mind may embrace.

CHAPTER XIV

A synopsis of the remaining plates to be exhibited in this first edition of the Würzburg Lithography.

THUS FAR WE HAVE DISCOURSED on the figured stones of the field of Würzburg: on all of them in general, on some in particular, supplementing our written word with plates inserted at various points.[1] It now remains to submit to your critical inspection the remaining plates, in order to complete the number of iconoliths, which we claimed to be in excess of two hundred. First, however, I should like to caution you, kind reader, that in selecting and arranging these stones I have not followed the order which the zoölogists and lithographers, in the interest both of ingenuity and of elegance, customarily observe in drawing up the various species of plants and animals which abound in the several realms of Nature. I have been constrained to employ a method which is perhaps less perfect, under pressure of time, because of the wish to hasten the completion of my work in spite of the interruptions of my public duties and functions, and, more than all else, because of the paucity of the stones which I had by then collected—the aggregation being much smaller than that which I have at present. From those relatively few I could not choose at will, but was obliged simply to arrange them in the order of their unearthing, and in that same order submit them to the artist and the engraver. Thus, omitting the first seven plates, which I have presented in the preceeding pages, I will begin with number eight.

The stones here shown (Plate VIII), (with few exceptions, in life size and, as far as possible, in their actual thickness) contain earth insects, bloodless animals, and the greater and lesser apoda; i.e., slugs, snails, and earthworms.

Plate IX: Lesser wingless earth insects, both multipedes and oligopods, such as ants, forbicines, earth scolopendrae, etc.

Plate X: Lesser wingless earth insects and oligopods, i.e, various species of spiders, with and without webs.

Plate XI: Lesser wingless multipede earth insects, i.e., several species of caterpillars.

Plate XII: Greater insects, with feet but no tails, both earth and amphibious: earth toads, green frogs, water toads, and swamp frogs.

Plate XIII: Greater earth insects, with tails and feet, lizards, among them, one with two heads, a salamander.

Plate XIV: Flying insects, with wings uncovered; i.e., flies, bees, hornets, wasps, and dragon flies.

Plate XV: Other winged insects: various species of butterflies.

Plate XVI: Still others of the same genus: stone flies, dragon flies, and obviously foreign and exotic species.

Plate XVII: Winged insects of the coleopter genus, having covered wings: species of locusts and crickets.

Plate XVIII: Winged insects of the vaginipennate genus, coleoptera, scarabs, cantharides, deer flies.

Plate XIX: Earth insects, with feet and tails, also aquatic insects, bloodless, crustaceous, with feet and tails: scorpions, astaci, or river crabs, shrimps, etc.

Plate XX: Marine animals, crustaceous, rotund and with feet; as marine crabs, pungers, oysters.

Plate XXI: Various species of marine and river fish, but in unusual form: especially a sucker with small mussels only partly petrified.

These, then, are the first fruits of the Würzburg Lithography, which I have edited under the promptings of zeal for the glory of our country, and of love of most noble learning. I must confess that I often put down my pen, distracted and worn out as I was by the demands made on me day and night by my duties, which left me scarcely more than the small hours of the night to compose a work that would be subjected to critical examination by those outside our land. Then came the indiscreet and importunate eagerness on the part of The Pair—not to propose objections (which men of letters expect and gladly receive in theoretical controversies), but to undo my efforts by insults and mockeries. One of these was entirely out of his proper field, the other laid his scythe to another man's harvest. Both would have impeded the progress of a dissertation dealing with things that concerned neither of them, nor their studies, nor their doctrines, nor their business—a dissertation which was mine alone, within the field of physics not only harmless to all, but highly desired by reason of the newness of the controversial objects discovered in Franconia, and undertaken at my own expense. This ignoble end they would have attained, had I not risen above the pressure of work with which they sought to wear me down, and carried on in the spirit of the text:

Give not way to evil men, but oppose them more boldly.[2]

Nor have I given way, as the crowning work of this first edition clearly proves. Further, I shall not yield in the future. I am as determined to champion this most righteous cause, as I have been prepared to throw open this new stone collection of Franconia to the whole world.

To the men of letters, to the scholars and patrons of the finer and more profound disciplines, I submit myself and my writings, with all the willing devotion which I have ever tendered them. I stand ready to acquiesce to their judgment, provided only that they weigh carefully my opinions and my reasonings. If, however, a greater portion of truth shall enlighten me, I shall perhaps set it forth in a subsequent edition of the Würzburg Lithography, with a more ample set of illustrations, better arranged, and augmented by new and very rare stones of exotic figures. This shall be done with that moderation which has ever been prized and cultivated by Christian and pagan philosophers alike, so that both this dissertation and its companion may be a search for truth without gall or aloes.

APPENDIX A

Bibliographical Citations from Chapter I

THAT BERINGER was well acquainted with the popular lithological writings of his day is clearly evidenced in Chapter I, in which he lists fifty-two authors whose "very names . . . should suffice to brand the idleness of that avaricious and crude pack of Academicians who attack Lithology as a useless pursuit." This "brief alphabetical synopsis of Lithographers" is in a class with the Grolier Club One-Hundred, although lacking the latter's bibliographical completeness. Since these works were considered by Beringer to be the pillar on which Lithology was built, it seems a loss to leave them in the muddled state in which Beringer presented them—although to Beringer's contemporaries, who must have had daily familiarity with the works cited, the synopsis was doubtless not nearly as formidable or confusing as it is to the twentieth-century reader.

The hope of being able to give complete bibliographical citations for all fifty-two was frustrated many times over until a stroke of good fortune turned up a copy of the title by Heraeus.

The Heraeus paper is really a double listing, having appeared under two titles, as will be seen later; it was perhaps the ultimate source of Beringer's citations. In Heraeus are to be found twenty-five of the works cited by Beringer (though often more completely given), with six additional authors mentioned by name only. As an example, Beringer cites for Tenzelius: "In Colloquiis Menstruis [In His Monthly Conferences]," but for what month and year he leaves us blank. On the other hand Heraeus cites: " . . . ex relat. Tenzelii in colloquiis menstruis de 1696." The addition of the year permits the well-founded assumption that what is being referred to is Tenzelius' "Epistola de Sceleto Elephanto Tonnae nuper effosso . . ." and not another of his myriad of writings.

Another source for Beringer's list seems to have been Spener's disquisition, in which are cited by title eight of those appearing in Chapter I and fourteen additional citations by author's name alone. Heraeus and Spener taken together leave only thirteen to be accounted for, of which three can be eliminated: Assalti and Lancisius, who are mentioned in connection with Mercati, and Leibnitz, whose dissertation immediately follows Spener's in the *Miscellanea Berolinensia* for 1710.

Although an attempt has been made to take bibliographical data from the actual books, many were impossible to obtain. Where such was the case, the second or even third edition (if such exists) was used for this purpose, and dates of previous editions were taken from printed bibliographies—the most useful of which were the *British Museum Catalogue*, the *Catalogue of the Library of Congress*, Brunet's *Manuel Libraire*, and G. R. Boehmer's *Bibliotheca Scriptorum Historiae Naturalis*. Another invaluable source of data for these works is the *Acta Eruditorum*, a journal published at Leipzig from 1682 to about 1755.

The following is an attempt at a revision of Beringer's synopsis, and the reader should refer back to Chapter I for his actual citations. Cognates of authors' names are given in square brackets following Beringer's listings, and titles have been fully corrected where possible. Annotations, including Heraeus' and Spener's citations, follow the date of publication. When Heraeus is mentioned as the source of Beringer's citation, the page reference was taken from his "De Ossium petrificatorum ortu diluviano" (*Ephemerides Academiae Caesareae-Leopoldino Carolinae Naturae Curiosorum*, [1722], 231–246). This article is identical with Beringer's citation for Heraeus, which appeared in a volume of his collected works. The page reference following Spener was taken from his "Disquisitio" as cited by Beringer. Reviews of works appearing in the *Acta Eruditorum* are given as AE: year, pagination. Where the actual title cited by Beringer could not be verified, Beringer's citation is given plus those data which were uncovered.

AGRICOLA [BAUER,] (GEORGIUS).
   De Re Metallica Libri XII. Quibus Officia, Instrumenta, Machinae, ac omnia denique ad Metallicam spectantia, non modo luculentissime describuntur, sed et per effigies, suis locis insertas, adiunctis Latinis, Germanicisque appellationibus ita ob oculos ponuntur, ut clarius tradi non possint. Eiusdem de Animantibus Subterraneis Liber, ab Autore recognitus: cum Indicibus diuersis, quicquid in opere tractatum est pulchre demonstrantibus. Basileae, 1556. (Other Latin editions, 1561 and 1657.)

Heraeus mentions Agricola only by name (p. 244), as does Spener (p. 101).

—————.

*De ortu et Causis Subterraneorum Lib. V. De Natura eorum quae effluunt
ex terra Lib. IIII. De natura fossilium Lib. X. De veteribus et novis metallis,
Lib. II. Bermannus sive De re Metallica dialogus. Interpretatio Germanica
vocum rei metallicae addito Indice faecundissimo.* Basileae: Hieron Fro-
benium et Nicolaum Episcopium, 1546.

ALDROVANDUS [ALDROVANDI], (ULYSSES) [ULISSE].
    De Simia in Lapide.
    Heraeus: "de simia in lapide Aldrovandi" (p. 244). A search of the
Opera Omnia of Aldrovandi has failed to turn up as much as a paragraph
heading concerned with an Ape in Stone. In Aldrovandi's *De Quadrupedibus
Digitatis Viviparis Libri Tres et de Quadrupedibus Digitatis Oviparis Libri
Duo* (Bononiensis: Nicolaum Tebaldinum, 1645), Book II, Chapter 5, is
entitled "De Simia"; however no mention of petrified apes was found in
it. Further, no listing of such a title or subdivision was to be found in either
of the comprehensive bibliographies of Aldrovandi listed below.
    Fantuzzi, Giovanni. *Memorie della vita di Ulisse Aldrovandi . . . Con
        alcune Lettere scelte d'Uomini eruditi a lui scritte, e coll'Indice delle
        sue Opere Mss., che si conservano nella Biblioteca dell'Instituto . . .*
        Bologna: Lelio dalla Volpe, 1774.
    Frati, Lodovico. *Catalogo dei Manoscritti di Ulisse Aldrovandi.* Bologna:
        Nicola Zanichelli, 1907.
    While Aldrovandi did not, it would seem, mention an "ape in stone,"
there is extant a remark on this occurrence. It is given by Benedictis Cerutus
in his *Musaeum Franc*[-isci]. *Calceolari* (Verona, 1622), p. 425: "There is
a stone naturally fashioned in the likeness of a monkey, concerning which
I am hesitant to say whether it causes more wonderment in the beholder
than that live and natural monkey about which the great Scalinger writes
[*Exotericarum* Exercitationum. Exerc. 213, pp. 679–680]." There is no mention in Cerutus' work of Aldrovandi's several volumes, of which four had
appeared by 1605, the remainder being issued between 1616 and 1668.

ASSALTUS [ASSALTI], (PETRUS).
    See Mercati, (Michaelis) for citation.
    Assalti is mentioned by neither Heraeus nor Spener. He evidently com-
piled the notes for the *Metallotheca* of Mercati. (See also Lancisius.)

BAJERUS [BAIER], (JOANNES JACOBUS).
    'Ορυκτογράφια (*Oryctographia*) *Norica, sive Rerum Fossilium et ad
Minerale Regnum Pertinentium, in Territorio Norimbergensi Ejusque
Vicinia Observatarum succincta Descriptio. Cum Iconibus Lapidum Figura-
torum Fere Ducentis.* Norimbergae: Wolfgangi Michahellis, 1708.
    Heraeus: "In Norico ex Oryctographia Nov. Jo. Jacobi Baieri" (p. 235).

APPENDIXES

BALBINUS, (BOHESLAUS) [BOHUSLAI ALOYSIUS].
Miscellanea historia regni Bohemiae, decas prima, libris VIII comprehensa.
Pragae: G. Czernoch, 1679–1688.
Heraeus: "Bolesl. Balbini in Miscell. Regni Bohemiae" (p. 235). AE:
1682, 241–247, 265–271, 400–401; 1685, 18–22; 1687, 605–607; 1688, 51–54,
405–408.

BAUHINUS [BAUHIN], (JOANNES).
Historia novi et admirabilis fontis balneique Bollensis in Ducatu Wirtem-
bergico, ad Acidulas Goepingenses . . . *Adiiciuntur plurimae figurae novae*
variorum Fossilium, Stirpium et Insectorum quae in et circa hunc Fontem
Reperiuntur. Montisbeligardi, 1598.
Cited by neither Heraeus nor Spener.

BAUSCHIUS [BAUSCH], (CAROLUS) [JOANNES LAURENTIUS].
De Unicornu Fossili ad Normam et formam Academiae Naturae
Curiosiorum Schediasma. Jenae, 1666.
Heraeus: "Caroli Bauschii in Schediasmate curioso de Unicornu fossili"
(p. 235).

BECANUS, (GOROPIUS) [JOH. GOROPIUS].
Origines Antwerpianae, sive Cimmeriorum Becceselana novem libros
complexa. Antuerpiae: Chr. Plantin, 1569.
Heraeus: "Goropii Becani in Origin. Antwerpiae." (p. 235).

BEHR [BEHRENS], (GEORGIUS HENNINGIUS).
Hercynia curiosa, hartz-wald, das ist sonderbahre beschreibung und
bezerichnen derer curiösen holeuseen, brunnen, bergen, und vielen andern
und auf dem hartz vorhandenen dendtuurdigen sachen, mit unterschiedenen
nütslichen, und ergetslichen medicinischen, physicalischen, und historischen
anmerckungen denen liebhabern solcher curiositaten zur lust. Nordhausen:
Carl Chr. Nevenhahn, 1703.
Heraeus: "Hennigii Behrens Hercinia curiosa" (p. 235). There is also
an English edition printed at London in 1730: *The Natural History of the*
Hartz Forest . . . [translated by John Andree].

BEL [BELIUS], (MATHIAS) [MATTHIAS].
Hungariae Antiquae et Novae Prodromus, cum Specimine, quomodo in
Singulis operis partibus elaborandis versari constituerit Auctor Matthias
Belius, Pannonius. Norimbergae: Petri Conradi Monath, 1723.
Heraeus: "In Hungaria antiqua & nova Matthiae Bel." (p. 235). AE: 1724,
99–101.

BOCCONE, (PAULUS).
Recherches et Observations Naturelles De Monsieur Boccone Gentil-
homme Sicilien; Touchant Le Corail, la Pierre Etoilée, les Pierres de figure

de Coquilles, la Corne d'Ammon, l'Astroite Undulatus, les Dents des Poissons pétrifiées, les Herissons alterez, l'Embrasement du Mont Etna, la Sangsue du Xiphias, l'Alcyonium stupposum, le Bezoar Mineral, et les Plantes qu'on trouve dans la Sicile, avec quelques Réflexions sur la Végétation des Plantes. Amsterdam: Jean Jansson à Waesberge, 1674.
Cited by neither Hereaus nor Spener.

BÜTTNERUS [BÜTTNERS BÜTTNER], (DANIEL SIGISMUNDUS) [DAVID-SIGISMUNDUS].
Rudera Diluvii Testes, i.e. Zeichen und Zeugen der Sündfluth, In Ansehung des itzigen Zustandes unserer Erd- und Wasser- Kugel, Insonderheit der Darinnen vielfältig auch zeither in Querfurtischen Revier Anterschiedlich Angertroffenen . . . Leipzig: Johann Friedrich Braunen, 1710.
Heraeus: "De Querfurtensibus (Rudera Diluvii Testes) Buttnerus" (p. 235). AE: 1711, 222–224.

————.
Coralliographia Subterranea. Seu Dissertatio de Coralliis Fossilibus, In Specie, De Lapide Corneo Hornoder gemeinem Feuer-Stein cum Tabulis aeneis. Lipsiae: Friderici Groschuffii, 1714.
This work of Büttner's is mentioned in neither Heraeus nor Spener. AE: 1714, 326–330.

COLUMNA [COLONNA], (FABIUS) [FABIO].
Purpura Hoc est de Purpura ab Animali testaceo fusa, de hoc ipso Animali alijsq. rarioribus testaceis quibusdam . . . *Cum Iconibus ex aere ad viuum representatis, Elencho rerum, et Indice Superiorum Permisso.* Romae: Jacobum Mascardum, 1616.
Spener: "Fabius Columna in peculiari Dissertatione, egregio ipsius de Purpura" (p. 112).

CORINGIUS [CONRINGIUS, CONRING], (HERMANNUS).
De Antiquissimo Statu Helmstadii et Viciniae Conjecturae. Helmestadii, 1665.
Heraeus: "Conringii de antiquo statu Helmstadii" (p. 235).

CROLLIUS, (OSWALDUS).
Basilica Chymica, Continens Philosophicam Propria laborum experientia confirmatam descriptionem et usum remediorum Chymicorum selectissimorum e Lumine Gratiae et Naturae desumptorum. In fine libri additus est eiusdem Authoris Tractatus nouus De Signaturis Rerum Internis . . . Francofurti: C. Marnium et heredes J. Aubrii, 1609.
Heraeus: "Crollii de Signaturis" (p. 235).

ERHARD [EHRHARTUS, ERHART], (BALTHASAR).
Dissertatio Medica Inauguralis, De Belemnitis Suevicis. Quam Annuente

Deo Ter Opt. Max. Ex Auctoritate Magnifici Rectoris, D. Francisci Fabricii . . . Author. Balthasar Ehrhart. Memminga Suevus. Ad diem 21. Septemb. 1724. hora locoque solito. Lugduni Batavorum: Apud Conradum Wishoff, 1724.

Cited by neither Heraeus nor Spener. The citation in Appendix B was taken from the *Editio Altera* (Augustae Vindelicorum, 1727).

FABRICIUS, (GEORGIUS)

De Metallicis Rebus ac Nominibus Observationes Variae et eruditae, ex schedis Georgij Fabricii: quibus ea potissimum explicantur, quae Georgius Agricola praeteriit. Tiguri, 1565.

Cited by neither Heraeus nor Spener. The Fabricus title is one of eight treatises bound as *De Omni Rerum Fossilium genere. De Metallicis Rebus* is the third work in the volume, with the collation: (3) + 31 leaves; a–d⁸e² (see Gesner).

GESNERUS [GESNER], (CONRADUS) [KONRAD].

De Omni Rerum Fossilium Genere, Gemmis, Lapidibus, Metallis, et Huiusmodi, Libri Aliquot, Plerique nunc Primum Editi. Tiguri: (Apud Gesnerum), 1565–1566.

Spener mentions Gesner by name only (p. 102). The Gesner title consists of eight treatises on mineralogy and allied subjects, of which all save the first have separate title pages. The Gesner title proper is the eighth title, with the following collation: (7) + 169 leaves; Aa–Yy⁸. The separate title page reads:

> Conradi Gesneri / De Rerum Fossilium, La- / pidum et Gemmarum / maxime, figuris & similitudinibus Li- / ber: non solum Medicis, sed omnibus / rerum Naturae ac Philologiae / studiosis, utilis & iucun- / dus futurus. / Tiguri: 1565.

GUERICKE, (OTTO VON).

Experimenta Nova (ut vocantur) Magdeburgica de Vacuo Spatio Primum a R.P. Gaspare Schotto, e Societate Jesu, et Herbipolitanae Academiae Matheseos Professore: Nunc vero ab ipso Auctore Perfectius edita, variisque aliis Experimentis aucta. Quibus accesserunt simul certa quaedam De Aëris Pondere circa Terram; de Virtutibus Mundanis, et Systemate Mundi Planetario; sicut et de Stellis Fixis, ac Spatio illo Immenso, quod tam intra quam extra eas funditur. Amstelodami: Joannem Janssonium a Waesberge, 1672.

Heraeus: "Prope Quedlinburgum, ex relat. Ottonis Guerike, clari Experimentis de Vacuo" (p. 235). The "Quedlinburg Findings" will be found in Liber V, "De Terraqueo Globo et ejus Socia quae vocantur Luna," Caput III: "Telluris Glopus, sicut externe innumera rerum varietate est exstructus, sic etiam interne" (pp. 154–156). The actual findings are mentioned on page 155, with a marginal note: "Sceleton Unicornis sub terra repertum." Beringer's citation consists of the following two sentences:

"It happened that in the same year, 1663, at Quedlinburg on the mountain called Zeunickenberg, where calcium matter was dug up, in one of the rocks there was discovered the skeleton of a unicorn resting, as beasts are wont to do, on its hind quarters, its head erect. A single horn projected from its forehead, weighing about as much as a human leg, and approximately the length of five forearms.

"At first the skeleton of this animal was thoughtlessly broken up and dismembered; but finally the head and horn, along with several ribs and part of the spine, was presented to the Most Reverend Princess Abbess who resided there."

HELWINGUS [HELWINGS HELWING], (GEORGIUS ANDREAS).

Lithographia Angerburgica, sive Lapidum et Fossilium, In Districtu Angerburgensi et ejus vicinia, ad trium vel quatuor milliarum spatium, in Montibus, Agris, Arenofodinis et in primis circa lacuum littora et fluviorum ripas, collectorum brevis et succincta Consideratio Additis rariorum aliquot figuris aeri incisis, cum Praefatione Autoris et Indicibus necessariis. Regiomonti: Johannis Stelteri, 1717.

Cited by neither Heraeus nor Spener. AE: 1717, 505–507; 1718, 322–325.

————————.

Lithographiae Angerburgicae Pars II, in Qua de Lapidibus figuratis ad Triplex Regnum Minerale, vegetabile et animale redactis, aliisque fossilibus in Districtu Angerburgensi ejusdem Vicinia Noviter Detectis, et in Specie de Origine Lapidum Literas Exprimentium, Occasione Lapidis Cujusdam Resaviensis, Literas Latinas L.V.R. Repraesentantis, Succincte Disseritur; Additis Iconibus Rariorum Lipsiae: Immanuelis Titii, 1720.

AE: 1720, 140–143.

HERAEUS (CAROLUS GUSTAVUS) [CARL GUSTAV].

"Hanc ordinis expertem materiarum varietatem claudat Dissertatiuncula oblata Illustr. Gall. Scientiarum Academiae; et, ne cum nostra Naturae Curiosorum Academia et cum aliis hanc quaestionem sua dijudicatione dignaturis sit communicata, impedita forte Directoris Doctissimi Viri D. Lochneri obitu praematuro. Nam Virorum bene meritorum funus nulla non aetate crudum et acerbum habetur."

The above citation (given in part by Beringer) is to be found on pages 329–344 of Heraeus:

Bedichte und Lateinische Inschriften des Kaiserl. Raths, auch Medallien- und Antiquitäten-Inspectors . . . Nürenberg: Peter Conrad Monath, 1721.

The same article appeared under a new title in 1722, although identical with the above:

"De Ossium petrificatorum ortu diluviano" (*Ephemerides Academiae Caesareae-Leopoldino Carolinae Naturae Curiosorum*, V (1722), Part 2 (Physico-Medicarum), 231–246.

HIEMERUS, (EBERHARDUS FRIDERICUS).

Caput Medusae, utpote Novum Diluvii universalis monumentum, detectum in agro Wurtembergico et brevi Dissertatiuncula epistolari expositum ab

Eberh. Frider. Hiemero . . . Stuttgardiae: Christiani Theophili Koeslini, 1724.
Cited by neither Heraeus nor Spener. AE: 1725, 376–377.

KENTMANUS [KENTMANN, CHENTMANNUS], (BER. [?] JOHANNES).
Nomenclaturae Rerum Fossilium, que in Misnia praecipue, et in aliis quoque regionibus inueniuntur. Tiguri, 1565.
Calculorum qui in Corpore ac Membris Hominum innascuntur, genera XII. depicta descriptaque cum Historiis singulorum admirandis . . . Tiguri, 1565.
Cited by neither Heraeus nor Spener. The Kentmann titles, like Fabricus, are two of the eight treatises bound as *De Omni Rerum Fossilium genere.* *Nomenclaturae Rerum Fossilium* is the first work in the volume, with the collation: gathering "a" (leaves unnumbered); gatherings A through M^8, consisting of 95 numbered leaves. *Calculorum* is the second work in the volume, with the collation: (2) + 22 leaves; Aa–Cc^8 (see Gesner).

KIRCHERUS [KIRCHER], (ATHANASIUS).
Mundus Subterraneus, in XII Libros Digestus; quo Divinum Subterrestris Mundi Opificium, mira Ergasteriorum Naturae in eo distributio . . . *Protei Regnum, Universae denique Naturae majestas et divitiae summa rerum varietate exponuntur, abditorum effectuum Causae acri indagine inquisitae demonstrantur, cognitae per Artis et Naturae conjugium ad Humanae vitae necessarium usum vario Experimentorum apparatu nec non novo modo et ratione applicantur.* (Editio Tertia.) Amstelodami: Joannem Janssonium a Waesberge et Filios, 1678. (First Edition: 1664–1665.)
Heraeus: "Kircheri in Mundo subterr." (p. 236). Spener mentions Kircher by name only (p. 115).

LACHMUNDUS, (FRIDERICUS).
Ὀρυκτογράφια (*Oryctographia*) *Hildesheimensis, Sive Admirandorum Fossilium, Quae in Tractu Hildesheimensi reperiuntur, Descriptio Iconibus Illustrata Cui addita sunt alia de calculis, de fontibus, etc.* Hildesheimii: Jacobi Mulleri, 1669.
Heraeus: "De Hildesheimensibus Lachmundus" (p. 235).
Spener mentions Lachmund on page 103.

LAMBECIUS [LAMBECK, LAMBECCUS], (PETRUS).
Commentariorum de Augustissima Bibliotheca Caesarea Vindobonensi Libri I (–VIII). Vindobonae: M. Cosmerovij, 1665–1679.
Heraeus: "Lambecius Bibl. Vindob. Appendici." (p. 234).
The citation refers solely to the Appendix to Peter Lambeck's *Commentaries on the Vindobonian Library.* Antonius de Pozzis, Physician to the Emperor whose library Lambeck catalogued, described for and communicated data to Lambeck on the subject of a large tooth housed in the Emperor's library. This information was published in an Appendix to

Volume VI. The tooth was determined to be the "grinder of an elephant," and certain "*os tibiae* and *femoris*" in the collection were also attributed to the elephant.

These were recognized to be petrified, by virtue of the earth in which they were buried, which "insensibly, by its concentrating principle, extracts and hardens the Seeds of Petrifaction."

LANCISIUS [LANCISI] (JOANNIS MARIAE).
See Mercati, (Michaelis) for citation.
Lancisius is mentioned by neither Heraeus nor Spener. He edited the *Metallotheca* after Mercati's death, and compiled the Appendix to the work. (See also Assalti.)

LANGIUS [LANGY, LANG], (CAROLUS NICOLAUS).
Historia Lapidum Figuratorum Helvetiae Ejusque Viciniae, in Qua non Solum Enarrantur Omnia eorum Genera, Species et Vires Aeneisque Tabulis Repraesentantur, sed insuper adducuntur eorum Loca Nativa . . . Venetiis: Jacobi Tomasini, et Lucernae: Haeredes Gottofredi Hautt et Joannem Judocum Halter, 1708.
Heraeus mentions Langius by name only (p. 246). Spener: "Idem Histor. Natural. Lapid, Figurat. Helvet." (p. 102). AE: 1709, 17–23.

————————.

Tractatus de Origine Lapidum Figuratorum in Quo diffuse disseritur, utrum nimirum sunt Corpora Marina a Diluvio ad Montes Translata, et Tractu temporis petrificata vel an a Seminio Quodam e Materia Lapidescente intra Terram generentur, Quibus accedit accurata Diluvii, Ejusque in Terra Effectuum Descriptio cum Dissertatione De Generatione Viventium, Testaceorum praecipue, plurimorumque corporum, a vi plastica aurae seminalis hinc inde delatae extra consuetam matricem productorum. Lucernae: Annae Felicitatis Hautt, 1709.
Cited by neither Heraeus nor Spener. AE: 1710, 81–87.

LEIBNITIUS [LEIBNITZ], (GODEFRIDUS GUILIELMUS) [GOTTFRIED WILHELM VON].
"Epistola Godofredi Guilielmi Leibnitii, ad Auctorem Dissertationis de figuris animalium quae in lapidibus observantur, et Lithozoorum nomine venire possent." *Miscellanea Berolinensia,* I (1710), Pars Segunda, 118–120.
Cited by neither Heraeus nor Spener, whose disquisition the above immediately follows.

LEIGH, (CAROLUS) [CHARLES].
The Natural History of Lancashire, Cheshire, and the Peak in Derbyshire, with an Account of the British, Phoenician, Armenian, Greek, and Roman Antiquities in those parts. Oxford, 1700.
Heraeus: "Car. Leigh in historia naturali Lancastriae" (p. 243, misnumbered as 143). AE: 1701, 511–519.

APPENDIXES

LUIDIUS [LHWYD, LHUYD], (EDWARDUS).
Lithophylacii Britannici Ichnographia sive Lapidum aliorumque Fossilium Britannicorum singulari figura insgnum, quotquot hactenus vel ipse invenit vel ab amicis accepit, Distributio Classica, Scrinii sui lapidarii Repertorium cum locis singulorum natalibus exhibens. Additis rariorum aliquot figuris aere incisis cum Epistolis ad Clarissimos Viros de quibusdam circa marina fossilia et stirpes minerales praesertim notandis. Londini: Ex Officina, 1699.
Heraeus mentions Luidius by name only (p. 246). AE: 1699, 333–335.

MAJOR (JOHANN DANIEL).
Dissertatio epistolica de Cancris et Serpentibus Petrefactis ad Dn. 'D. Philippum Jacobum Sachs a Lewenheimb . . . cui accessit Responsoria Dissertatio Historico-Medica Ejusdem Philippi Jacobi Sachs . . . De Miranda Lapidum Natura. Jenae: Esaiae Fellgiebeli, 1664.
Spener: "Dn. D. Major. Dissert. Epistol. de Cancris et serpentib. petrefactis" (p. 101).

MASCARDUS [MOSCARDO], (LUDOVICO).
Note overo memorie del museo di Ludovico Moscardo nobile veronese, academico filarmonico, dal medesimo descritte, et in tre libri distinte. Nel primo si discorre delle cose antiche, le quali in detto museo si trouano. Nel secondo delle pietre, minerali, e terre. Nel terzo de corali, conchiglie, animali, frutti, et altre cose in quello contenute . . . Padua: Paolo Frambotto, 1656.
Heraeus: "Mascardus in Museo" (p. 236).

MERCATUS [MERCATI], (MICHAEL).
Michaelis Mercati Samminiatensis Metallotheca Opus Posthumum, Auctoritate, & Munificentia Clementis Undecimi Pontificis Maximi E tenebris in lucem eductum; Opera autem, & studio Joannis Mariae Lancisii Archiatri Pontificii Illustratum. Romae: Jo. Mariae Salvioni Romani, 1719 (colophon dated 1717). Also a second title-page for the appendix:
Appendix ad Metallothecam Vaticanam Michaelis Mercati, In qua Lectoribus exhibentur XIX. Icones ex Typis aeneis nuper Florentiae inventis, quorum XIV. Pontificia liberalitate suppleti jam fuerant: Quinque vero penitus desiderabantur. Additis Notis, Et novis Iconibus choclearum Cornu Ammonis forma. Romae: Jo. Mariam Salvioni, 1719.
Spener: "in Italia Mercatum commentatori inverecundo judicio" (p. 246). AE: 1720, 169–172. (See also Assaltus and Lancisius.)

MONTI, (JOAN.) [JOSEPHUS].
De Monumento Diluviano Nuper in Agro Bononiensi detecto, Dissertatio, in qua permultae ipsius inundationis vindiciae, a Statu Terrae Antediluvianae et Postdiluvianae desumptae, exponuntur . . . Bononiae Studiorum: Rossi et Socios, 1719.
Cited by neither Heraeus nor Spener. AE: 1720, 17–21.

Mylius, (Godefridus) [Gottlob Friedrich].
Memorabilium Saxoniae Subterraneae (Pars Prima [and] Secunda). *i.e.*
Des Unterirdischen Sachsens Seltsamer Wunder der Natur . . . Leipzig:
Friedrich Groschussen, 1709–1718. (A second edition appeared with the
Volckmann work in 1720.)
Heraeus: "in Memorabilibus Saxoniae subterraneae G.F.M." (p. 235).
AE: 1709, 173–176.

Rueius [Rueus], (Franciscus).
De Gemmis aliquot . . . *libri duo*. Parisiis, 1547.
Cited by neither Heraeus nor Spener. The Rueius title (editio secunda),
like Fabricus and Kentmann, is one of the eight treatises bound under *De
Omni Rerum Fossilium genere. De Gemmis* is the seventh work in the
volume, with the collation: (2) + 85 leaves + misnumbered extra page 2
after page 2; †alpha †lambda⁸. Title page:
De Gemmis / Aliquot, Iis / Praesertim Quarum / Diuus Ioannes Apostolus
in sua Apocalypsi / meminit: De aliis quoque, quarum usus hoc / aeui apud
omnes percrebruit, Libri duo: Theo / logis non minus utiles quam Philoso-
phis, & / omnino felicioribus ingeniis periucundi, e non / vulgaribus utriusque
philosophiae adytis de- / prompti: authore Francisco Rueo, / Doctore
medico Insu- / lano. / Editio secunda, nam prima mutila, & in- / scio
authore edita fuerat. / Tiguri: 1566.

Sachs [Sachsius], (Philip Jacob) [Philipps Jacobi].
*Gammarologia, sive Gammarorum, vulgo Cancrorum consideratio physico-
philologica-historico-medica-chymica, in qua Praeter Gammarorum Singularem Naturam, Indolem et multivarium usum non minus reliquorum Crusta-
torum instituitur Tractatio.* Francofurti et Leipzig, 1665.
Spener cited Sachs by name only (p. 102).

Scheuchzer [Scheuchzerus], (Joannes Jacobus).
*Meteorologica et Oryctographia Helvetica, oder Beschreibung der Luftge-
schichten, Steinen, Metallen und andern Mineralien des Schweitzerlands,
absonderlich auch der Ueberbleibseln der Sundfluth.* Zurich, 1718.
Heraeus mentions Scheuchzer in several places by name only, and cites
but one work: "Scheuchzeri in Oryctographia Helvetiae Germ." (p. 235).
Spener mentions him by name only (p. 102). There is some doubt regarding the correct citation for "Oryctographia Helvetiae," as Scheuchzer
wrote a great quantity of works on that subject. The above was taken from
Agassiz. The *British Museum Catalogue* gives the following:
*Helvetiae Stoicheiographia, Orographia et Oreographia, oder Beschrei-
bung der Elementen, Grenzen und Bergen des Schweitzerlands, etc. (Hydro-
graphia Helvetica.—Meteorologia et Oryctographia Helvetica, etc.).* Zurich,
1716–1718.
It is very possible that Beringer (and Heraeus) refers to an earlier work
of Scheuchzer's:

APPENDIXES

'Ουρεσιφοινης (Ouresiphoites) *Helveticus, Sive Itinera Alpina Tria: In Quibus Incolae, Animalia, Plantae, Montium Altitudines Barometricae, Coeli et Soli Temperies, Aquae Medicatae, Mineralia, Metalla, Lapides Figurati, aliaque Fossilia; et quicquid insuper in Natura, Artibus, et Antiquitate, per Alpes Helveticas et Rhaeticas, rarum sit, et notatu dignum, exponitur, et Iconibus illustratur.* Londini: Henrici Clements, 1708. (Originally printed at Tiguri in 1702.)

———.
Specimen Lithographiae Helveticae Curiosae, quo Lapides ex Figuratis Helveticis selectissimi aeri incisi et describuntur a Johanne Jacobo Scheuchzero . . . Tiguri: Davidis Gesneri, 1702.
AE: 1705, 479–480.

———.
Herbarium Diluvianum Collectum a Johanne Jacobo Scheuchzero, Med. D. . . . Tiguri: Davidis Gesneri, 1709.
AE: 1710, 451–454; 1723, 79–80.

———.
Piscium Querelae et Vindiciae Expositae a Johanne Jacobo Scheuchzero. Med. D. Acad. Leopoldin . . . Tiguri: Typis Gessnerianis, Sumtibus Authoris, 1708.
AE: 1709, 23–24.

SCILLA, (AGOSTINO).
La Vana Speculazione disingannata dal Senso. Lettera risponsiva circa i corpi marini, che petrificati si trouano in varij luoghi terrestri. Di Agostino Scilla . . . Napoli: A. Colicchia, 1670.
Cited by neither Heraeus nor Spener.

SPENERUS, (CHRISTIAN MAXIMILIAN).
"Disquisitio de Crocodilio in Lapide Scissili Expresso aliisque Lithozois." *Miscellanea Berolinensia,* I (1710), Pars Segunda, 99–118.

SPONIUS [SPON], (JACOBUS) [JACOB].
In Itinerario Hispanico de Regno Valentiae.
Heraeus: "In Hispania, & quidem regno Valentiae, ex relat. Jacobi Sponii in Itinerario" (p. 235). AE: 1683, 369–371, 519–520; 1684, 231–233, 272–273, 429–430; 1685, 349–351. The Spon title presents certain inherent problems. The first is in "Valentiae." There are two "Valentias": one in Spain (Valencia) and one in France (Valence, but Valencia in Latin). Heraeus maintains that Spon visited Spain and the Kingdom of Valentia. This may be incorrect, as Spon describes in his *Voyage D'Italie, de Dalmatie, de Grèce, et du Levant, Fait aux années 1675 et 1676* (pp. 1–4 of the French edition of 1724) a visit to Valencia (Valence), an area in France. There are several

arguments in favor of assuming an error on the part of Heraeus: first, that Spon describes some "natural rarities" in Valence, the very subject which would have brought Spon to his notice; second, that while the work was originally in French, it was translated into German (1690), into Italian (1688), and into Dutch (1689). The principal argument against this supposition is that the title of the work was given by Heraeus in Latin, and the *Voyage D'Italie* did not appear in that language.

STENO [STENONIUS, STENSEN], (NICOLAUS) [NIELS].
De Solido Intra Solidum Naturaliter Contento Dissertationis Prodromus.
Florentiae: Typographia sub signo Stellae, 1669.
Spener: "Stenonis illa de Solido intra solidum" (p. 112).

TENZELIUS [TENTZEL], (WILHELM ERNEST).
Epistola de Sceleto Elephantino Tonnae nuper effosso, ad Virum toto orbe celeberrimum, Antonium Magliabechium, Serenissimi Magni Hetruriae Ducis Bibliothe-carium et Conciliarium. Gothae: Litteris Reyherianis, [Quinto Nonas Maias], 1696.
Heraeus: "Tenzelii in Colloquiis menstruis de 1696" (p. 235); Heraeus also, on page 239, mentions the paper by title. Spener mentions Tenzelius and his "Epistola" on pages 103, 111, and 116.
AE: 1697, 10–14.

VALENTINI, (MICHAELIS BERNHARDI).
Museum Museorum, oder vollständige Schaubühne aller Materialien und Specereyen, nebst deren natüralische Beschreibung, Election, Nutz und Gebrauch. Francofurti ad Moenum: Joh. David Zunnerum, 1704–1714.
Spener: "Museum Valentiniam" (p. 107), and "Mich. Bernh. Valentini . . . Museum Museorum" (p. 108). AE: 1704, 363–364; 1714, 376–380.

VOLCKMANNUS [VOLCKMANNS], (GEORG ANTON).
Silesia Subterranea, oder Schlesien, mit seinen unterirrdischen Schatzen, Seltsamheiten, welche dieses Land mit andern gemein, oder zuvoraus hat . . . Leipzig: Georg Weidmann, 1720. (Bound with a second, though abridged, edition of Mylius.)
Heraeus: "Volckmannus Silesia Subterranea" (p. 235).
AE: 1721, 85–88.

WELSCHIUS [VELSCHIUS], (GEORGIUS HIERONYMUS).
"Lapides engraphi. Astroites. Dendrites. Rhodites. Hydatites sive Cymatites. Stigmites glossopetroides. Cometites." Hecatostea I, observat. xliv, pp. 60–61 of:
Georgii Hieronymi Velschii Hecatosteae II. Observationum Physico-Medicarum ad Illustrem Societatem Naturae Curiosorum in Germania.
Augustae Vindelicorum: Theophili Goebelii, 1675.
Spener: "Georg. Hier. Velschius, varias Astroitae, nec non Cometitae sive lapidis Cometen caudatum referentis, item Stigmitae, Hydatitae sive

Cymatitae undarum & fluctuum effigiem repraesentantis species. Hecatost I. observ. XLIV. p. 60.61" (p. 106).

WINCKELMANNUS, (JOHANNES JUSTUS).
Wahrhaffte Beschreibung von Hessen und Hersfeld. i.e. Vera Descriptio Principatuum Hassiae et Hersfeldiae. Bremae: Hermannum Brauer, 1711.
Heraeus: "Winckelmanni in Descript. Hassiae" (p. 235).
AE: Supplementa V (1713), 519–520.

WOLFARDUS [WOLFART], (PETRUS).
Historiae Naturalis Hassiae Inferioris . . . qua Potiora et Elegantiora hujus Fossilia, Figurata aeque ac certa quadam et regulari figura carentia, eaq; vel lapidea vel metallica, ita in lucem protrahuntur publicam necessariisq; Iconismis illustrantur, ut cuilibet curioso in illis conchas genuinas Marinas, Plantas, Pisces aliaq; naturae admiranda cernere et per haec magnum Creatorem laudare liceat . . . Cassel: Henrich Harmes, 1719.
Heraeus: "D. Wolfarti in Hist. Natur. Hass. Inf." (p. 235).

WODWARDUS [WOODWARDUS, WOODWARD], (JOANNES) (JOHN).
An Essay toward a Natural History of the Earth: and Terrestrial Bodies, Especially Minerals: as also of the Sea, Rivers, and Springs. With an Account of the Universal Deluge: and of the Effects that it had upon the Earth. London: R. Wilkin, 1695.
Heraeus mentions Woodward by name only (pp. 232 and 246) as Whodwardi. Spener also mentions him only by name (p. 102) as Woodwarti. Beringer refers not to the English edition, cited above, but to a Latin translation made from the original English by Johann Jacob Scheuchzer:
Specimen Geographiae physicae quo agitur de terra, et corporibus terrestribus speciatim mineralibus: nec non mari, fluminibus, et fontibus. Accedit diluvii universalis effectuumque ejus in terra descriptio. Authore Joh. Woodwardo. Tiguri: Davidus Gessneri, 1704.

WORMII [WORMIUS, WORM, WURM], (OLAO).
Museum Wormianum. Seu Historia Rerum Rariorum, tam Naturalium, quam Artificialium, tam Domesticarum, quam Exoticarum, quae Hafniae Danorum in Aedibus Authoris servantur. Lugduni Batavorum, 1655.
Heraeus: "De Wormii homine siliceo Mus. p. 82" (p. 143).
Spener mentions Wormius by name only (p. 102).

ZAHN [ZAAN], (JOANNE).
Specula Physico-Mathematico-Historica Notabilium ac Mirabilium Sciendorum, in qua Mundi Mirabilis Oeconomia, nec non Mirifice Amplus, et Magnificus ejusdem abdite reconditus, nunc autem ad lucem protractus, ac ad varis perfacili methodo acquirendas Scientas . . . quo universae Naturae Majestas in triplici Mundo Coelesti, Aereo, et Terrestri . . . Norimbergae: Joannis Christophori Lochneri, 1696.
Cited by neither Heraeus nor Spener.

APPENDIX B

An Account of the Beringer Hoax and of the Subsequent Trials

THE ROMANCE of the *Lithographiae Wirceburgensis* has made immortal the name of Johann Bartholomew Adam Beringer (Behringer): an overzealous savant and backward worthy duped by person or persons unknown (heretofore supposed to be his students) into accepting certain carved stones as "fossils" (or more properly as *lapides figurati*). Beringer has become something of a joke with a ready-made moral attached. The work itself is of almost legendary rarity and has come to be a prize among bibliophiles—a catalogue from a recent sale at Sotheby's auction rooms, in which a copy of the work was listed as item 50 (it was knocked down for as many pounds), contained the following annotation: "A famous hoax in the history of science. Beringer's students manufactured curious 'petrified fossils' and planted them in the neighbourhood of Würzburg, where the professor was led to discover them. He published the present book about them before he discovered the fraud." [1] This was only the third copy of the work to be sold in the past five years, to the best of our knowledge. Although the collation of the *Lithographiae Wirceburgensis* has been noted in the introduction, it might be well to mention that complete copies are evidently scarce. We have examined four copies of the work, and only one of the four contains the Medical Corollaries of Hueber. It has been contended that this represents a second issue of the work, but the rapidity with which the judicial proceedings followed the actual publication would seem to be against this. [2] In any case the legendary figures of the man and his work have conspired to create a truly Barnumesque and Rosenbachian aura in histories of science and in booksellers' catalogues.

Very little in fact is known of Beringer's life; unhappily not even a portrait of the learned doctor is extant. He was born sometime in 1667, the son of Professor Johann Ludwig Beringer (Behringer); he died sometime in 1740, fourteen years after the publication of the *Litho-*

graphiae Wirceburgensis.[3] During his lifetime he acquired the titles of Doctor of Philosophy and Medicine, Senior Professor and Dean of the Faculty of Medicine of the University of Würzburg, Advisor and Chief Physician to the Prince-Bishop of Würzburg [Christopher Franz], and Chief Physician to the Julian Hospital. Beringer was considered to be an indefatigable scholar, perhaps even "the most active man of his time."[4] His life and works have, however, been eclipsed by the unfortunate occurrences of 1725–1726, and only the "intellectual dementia" of the man remains to us.

Even within his lifetime the legend of Beringer and his "Lügensteine" had begun to gain momentum. Balthasar Ehrhart, writing only a year after the publication of the *Lithographiae Wirceburgensis*, remarks, in the Editio Altera of the work cited by Beringer:

> ". . . Similarly there are the figured stones, of still uncertain origin, found near Herbipoli, which the illustrious Doctor Beringer, Councillor and Chief Physician, described in his *Lithographiae Wirceburgensis*. Now this most inquisitive scholar could not better have countered the untimely suspicions of certain persons [mentioned in Chapter XII] than he did by his sincere and candid exposition of all circumstances attending the acquisition of these extraordinary fossils."[5]

Twenty-six years after, in 1752, Johanne Gesner, seemingly lacking much detail, blatantly condemns Beringer: "Concerning the figured stones of Würzburg, displaying a variety of strange insects, wherewith that malicious imposter Beringer made wonderful, if opprobrious sport of the Science of Lithology, it were better to say nothing."[6] Yet Gesner remarks in the succeeding sentence: "A description of the petrified beehives observed in Ethiopia by Lippi may be read in *Acta Parisina* . . ."[7]

James Parkinson, 78 years after, in his widely circulated *Organic Remains of a Former World*, mentions Beringer with ambiguous detail:

> "One work published in 1726, deserves to be particularly noticed; since it plainly demonstrates, that learning may not be sufficient to prevent an unsuspecting man, from becoming the dupe of excessive credulity. It is worthy of being mentioned, on another account: the quantity of censure and ridicule, to which its author was exposed, served, not only to render his contemporaries less liable to imposition; but also more cautious in indulging in unsupported hypotheses. The work is intitled *Lithographiae Wirceburgensis Specimen Primum*, and was written by Dr. John Bartholomew Adam Beringer. We are here pre-

sented with the representation of stones, said to bear petrifactions of birds; some with spread, others with closed wings: bees and wasps, both resting in their curiously constructed cells, and in the act of sipping honey from expanded flowers: spiders weaving their webs: moths and butterflies engendering: and, to complete the absurdity, petrifactions representing the sun, moon, stars, and comets, with many others too monstrous and ridiculous to deserve even mention. These stones, artfully prepared, had been deposited, purposely to dupe the enthusiastic collector, in a mountain, which he was in the habit of exploring. Unfortunately, the silly and cruel trick succeeded so far, as to occasion to him, who was the subject of it, so great a degree of mortification, as, it is said, shortened his days." [8]

The legends of Beringer, the Würzburg "Lügensteine," and the *Lithographiae Wirceburgensis* have grown with time. Again and again the story of the students' pranks is repeated—and each time with a little more gusto. We read of an "original" theory supposedly advanced by Beringer—that the stones were merely "capricious fabrications of God," hidden in the earth for some inscrutable purpose, possibly to test the faith of man. In other accounts detailed descriptions are given of the students' machinations to undo Beringer. These fables have been printed innumerable times and can be found in most biographical encyclopedias and dictionaries. We had thought of giving several extracts from noted works of this type on the subject—say in English, Italian, German, and French—but decided that this would do nothing for the edification of the reader since the tale is the same in any language.

There are many factors to be considered in "judging" Beringer, not the least of which is the state of science in 1726. The factual or theoretrical comprehension of the seventeenth and eighteenth centuries is not overly difficult, but *understanding* is another matter. With sufficient reading we can know the diluvial theory or the spermatic principle, but do we catch the subtle nuances? Do we see the often censurable workings of the seventeenth-century mind, with its clandestine activity of concealing vagaries with positive statements? It is difficult to perceive the true depths of learning in as "fallacy-ridden" a century as the seventeenth, even though the very substance of modern science is founded upon the researches of such virtuosi as Scheuchzer, Beringer, Morton, and a host of others. To identify with a savant of this period—that quixotic, often pedantic paragon of learning—to conceive him as a living man, researching in his laboratory, teaching in his classroom, communicating ideas via learned journals, is even more difficult. If he was florid in his style of writing, we are little better for the asceticism of ours. If he wrote in Latin, the common language of learning, we are the worse for having to learn many tongues. If academic circles were pretentious, we must recall that it was not a democratic age, but one of an autocratic aristocracy, part of a pretentious society.

The true story of the hoax is difficult to piece together, even as revealed in the judicial action taken against the perpetrators and in Beringer's own apologia for his stones (Chapter XII). We are no longer dealing with the simple students' pranks of history. The hoax becomes an act seemingly motivated by revenge and envy—an act propagated more by cold wickedness than by pranks of youth which had got out of hand.

The hoax, as will be shown, must never be separated from an academic atmosphere. The desire for revenge began in this setting, and was evolved and completed here. Behind the hoax are two Iagolike academicians: J. Ignatz Roderick (Roderique), Professor of Geography, Algebra, and Analysis at the University of Würzburg, and the Honorable Georg von Eckhart (Eccard), Privy Councillor and Librarian to the Court and to the University. It is impossible here to make a detailed character analysis of either Roderick or Eckhart, but certain salient characteristics should be brought out.

Roderick was an academic parvenu of unscrupulous character, and did all in his power not only to ruin Beringer, but to place the blame on at least two of Beringer's three hirelings. Eckhart was doubtless the better scholar of the two, and left a wealth of unpublished manuscript material at his death. He had, it seems, been engaged in preparing a history of the Duchy of Würzburg for some years, but because of his involvement in the hoax was denied future access to the archives. That the motive behind the conspiracy was revenge and perhaps even envy is brought out in the subsequent hearings, in which we learn that they wished to ruin Beringer because "he was so arrogant and despised them all."

There was in the background the intriguing figure of a German nobleman: Baron von Hof. We know only that he participated in the conspiracy and was carried about in a sedan chair.

The story then is this:

Beringer, following his interest in oryctics, employed three youths of Würzburg to work for him in the field and to bring to him any figured stones they found there. The young men were Christian Zänger (aged 17), and two brothers: Niklaus and Valentin Hehn (aged 18 and 14 respectively). These young men encountered nothing remarkable until May 31, 1725, on which date the first three "Lügensteine" were found. Just how long the diggers were employed by Beringer previous to this date is unknown.

Accepting Christian Zänger's statement that Roderick and his associates (including Eckhart and Baron von Hof) had already determined to undo Beringer's arrogance, we come to the *modus operandi*. Whether Roderick and Eckhart were familiar with the possibly apocryphal story of Athanasius Kircher's encounter with the pranks of students [9] and decided merely to emulate it, or by some act of fate hit upon Beringer's oryctological enterprises as a means of undoing him, we will probably never know. Once the *modus operandi* had been decided upon, specifically the filling of Beringer's cabinet with fraudulent figured stones, it became necessary to bring at least one of the three diggers into the confidence and pay of the conspirators. Accordingly Christian Zänger gained double employ. The stones (of shell-limestone) were carved principally by Roderick and later polished by Zänger. Some of the stones were hidden about Mount Eivelstadt and others were delivered directly to Beringer by Zänger. Only those hidden on the mountain were brought to the unsuspecting physician by the Hehn brothers.

Sometime between May, 1725, and the publication of the *Lithographiae Wirceburgensis* the perpetrators of the hoax decided that things had gone far enough—perhaps they learned Beringer had had plates engraved and was preparing a dissertation on the stones, which if published could bring ruination on the conspirators as well as on the object of their vindictiveness. For whatever reason, they circulated the rumor that the stones were fraudulent and even went so far as to sell Beringer some stones and then inform him of their manufacture. But Beringer would have none of this! He could not be made to understand that all of the stones were of this same origin, and his reasons perhaps had basis (these he gives in Chapter XII). Besides, had not other learned virtuosi received and seemingly accepted similar stones: Herr König of the Hospital, Herr Balthasar Neuman, and the gentleman at the Hirsch Pharmacy?

Just how Beringer was forced to the realization that he had been hoaxed and that *all* his remarkable stones were of recent manufacture, it is impossible to say. Perhaps he did find his own name within the rocks. Or perhaps it was his Grace, the Bishop of the Church, who made the situation painfully clear to his physician. We will probably never know.

We do know that judicial proceedings were begun on April 13, 1726, at the special request of Beringer, for the "saving of his honor." The judicial process was in three steps: first the hearing at the Würzburg Cathedral Chapter on Saturday, April 13, 1726; second and third were the municipal trials of April 15 and June 11, 1726. Following are the accounts as they exist today.

PROCEEDINGS AT THE WÜRZBURG CATHEDRAL CHAPTER ON APRIL 13, 1726

As the Acts concluded in the previous Cathedral Chapter Session had been read and approved, the Dean of the Church came forth with the statement that his Grace's personal physician, Dr. Beringer, had requested that certain young people of Eivelstadt—who had purposely brought figured stones, up to the present time found in this vicinity, not only to himself but to sundry others—be heard *per syndicum* as to whether they had mingled false stones with true ones, and sold the former as genuine. As the saving of his honor depends upon it, since some impostor wishes to saddle the responsibility for the forgery [of the stones] on him, Dr. Beringer hopes to obtain justification *in subsidium veritatis et iustitiae.*

Whereupon it was agreed by common consent, in response to the supplications of his Grace's personal physician, presented in his reasonable petition, that the *syndicus* should undertake this examination as soon as possible.

Interrogation of the Young Diggers

1. Did any of them ever learn the art of sculpting?
2. Did they not subsequently, by the work of their own hands, sculpt some sort of figures either in wood or in stone?
3. Were they ever hired or induced by any mortal to sculpt images?
4. Did they ever see in any book representations of the figures and characters found in these stones?
5. What occasioned their digging on this mountain, and how did they find the figured stones?
6. Did they ever see anyone secrete such sculptured stones on the mountain, and did they not dig up such stones?
7. How many times and about what matters were they examined and questioned by Messrs. Eckhart and Roderick?

8. Were they threatened, and what was the nature of the threats?
9. Were they ever induced by Messrs. Eckhart and Roderick to sculpt stones, then to bring such stones into the city and pass them off as discovered and dug up?
10. Did they not receive certain sketches according to which they sculpted the stones?

Finally, who is the digger, or who were the diggers whom these two men employed and whom they frequently examined?

Also, information may be sought from the Reverend Pastor and from the more honored citizens of Eivelstadt concerning the skills, the mode of life, the employment, the education, etc., of these youths.

N.B.: If the boy or boys whom Eckhart and Roderick employed can be found, they are to be arraigned and severely questioned on the following points:

1. Did they dig of their own accord, or by someone's orders? If the latter, by whose orders?
2. Where did they take the discovered stones? For what fee? How many did they take?
3. Did they ever make such stones artificially?
4. On what matters were they examined and questioned by Eckhart and Roderick? How did they reply?
5. Were they ever ordered by these two men to make such stones? How many did they make?
6. Were they not ordered to spread the rumor among all and sundry that these stones were spurious?

Interrogation of the young Zänger of Eivelstadt

1. Whether Zänger declares that Eckhart and Roderick offered him twelve ducats if he would say that the diggers [the Hehn brothers] had made the stones? Also if recently Roderick's servant had offered him two Reichsthaler along with the "Commination mit dem Degen" ["commination" with the sword]?
2. Whether Zänger does not declare that he spent entire weeks at Eckhart's house grinding and making stones?
3. Whether Zänger declares that Roderick and Eckhart had promised him a new suit of clothes and thereafter to take him with them to Coblenz, as a servant, before Easter-time?
4. Whether he does not declare that he heard from Eckhart and Roderick that they would not rest until Dr. Beringer was suppressed and forced to pay a fine of 1,000 Reichsthaler—toward which end a Baron, carried in a sedan chair, and five other persons wished to meet? Who was this Baron? And in addition, who were the others who spoke such words?
5. Where did Zänger get the "dragon-stones," the stones on which were the Hebraic letters and others upon which the knife was used?

Was he not ordered by Roderick or Eckhart to deliver up diligently such stones to Beringer? To whom else were they delivered?

6. How many stones did he copy [from sketches] while he worked in Eckhart's house? Where can these stones be found? Did he [Zänger] or some other person besides hide these stones in the mountain? How deeply were they buried, where they are now found?

7. Did not Zänger declare in the presence of the mother of the Hehn brothers that during the recent visit of his Grace [the Sovereign Bishop?], Eckhart and Roderick gave him [Zänger] a carved stone and ordered him to give this stone to his Grace? But as he [Zänger] did not wish to do this, they [Eckhart and Roderick] emphatically assured him that he had no cause for fear, as his Grace already knew of the matter, i.e., what there was about the stone and what figure was on it.

8. Did not Zänger receive from Roderick and Eckhart a little sketch of a mouse and Hebraic letters? For what purpose were these given him?

9. Did he [Zänger] ever work in alabaster? What was the figure he made in it, which he described to Eckhart and Roderick?

Other Questions to be posed to the Hehn brothers of Eivelstadt:

D.G. Had not the priest of that place [Eivelstadt] cautioned them against Eckhart and Roderick, because they [Eckhart and Roderick] had been burying their stones in the mountain?

2. Did not Roderick threaten Zänger and Hehn [Valentin] with immediate imprisonment in irons and fetters, if they did not admit to the authorship of the stones?

Questions to be posed to the innkeeper's wife:

Had not Roderick not long ago passed himself off as a nobleman or country squire in the inn of that place [Eivelstadt]?

PROCEEDINGS AT THE CITY HALL OF EIVELSTADT
ON THE 15TH OF APRIL 1726

Present: Joh. Casp. Christian Papius, the Sovereign Episcopal Official [Secretary to the Prince-Bishop]; the High Bailiff Ferd. Wolffg. Stadler; and myself, Johann Georg Molitor, Town Clerk of Eivelstadt, as recorder.

After the petition of Dr. Beringer, the personal physician of his Grace the Prince-Bishop, had been presented to the Right Reverend Gentleman, the Provost of the Cathedral Chapter, and the entire body of the Cathedral Chapter, certain young people of Eivelstadt were arraigned concerning figured stones found in the vicinity, which they had dug up and brought forth. They were to be heard *in subsidium iuris et veritatis probandae*, as to whether they had actually discovered such stones as they had delivered or whether they had carved them or at least learned from someone else the name of the person who had actually manufactured such stones—in this manner the *syndicus*, to whom the commission of this case had been entrusted, took up the trial, which was proffered by the High Bailiff, from this day forth. This was done with the purpose of examining the various citizens' sons in the following manner concerning the above-mentioned events.

Examination of Niklaus Hehn (aged 18 years)

1. Whether he knows that some time ago stones with various figures were found in this vicinity?
   ANSWER: To this he gave full acknowledgement.
2. Whether he did not himself dig after and discover stones of this sort [i.e., "Lügensteine"]?
   ANSWER: Affirmative. He searched for and discovered many such stones.
3. What particular figures did these stones have? What did he do with them?
   ANSWER: There were crabs, toads, frogs, flies, lizards, worms, water snakes, and many other things engraved on the stones, which he had carried and handed over to Dr. Beringer.
4. How long ago had he searched for and dug after these stones?
   ANSWER: On the holy Blutstag of last year he had discovered the first three stones.
5. What figures were on these three stones?
   ANSWER: On one was a circle, like the sun with its rays. On the others, however, were worms.
6. Did he polish or carve a little, or do anything else with an instrument, on any of the stones he discovered and subsequently delivered to Dr. Beringer?
   ANSWER: He never did anything to the stones, but such stones as he found he delivered to Dr. Beringer *as* he found them—just as he had long before brought him shell-stones.
7. Had anyone else done anything to these stones, such as grinding, polishing, or cleaning?
   ANSWER: Neither he nor anyone else had done even the slightest thing to them, except that he had cleaned them of the dirt.
8. Had any other persons, besides Dr. Beringer, requested like stones from him?
   ANSWER: There were many who had requested such stones, specifically Herr König in the Hospital, and the journeyman of the Hirsch Pharmacy in Würzburg, as well as a gracious gentleman who lives next to the Franciscan brothers, to which persons he had, however, *de facto* not yet brought in any stones.
9. Does he still remember which persons had requested these stones from him?

ANSWER: In the parsonage here there was also one, who was with von Eckhart, who asked for like stones and the promise that Hehn give him ten times as many stones as he had given Dr. Beringer.

10. Does he know the name of this man?

ANSWER: He had heard that he is called Roderick.

11. Did this Herr Roderick say anything further or make any other requests?

ANSWER: He [Roderick] said that his Grace had sent him out to discover whether they themselves [the Hehn brothers] had not carved the stones and hidden them in the mountain. To this he [Hehn] answered that they had done no such thing, for they gave out the stones as they had found them. As Roderick now saw that he could do nothing with him [Niklaus Hehn], he turned to his younger brother to ask him the same question. He also threatened to have him put into irons and fetters if his brother would not admit to having carved the stones with a knife.

12. How did his brother answer to this?

ANSWER: He [Valentin Hehn] answered the same as the older brother [Niklaus]: If they could *make* such stones, they wouldn't be mere diggers.

13. Had either of the brothers learned the art of carving, so that he could fashion such figures?

ANSWER: Neither of them had learned to work in stone.

14. Had they at least learned to carve in wood?

ANSWER: They had never learned to carve and they would not be able to do it.

15. Did he ever deliver any stones to the aforementioned Roderick?

ANSWER: He had brought Roderick three stones from his home. One of these same stones Zänger produced in the presence of his Grace, as if he had just found it. Zänger then put next to it, for comparison, another stone, which Roderick had carved in Würzburg, with the figure of a sea horse on it.[10]

16. How is it that he knew that one of these selfsame stones, which he had handed over to Roderick, was brought out by Zänger? Further, how did he know that the stone with the sea horse on it was carved by Herr Roderick in Würzburg?

ANSWER: He knew his stones well, and had never found another of this type. Of the other stone, however, the one with the sea horse, Zänger had told him and confessed that Roderick had made that particular one. In addition to this Zänger had drawn three figures for him [Hehn] on paper and explained that Roderick had promised him money when he would deliver up such stones.

17. Of what were the figures that were drawn on the paper, and what did Zänger do with them?

ANSWER: It was the drawing of an elephant, as if he had a "*Doll-fues*"[?], then there was a lion and letters. The paper he then took from him and carried to Dr. Beringer.

18. Was he not warned by anyone to keep watch, since these stones could have been hidden in the mountain?

ANSWER: The priest had warned him to beware. And this he did and followed the warning, but nothing came of it.

END OF THE QUESTIONING

Examination of Valentin Hehn (aged 14 years)

[The questions are the same as those put to Niklaus, and only the answer was recorded in the transcript.]

1. ANSWER: Affirmative.
2. ANSWER: Affirmative.
3. ANSWER: He did not know of any figures except those of plants, horseflies, and fish, all of which he delivered to Dr. Beringer.
4. ANSWER: On Fronleichnamstag of last year they had found the first stones.
5. ANSWER: There were worms on these stones. The other figure he didn't understand.
6. ANSWER: He had done nothing to these stones.
7. ANSWER: He isn't aware that anything was done to the stones by any other person. When they [the Hehn brothers] found the stones, they washed them off and carried them into Würzburg without delay.
8. ANSWER: No one had requested like stones.

9.
10.
                    QUESTIONS CAME TO NOTHING
11.
12.

13. ANSWER: Neither of them had learned such a craft.
14. ANSWER: Neither of them had learned to make such figures.
15. ANSWER: Negative. Roderick did not request any stones from him, but he [Roderick] stated that he knew how it happened with the stones: namely that they [the Hehn brothers] had filled the mountain from top to bottom with stones. And since they had left the mountain, there were no more stones. He [Roderick] also knew how the stones were made. And that the Hehn brothers had stuck the stones under the boulders on the mountain. Whereupon he [Valentin Hehn] had answered that all this was a lie. How could they have buried the stones? He wanted to go to Würzburg on the morning of the next day and accuse Roderick to his Grace, so that he [Roderick] had to leave the city. No honest man would say that of him [Valentin], only a ———.

QUESTION: What then had Herr Roderick to say upon hearing this sharp talk?

ANSWER: He said nothing, but went away.

The city clerk explained that Roderick, according to his knowledge, had not heard Hehn's remark, because the boy had so quickly run off, as he himself had seen. He believed, however, that the others, who had spoken French with him [Roderick] had told him of the reproaches of the boy, because Roderick had become pale and looked after the departing youth.

TO THE QUESTION: If the young Hehn brothers knew anything further about the matter, the response was negative.

The testimony of the third witness:
Christian Zänger (aged 17 years)

1. Does he know the truth about the stones, discovered some time ago, which bore divers figures?

    ANSWER: Affirmative.

2. Had he dug after and found such stones? To whom had he delivered them?

    ANSWER: He had given Herr Stück-Major [Balthasar Neuman] and Dr. Beringer such stones. A tree was carved on the one received by Herr Stück-Major.

3. Had he found all the stones which he delivered to both Herr Stück-Major and Dr. Beringer, or had he occasion to do any work on the stones, such as polishing?

    ANSWER: He had done nothing to the stones, but left them as he had found them.

4. How could he say that he had left the stones as they were found, since he admittedly had brought some which had been copied to Dr. Beringer, and received payment for them?

    ANSWER: He had done nothing except receive stones from Herr Roderick—to which Roderick had applied a knife and carved the letters and the rest of the things.

5. Had he not received other such stones from this gentleman?

    ANSWER: Roderick had also given him one with a dragon on it, another with a pomegranate,[11] and a third on which was a lion with a long tail. He did as he was ordered and delivered these to Dr. Beringer. For the four copied stones, in addition to the ones which he had actually found, he had received 22 Batzen.

6. How did he know that the accused Herr Roderick had made the stones?

    ANSWER: He was present when Herr Roderick had made two of them, and the other two Herr Roderick had admitted carving.

7. What was he doing at the time that Roderick had carved the first two stones? Where had this work been undertaken?

    ANSWER: Herr Roderick had summoned him to the residence of the Privy Councillor [von Eckhart] at the Sandter Gate and asked him if the Hehn brothers could carve stones for Dr. Beringer. To which he replied that they could carve small altars, and had in fact made one for him. About all this Roderick wished further information. Could they carve in stone? Had he not seen them make such things? To which he denied that he had seen anything. After this Roderick had mentioned that he was suspicious of the stones and believed them to be fraudulent. He [Roderick] requested hard marble, which he [Zänger] delivered to him. Then Roderick had him polish the marble and afterwards ordered him to deliver the copied stones to Dr. Beringer.

8. Had he received from Roderick only these four carved stones which he had given to Dr. Beringer, or were there still more of them? Who else received such stones from him?

    ANSWER: As his Grace intended to come to Eivelstadt, Roderick had given him another stone upon which there was a sea horse. This he was ordered to deliver with other stones to his Grace. Should other gentlemen be present, he should say that he had found it, but if his Grace were alone, he should tell him that Roderick had made the stone, since his Grace already knew about it.

9. Was he offered any money, and how much, if he would say that the Hehn brothers had made such stones?

    ANSWER: The Privy Councillor and Herr Roderick had promised him, at the former's residence, much money and many favors if he would state that the Hehn brothers had made the stones.

10. Was anything else talked about when this promise was made?

    ANSWER: He knows nothing else save that at one time a Baron von Hof, who was afterwards carried away in a sedan chair, was at the residence of the Privy Councillor; and that there they had discussed how they wished to accuse Dr. Beringer before his Grace, because he was so arrogant and despised them all.

11. Had he ever buried stones in the mountain, which he received from Herr Roderick, and which are actually still to be found there?

    ANSWER: He had buried none. Roderick, however, had said that he had still more buried there.

12. Had he received a paper upon which were drawn Hebrew letters, mice, and other animals? For what purpose had he been given this?

    ANSWER: Herr Roderick had said that this is how the stones which he had buried looked. And recently when Herr Major [Balthasar Neuman] found one of the same stones, Roderick laughed over it with the inference that it could be one of his stones.

[RECESS]

Meanwhile, after this morning's examination, young Zänger was persuaded *in ipso discessu* that he improve his memory of the actual events and truth, so that whatever may happen to occur to him this afternoon should be brought out. He appears with a more challenging contestation: that he in his conscience did not intend to declare a disadvantage for anyone; that Herr Roderick said that he had buried three stones at the Wolfsgraben, which he would still like to show him, so that when gentlemen come and ask to see them, he could show them the same. And in addition he had to report to them that when he had delivered the false stones to Dr. Beringer and returned to the residence of the Privy Councillor, they all had a big laugh that Dr. Beringer was deceived by the stones. For this reason the lady [von Eckhart's wife] had shown her feelings of great jubilation, and had honored him with six Batzen, remarking that Christian could certainly sell his stones well. Moreover, he gave to the commission the very powder which he had been given to polish the stones.

The commission then showed this Zänger a newly found stone in the shape of a field dove lying on its back, with the question: "Could this be one of those which Herr Roderick, according to his own statement, had carved, or do you judge such a one to be a natural stone or at least from antiquity?" To which he answered, that the marks and imprinted masses of sand and other little stones, besides the roughness, are sufficient proof that this stone could not have been brought to its present state in modern times.

The commission then repeated the question: "For what reason does the defendant believe that he was sent to Dr. Beringer, so that Dr. Beringer might buy false stones?"

ANSWER: They said that he [Zänger] should try Dr. Beringer, to see if he could be tricked into buying the false stones. After which they ordered him to remain there through the same night so they could make enough stones for him [Zänger] to deliver to Dr. Beringer.

The young Valentin Hehn was then called and testified that Herr Roderick was considered in high repute, since he had passed himself off first as a canon and then as a nobleman. This statement Zänger affirmed.

Finally Zänger was again called by the commission and asked if he judged the stone in the shape of a stag beetle, collected near the mountain, to be authentic or false. To this he answered: It is certain that this stone had been worked on. But whether the entire figure had been carved on it or only changed, he could not be certain. However, he must admit that Herr Roderick had said that he had hidden his false stones in the Wolfsgraben, where this stone was found.

The defendant pointed out again that Roderick had ordered him to tell Dr. Beringer—should he have any misgivings about the stone on which was carved a dragon and on which the Praeceptor in the house had carved a mouse on the backside so unsatisfactorily that he [Zänger] had to grind it off again—that his brother had broken off the figure on the side.[12] He asked the commission for help in obtaining the wages owed to him by Roderick for eight days of stone polishing, for which he had received no compensation.

PROCEEDINGS AT THE MAGISTRATE'S ON 11TH JUNE 1726

Christian Zänger of Eivelstadt was heard out on further questions. He was warned above all else to speak only the pure truth about the things which he would be asked, and to speak out in this manner so that one would not be occasioned, in case his past testimony should be found to be false, to have his name entered into the Black List after his departure [from the trial, or from Würzburg?].

These questions were as follows:

1. How many stones did he copy after the time he gave evidence before the previous commission?

ANSWER: According to his testimony, he does not know of any stones which were made after that time, either by himself or any other, save for a single one which he already confessed to Dr. Beringer.

2. What was the figure on this stone and to whom was it sold?

ANSWER: On this single stone were carved the sun, moon, and stars. He had delivered it to the most distinguished gentleman at the Hirsch Pharmacy and was given in return four Schilling.

3. To what extent had he helped in the manufacture of the stones and further how had he achieved the effect?

ANSWER: He had not copied any, but had polished twenty hard pieces of stone at the residence of the Privy Councillor von Eckhart. Three of the soft stones he had received from the young Hehn at Eivelstadt before the meeting of the commission—of which two he could say certainly that they were copies. Two of the three he had handed over to Herr Stück-Major Neumann. On one of these there was a tree and on the other there were but letters. The one with the tree was copied. Previously he had also taken such stones to Dr. Beringer. Dr. Beringer, however, did not acknowledge them as authentic, and had sent him away again with the stones, after having given him ten Kreuzer for his trouble. Herr Neumann had kept both stones and had given him six Batzen drinking money. The third stone, upon which there was a bird and which was also false, he had taken to Herr König in the hospital. Herr König had given him four light Batzen and several shell stones.

This is the totality of the proceedings known today. Abruptly they began and abruptly they ended. Nothing further is heard of the three youths of Eivelstadt. Within four years of the trial, von Eckhart died, evidently leaving a legacy of unpublished manuscript material. Roderick was either cast from or found it convenient to absent himself from Würzburg. Beringer continued in his academic status, and wrote (after the *Lithographiae Wirceburgensis*) at least two additional books, which appear to have achieved a certain academic acclaim. He survived the ordeal by some fourteen years.

In February, 1730, Roderick wrote to the Prince-Bishop of Würzburg in the following plaintive terms:

Most Reverend and High Prince and Lord of the
Holy Roman Jurisdiction, Most Clement Lord:
Staggered by the tidings of the unexpected death of that excellent man, so dear to me in life, J. G. Eccard [Georg von Eckhart], I seek some balm for my grief, and can find none, unless it be possible for me to erect a memorial to him in my own modest fashion. But since I am well aware that this cannot be fittingly accomplished except under the most gracious auspices of your Most Reverend Highness, I prostrate myself at the feet of your great mercy, imploring these auspices. I know full well what an indignity I perpetrate by importuning Your Most Reverend Highness, occupied as you are with the most weighty matters of the Church and of the Christian Republic; yet I am raised from my trembling abjection by the thought of that undisguised esteem which the most eminent and most illustrious citizens of Schonborn ever tendered the Deceased, and which I confidently believe will never be wanting to him, to his memory, and to his bereaved children.

Wherefore, I would deem it a fitting tribute to the name of this celebrated man, were his life written up in compendium, to which should be added the vindications against Schannat, wherein as in one work the rights of Würzburg are defended; lastly, prefaces and a dedicatory letter should embellish his Commentaries on Eastern Franconia, and each of these should precede the former.

I am keenly conscious of my inability to perform this task in keeping with the desserts of this most egregious man; nevertheless, I would seem better fitted for it than any other, since I am apprised of all of his affairs and intentions, and, moreover, I frequently sponsored his esteemed Commentaries. Therefore, since there are many items in his library which could further this endeavor, I pray your Most Reverend Highness that the library be preserved intact until my health permits me to undertake the journey to Würzburg. I anticipate an early realization of this proposal. There is yet another reason for making this request. In this library are a number of books belonging to the splendid Geubach Library, others that belong to me and to other persons, and a host of other things, the use and purpose of which form a part of my plans.

And now, in all deference, I pray Your Most Reverend Highness to look with favor upon my ardent wish to render to this parent, as it were, the affectionate and pious honors of a son. Were I gifted with sufficient ability and learning so that I might pursue the works he so magnificently began, I would seek to appropriate his literary province. But, crushed by a sense of my own limitations, I dare not entertain such lofty ambitions. For the rest, although in other matters I am abysmally inferior to the deceased, still I yield neither to him nor to any other, Most Clement Lord, in my unswerving loyalty and profound devotion to Your Most Reverend Highness.

> Your most humbly and faithfully
> devoted servant,
> IGN. RODERICK

Cologne, Feb. 19, 1730.[13]

Roderick's request was granted in March, but not without innuendo regarding his past actions:

> From your letter to us, we have understood your plan of a memorial to the honorable Eccard [Eckhart], now deceased, and also what you propose concerning his library and other effects, and for the continuation of the work begun by him: a task to which you yourself consider yourself unequal. In good time we shall issue directives anent these matters as circumstances seem to require. Now, since you make mention of your preparation to return to Würzburg, we will not dissimulate the fact that in the past, both by reason of your gross neglect of duty and because of other irregularities in your life, you have gained an unenviable reputation and have suffered no small blight on your good name. Trusting, therefore, that henceforth you will acquit yourself more satisfactorily in your teaching of geography and algebra, and will so conduct yourself in all matters that whatever is deemed fitting may be more confidently entrusted to you,
>
> > We remain, meanwhile, affectionately
> > yours in grace,

Vienna, March 8, 1730.[14]

The story of the *Lithographiae Wirceburgensis* as revealed through the judicial proceedings is a far cry from the simple "students' pranks" of history. When one reads the transcript with a remembrance of Beringer's defense of his stones throughout the text of the *Lithographiae Wirceburgensis*, the tragicomedy takes on genuine pathos. Here was a savant hopelessly duped, and today remembered only for his credulity. Rather than being fated to a happy obscurity, along with Büttner, Langius, and a host of others, his name has become "a hissing and a byword." Perhaps this may be changed.

But now our case rests. We have willingly submitted our notes to the scrutiny of wise men, desiring to learn their verdict in this much-mooted question.

APPENDIX C

Lhwyd's Letter to John Ray

EDWARD LHWYD'S (Lhuyd or Luidius) celebrated *Epistola* to John Ray (discussed by Beringer in Chapters III and VI) exists in several versions. It first appeared in Lhwyd's *Lithophylacii Britannici Ichnographia* (1699: pp. 131–145; 1760: pp. 131–142), and was subsequently rendered into English by Lhwyd himself at the request of Ray. The latter included it to great effect in his *Three Physico-Theological Discourses.*

The English version in many places scarcely resembles the Latin, as in translation it was "enlarged with many additions." The version reproduced here is Lhwyd's translation. Care has been taken to note changes in the text where marked differences occur between the Latin and English versions.

Some of the annotations in the letter have been taken, by permisson, from Volume XLV (Life and Letters of Edward Lhwyd) of R. T. Gunther's *Early Science in Oxford*, which is probably the most comprehensive work on Lhwyd yet issued. The notes are of necessity brief, and the reader should refer to Gunther's work when any questions arise as to Lhwyd's life and associations.

Notes preceded by dagger were included by Lhwyd in the manuscript, while notes preceded by a double dagger were inserted by Ray into the letter.

OF THE ORIGIN OF MARINE FOSSILS;
AND OF MINERAL LEAVES, BRANCHES,
ETC.

Hon'd Sr
You are pleasd to ask whether after some years observations I have been at length able to satisfy my self, as to the origin of what we call *Marine Fossils;* & those other bodies no less surprizing, which, to distinguish them from other plants, I have taken the liberty to call *Mineral*

142

Leavs [=Lithophyta]: viz. whether I conclude, with ye general opinion, that they have been reposited in the places we find them at ye universal Deluge, & so preservd to our time; [1] or that they are original productions of Nature, there form'd from some plastic power of salts or other minerals, wch was ye conjecture of the late ingenious Dr. Plot [2] & other experienced Naturalists. To this I must needs answer that ye frequent observations I have made on such bodies, have hitherto affoarded litle better satisfaction, than repeated occasions of wonder and amazement; for as much as I often (I may say continually) experienced, that what one days observations suggested, was by those of ye next calld in question, if not totally contradicted & overthrown. Nevertheless so indefatigable is ye curiosity, & indeed so successfull have been the discoveries of this present age, that we are dayly encouraged to hope this so important a question will not much longer want its final determination, to the great advancement of that kind of real knowledge, wch relates to minerals or fossils. A part of Natural History, which you well know, hath been hitherto much more neglected than that of plants & animals; onely, as I presume, because these bodies are less obvious to our view, and much more abstruse and unaccountable as to their origin or production. I therefore at spare hours continue to improve my collection, in regard it may be hop'd that from an accurat inspection of it, some others hereafter may frame several usefull inductions, wch I my self never had the least thoughts of. And in the mean time because the communicating to our friends, what carries but the least shadow of probability, does often contribute somwhat towards ye speedier discovery of the truth, I shall here presume to submit to your examination a conjecture relating to the origin of these bodies, wch I know not whether any other have as yet thought of. But in regard it is necessary that before any new opinion be propos'd, reasons be produc'd against those already receiv'd, give me leave here to lay before you some objections against both the above mentiond accounts of the origin of these bodies. To begin therefore with that which referrs all these marine fossils & mineral leavs, stalks, & branches, &c. to the Deluge, I have several reasons to offer against it, whereof (because I would not too much presume on your time & patience) I shall at present propose onely these few.

I. Therefore had these bodies been marine spoils, brought on the dry land by an inundation, they would (for the generality at least) either have been left upon the surface of the earth, or have been lodg'd at no very great depth under it; but I have found them buryed or inclosd within solid marble on the *face* of broken sea cliffs, of the height of 200 fadoms & more at all depths from the tops thereof, to ye bottom; & observd them to be continued so under ye sea water. Nor was that onely on the face of these rocks, but even, more or less, throughout the whole mass of them. And this is manifest from divers rocks hewn down by workmen for making of lime, & other pieces casually fallen from the cliffs in the Isle of *Caldey* & elsewhere about Tenby in Pembrokeshire; as also in several other rocks & mountains that consist of such bastard marble or lime-stone, throughout Wales, Ireland & other countreys. Now although we should grant yt at the time of the Deluge, these rocks were no other than clay or earth; & that therefore, sea shells, coralls & other marine bodies, might by the violence of the inundation have been lodg'd; & that in tract of time that suppos'd clay or earth consolidated into lime-stone: I say although we should grant all this, yet can I not perceive by what force such bodies could be sunk into any clay or earth to so great a depth. If indeed these bodies constituted one continued mass; so as that one should bear hard on the other, something perhaps might be replyd: but the matter is clearly otherwise; for they are found confusedly dispers'd, throughout the mass of lime stone, some times at the distance (for example) of three foot from each other; some times two, some times within half an inch; & not seldome two or three or more of them contiguous.

II. Such marine fossils have been observ'd on ye sides or walls within our limestone caves; & are even some times found sticking to the roofs of them, for I have gather'd the Cuthbert Beads or *Entrochi*,[3] which are vertebrae of sea starrs, from ye roof a cave called Lhygad Ihwchwr near Kerrig Kennen Castle in the County of Caermarthen: and on the sides (as well as bottom) of a noted cave calld *Porth Gogo* at *Ystrad Velhte* in Brecknockshire, I have observd sevral remains of cockles half worn by the swift current of the River *Melhte* wch runs through this cave and polishes its limestone. Now although I can readily grant that the Deluge might have cast marine bodies into these & any other caves; yet can I not allow that it could ever fasten them to their polite roofs & sides: and that they should be sunk so deep from the top, is the difficulty of the former objection. To this may be added that such limestone caves are for ye most part wainscoted (as it were) with a stony crust of *stalagmites* wch is of no very old date; but owing to the continued dropping or distillation of the caves, in wch if any marine-like bodies are found, as I can assure you the *Entrochi* are, I leave it to your self & other unprejudiced observers to consider of their origin.

III. The third reason for my questioning whether all these things be the effects of the deluge, is for that the bones, horns & hoofs of land animals are very seldome if at all found inclosd in solid marble or other ston: whereas seeing all perishd in the Deluge, the spoils of ye land might be expected (in proportion) as well as those of the sea.[4]

IV. Some fossil shells are intirely composd of a spar or crystal, insomuch that there is no distinction of a containing & contain'd matter; but onely a crystalline body, of the figure of a shell, as is by Steno himself acknowledg'd,[5] and as may be seen in myne & other cabinets of form'd stones. How so great a change should happen to sea shells & yet their shape or outward form not violated, seems to me too difficult to explain. The like may be sayd of the fossil fish teeth;[6] for these are not always of ye same matter, as may be observd from diverse specimens in my collection.

V. That fossil shell which I have called *Pholas amygdaloides* in ye Catalogue [*Lithophylacii Britannici Ichnographia*] num. 877. is for ye most part found wrap'd up in an odd lamellated case of a peculiar structure. Now yt all or ye most part of ye shells of this kind, should by being driven to land be involved in a plated.[7]

V. Living animals are sometimes found in these fossil shells; For in Misson's *Travels* page . . . we read of a lobster found alive [8] . . . [in the midst of a Marble near Tivoli; and the late Description of *Orkney*, &c. gives us the like Account of Cockles.] [9] . . . and as I am credibly inform'd some workmen very lately digging for the foundation of a buylding near ye town of Mold in Flintshire; met with sevral muscles at about three foot depth in the gravel, which had living fish in them. Now as 'twould be asburd to imagine any animals could live since ye Flood; so neither can we suppose that such creatures being left there by the Deluge, should propagate their kind ever since; for in that case there must have been left in the same place, a heap of their shells.[10]

VI. Had these marine bodies been reposited in the earth at the Universal Deluge, such of them as adhere to each other, nay all of the same pits or quarries; unless their beds be of a different matter, must necessarily have undergone the same change; but Steno acknowledges that he had found Testaceous shells adhering to one perfectly crystalline; [11] and I have my self often gather'd some crystalline specimens & others Testaceous of the same sort of shell, in the same quarry & the same stratum or layer.

VII. The immense quantity we have of marine fossils seems no ways to plead for their origin from ye Deluge. For we may observe many thousands of great stones, & even broken pieces of limestone rocks throughout Wales and the North of England, almost wholy composd of those vertebrae; or broken pieces of the Radij of sea stars, which are commonly calld *Entrochi* (*Entrochos vulgo vocant*), Fayry Stones & Cuthbert Beads, wheras 'tis very rare to find on our shoars, three broken Radij or fragments of any sort of Sea starrs close together. Likewise one shall rarely find in ye same place two single of any fish on all our coasts; whereas thousands of these fossil teeth exactly answering those of diverse sorts of sea fish have been of late years found in quarries and gravel pits [at Faringdon] about Oxford; nor is their quantity at all diminished upon breaking new ground.

VIII. Some of these marine fossils are no other than as it were shadows or superficial representations of sea bodies: nor do they seem to have much more of ye matter or consistence of those bodies they mostly resemble, than a picture hath of ye person or thing it represents. And of this kind is Dr. Lister's *Pectinites membranaceus* out of the cole pits; [12] The Mock plaice or *Buglossa curta strigosa* of Caermarthenshire,[13] & the Islebian fish-stones in Germany,[14] of which Olaus Wormius gives us this following account: 'In the Islebian slat (sayth he) are seen some times a small dust of the Golden Pyrites; which represents various figures of animals. I have a large piece of this stone which so lively expresses all the lineaments of a Barbel in golden colour, that the scales, the fins, the tayl, the head &c. could not possibly by any artist be ever better painted. The bodies of these fish, are not converted into *Pyrites;* so that we have but just the outward lineaments of them; and not the least impression left of any bones or other parts. We find our selves therefore oblig'd to confess, that Nature reservs many things from our knowledge the true reasons wherof, no man will ever, so far discover, as to be enabl'd to render us a due account of them.'[15] Now as these representations are neither animals themselvs, nor the exuviae of animals; so neither can they be their impressions; for as much as these lineaments are prominent, not impress'd: And as for ye impression they make on one side it seems not satisfactory, because I can not well conceive, how all ye vertebrae of a fish, whereof many are frequently found in our midland quarries & gravel pits should here be totally consum'd, & the surface onely of one side, be converted into this Pyrites or Marchasite.

IX. An other obstacle of my assent to their being all of diluvian origin, is the vast number of unknown marine fossils so commonly met with throughout most counties of England; such as we have nothing like, neither on our sea shoars, nor rak'd by dredges out of the bottom of the sea, by the oyster fishermen & others who have been employ'd by curious persons on set purpose. I have in my collection above 40 different species of the fossil *Nautili* or those shell-stones, a great many sorts whereof are commonly calld *Cornua Hammonis;*[16] and have observ'd plenty of most of these species (broken or whole) in the fields, quarries and clay pits of the Midland Counties of England; Nor doe I question but in that excellent collection of Dr. Woodwards,[17] & in those of some others of our curious naturalists, several species may be found that are not in myne: And yet I can not understand that all our British seas affoard one sort of this shell. The like may be sayd as to several other kinds; particularly the *sea stars*, of the broken *Radij* whereof we find no less a variety,[18] and the *Echini*, to ye prickls or radioli of which, as well as to those of the sea stars, all sorts of *Lapides Iudaici*[19] (as many years since I hinted to you) must be referr'd, notwithstanding the excessive thickness of some of them, and that they have that very rough or grater-like superficies,[20] so as to be nothing like the spines of any of the *Echini* or starr-fish of our seas.[21]

X. I adde only one other argument, which though many have already objected, yet hath not that I know of, been hitherto answer'd to satisfaction. And that is that such marine substances are some times generated in human bodies. For to me it appears a far less wonder that shells and other marine bodies should be produc'd in the bowels of the earth, than their production in the bodies of men or animals at land.[22] And that they have been so found is sufficiently attested both by ancient

& modern authors of a credit and character beyond all exception. You know many instances of this kind are produc'd by Dr. Lister in the second part of his *Anatomy of Shells;* amongst which I remember very well to have seen that *Turbinulus* or *periwinckle* [23] discover'd by Dr. Pierce of Bath & sent to Dr. Musgrave then Secretary of ye Oxford Philosophical Society; & it was such as I believe none could have possibly distinguished from a sea shell. These Sr are the objections I had to offer against their opinion, who attribute the origin of all these marine fossils to the universal Deluge. For whatever their true origin is, *marine fossils* they ought to be term'd in order to their better distinction from all others. 'Tis also for the like conveniency of distinction, that I use the term of *mineral plants* for those fossil leavs & branches we find so commonly inclos'd in stone & blew marl at our cole-pits, & some iron mines.

And now to proceed we shall find much the like difficulties with what occur'd when we consider'd the marine fossils.

I. For in the first place these subterraneous Leavs frequently (indeed, most commonly) are found at ye depth of at least 20 or 30 foot: and how they should be layd so deep by an inundation seems to me not so easily accountable. For since 'tis the property of leavs to swim, its natural to suppose that all plants were left by the Deluge on the surface of the earth, in the manner we dayly find several American seeds of Leguminous trees cast up on the shoars of Ireland, Scotland, & Wales; and that consequently in a short space there would be no more remains of them, than we find of those sea plants we dung our land with.[24]

II. Allowing they might be by some accident we can not think of, buryed so deep, I can discover no reason for their being thus lodg'd so plentifully in cole-slat & iron stone; and never that I know of, in the mass of our flint, lime-stone & common rock; though there be infinitely the greater quantity of these latter: and this Note seems to deserve our consideration, unless it can be made out that though the matter of flint & limestone has very intirely preserv'd the Antediluvian shells, yet it could not leavs or other parts of vegetables.

III. Had they been owing to the Deluge we should find the leavs & branches of such plants as are natives of our own Island much more plentifully than such unknown plants as far as Dr. Richardson's observations [25] & my own have been able to distinguish, the generality of these mineral leavs are clearly distinct from those of our British plants.

IV. Had they been thus reposited at ye Deluge, some specimens of most, if not of each class of plants, would be found amoungst them; and especially of trees, in regard such leavs are not onely the most numerous, but also commonly the driest and most durable: But we have not hitherto discover'd that any of these mineral leavs answer to those of trees or shrubs; nor are we assur'd that any have been yet found, but what may be reduc'd to three or four classes.

V. The same curious and ingenious gentlman [Richardson] hath observd that these mineral leavs are, generally speaking, less than those they seem most to resemble, which is what in diverse specimens I have since taken notice of my self.

VI. Although some times mere flexible leavs are found amongst these mineral plants yet ye generality of them (as I have before observ'd of some of the marine fossils) are but mere delineations or superficial resemblances, nor yet could such representations be owing to the impressions of plants, since consum'd, because as I have sayd before of the *Mock-Fish* they are a litle rays'd above the surface of the stone, & not impress'd.

VII. It seems nothing more strange or unaccountable that delineations of leavs should be naturally produc'd in this cole slat &c. than that representations of gnats should be some times found in the fossil amber of Prussia [26] and of spiders in the cole-slat in England.[27] But if any assert that these were once living animals, they are to explain how they came so deep under ground; & afterwards how they got into these intirely close prisons of stone & amber. I meet with several more difficulties, but perhaps of less moment; which I shall not therefore trouble you withall, til some other occasion.

As to the other opinion, which maintains that all these bodies are form'd in the earth; the great difficulty it labours under, is that we find our selvs incapable of giving any satisfactory account of the causes and manner of the causes and manner of such a production. For if any have recourse with Dr. Plot, to the plastic power of salts; I see not (to go no farther) what they can answer to that objection proposed by your self long since in your *Physico-theological Discourses*.[28] For who can reasonably imagin that any mineral salts should so conspire, as that some of them should so exactly frame the points of the *Glossopetrae*,[29] which are fish teeth of one matter, & some their roots (adding now and then a piece of a jaw) which are of another: that some should form the polite convex side of a *Siliquastrum*, & others its Appendix; [30] that some should make ye *Socket* or Calix of the *Belemnites*, & others its *Alveolus* [31] &c. I therefore humbly offer to your consideration, some conjectures I have of late years entertain'd concerning the causes, origin, & use of these surprising phenomena.[32] I have in short imagin'd they might be partly owing to fish-spawn, receivd into the chincks and other meatus's of ye earth in the water of the Deluge, and so be deriv'd (as the water could make way) amongst the shelvs or layers of stone, earth, &c: and have further thought it worth our enquiry whether the exhalations which are raisd out of the sea and falling down in rains, fogs, &c. do water the earth to ye depth here requir'd, may not from the seminium or spawn of marine animals, be so far impregnated with as to the naked eye invisible animalcula (& also separat or distinct parts of them) as to produce these marine bodies, which have so much excited our admiration, and indeed bafl'd our reasoning throughout the whole globe of the earth.[33] I imagind farther that the like origin might be ascrib'd to the mineral leavs and branches, seeing we find that they are for the most part the leavs of ferns and other capillaries, & of mosses & such like plants as are calld less perfect; whose seeds may be easily allowd to be washd down by the rain into the depth here requir'd, seeing they are so minute, as not at all to be distinguished by the naked eye. And as to such of them as are not reducible to these classes of minute seeds; they are such as I know not at all whither to referr.

I am not so fond of this Hypothesis, as not to be sensible my self, that it lies open to a great many objections: and in all probability you will soon discover more difficulties than I shall be able to remove. However, those arguments that first led me to it, shall be here layd before you.

I. Because I observ'd that of all these extraneous figures or representations dug out of the earth, there is scarce one in a thousand but is reducible to such natural bodies as expose their seeds either to ye open air or the water: namely plants, insects or fish. For (as I have before hinted) had the spoils of the Deluge been preserved to our time, we might reasonably expect plenty of the skeletons and of the horns and hoofs of quadrupeds; and why should not either intire or broken skeletons of birds, be found preservd likewise in the same manner & in ye same places we find these leavs of plants? How happens it at least that we find none at all of their Penfeathers, which should seem of a constitution more dureable, if once inclosd in fine stone then, than that of plants? I am not ignorant that some very learned writers and those even eminent naturalists, have inform'd us that not onely bones of land animals have been frequently found inclosd on all sides in solid stone; but likewise the representations or lineaments of birds and beasts; and of men & their parts; nay even that *monks, hermits* & *saints* have been exactly pourtray'd in the midst of solid marble.[34] To these I must take leave to reply: 1st that some of these informations are manifestly erroneous; for they tell us that these delineations appear'd upon polishing the marbles; whereas all figures naturally delineated within stones, must upon polishing those stones be defaced. 2ly. When we discover any unknown fossils, we are very subject to make erroneous comparisons; assimilating many of them to the parts of land animals which indeed ought to be reduced to sea shells or other marine bodies; as may be observd in those stones calld *Hippocephaloides, Otites, Bucardites* & diverse others.[35] 3ly. Although it be granted that some times the bones, horns & hoofs of viviparous animals are dug out of the earth; yet seeing they are so very few; it seems much likelier that they might have been buryed by some other accidents, than that they have been there preservd ever since the Deluge. For in the Deluge all land creatures whatever perish'd, nor should we so much expect to find their single bones as whole skeletons, thus interr'd. 4ly. When ever I find any confirmation by competent and credible authors of such delineations of any sort of viviparous animals or birds as the *Islebian stones* exhibit of fish, I shall then readily grant these things may be also as well produc'd without previous seeds; & offer no further arguments for this Hypothesis.

II. I am, as to my own part, abundantly satisfied; and others will I presume upon sight and accurat observation of some fossils I have collected, be no less; that these bodies doe in tract of time quite loose their forms, & become such shapeless lumps as to be distinguished for marine, by none but such as are very conversant in observations of this kind, nor even, at last, by them neither. I say I am fully satisfied thereof; because I have collected sparry or crystalline bodies, whose surface do onely partly resemble *Entrochi;* Likewise shells, *Glossopetrae* and *Siliquastra,* consisting of a flinty sort of peble, and receding from their proper or common figures; and lastly *Ichthyospondyli* or *fish-vertebrae,* sometimes more, sometimes less deformed; exhibiting on their surface such small stellated figures as we find on a sort of the Astroites.[36] Now seeing that in tract of time, some of them loose their substance & form, degenerating into other bodies; may we not suspect that others (considering the intireness of many of them & their vast plenty,) might be in the interim produc'd?

III. If this Hypothesis be admitted; some account might probably be given of the fossil *Nautili* & other strange shells; by supposing 1st. That many of those clouds which fall here in rains &c. have been exhal'd in very remote parts: And 2ly. that such a generation as is here suppos'd, must be much more lyable to monstrous productions than the common. For as Agricola says, appositely to this purpose: *Quanto crassior est terra quam aqua, tanto imperfectiores gignit formas et quae animalibus careant.*[37]

IV. I have often in one and the same quarry, gather'd 20 or 30 different magnitudes of the same species of shell stones; whence I began to suspect that they might have a certain vegetative growth;[38] & that they had therefore their Generation & Corruption in the very place we find them, & that hence it is that we find some *Nautili, Lapides Iudaici, Glossopetrae* and *Astropodia* of such monstrous largeness, that no seas as far as our curious naturalists have hitherto discover'd, affoard any thing comparable to them.

V. To comprise the rest in few words: The burying of these leavs of plants so deep; the vast quantity of these marine bodies; the incredible variety of exotic or unknown shells, sea starrs, &c. in so narrow a compass, as this Island; their so frequently distorted and uneven surfaces; that they should be found at all depths from the tops of the highest rocks to the bottom; that they should be not rarely found adhering to the roofs, and to the walls or sides of caves as well as perpendicular clefts of rocks; and be also sometimes discoverd in animal bodies at land; & that there should be sea shells dug at land containing living animals: I say all these consider'd together seem inconsistent with the effects of a deluge; and if this Hypothesis may be admitted; not very difficult.[39]

But before it be I ought not to doubt but that your self and others will find many more objections than I can foresee. In the mean time such as occur to my thoughts, I shall here, however destructive they may prove to it fayrly lay down: for they who have no other aim than the search of Truth, are no ways concernd for the honour of their opinions: And for my part I have been always, being led thereunto by your example, so much the less admirer of *Hypotheses;* as I have been a lover of Natural History.

The maign difficulties that I can at present think of are these.

1. It will be questiond whether the suppos'd *seminium* can penetrate the pores of stones.

2. It will scarce seem credible that such bodies having no life should grow, especially when confind in so seemingly unnatural a place, as the earth &c.[40]

4. According to this Hypothesis, these bodies should be found in much the same manner, logd'd in all kind of stone, &c. throughout all countrys.

5. We should not find plenty of shells &c. adhering to each other; in the same manner as they are found at sea.

6. Some fossil shells should then be found so minute, as to be scarce visible, & others of the same kind in their complete magnitude.

7. It may be well question'd whether the essential parts of this suppos'd spawn of any fish, should being (e.g. must be here often supposd) separated, ever effect the end by Nature designd them, especially when brought out of their proper element.

8. It will be sayd that the remaining Tracks of Shells that once adhered on the surface of some of these Fossils; and the perls which (as has been related) have been found sticking to others are a plain proof that they are the spoils of once living animals; Also the change of the colour near the roots of some fossil fishteeth, as namely of some *Plectronitae*,[41] shew how far they were fastend in the jaws of once living fish; and that the worn extremities of some others do plainly discover that they have been once employd.

9. Many of these subterraneous fish as particularly several of the *Glossopetrae*, are taken for the teeth of viviparous fish; which being granted its impossible they should be produc'd in the manner here proposd.

10. Lastly such a production seems clearly beside the ordinary course of Nature, nor can we perceive any end or use of so praeternatural a generation.

To ye first I answer that its manifest from experience, upon which all solid Philosophy must be grounded that the spawn of animals may insinuat it self into the mass of stone. And this plainly appears from live toads found some times in the midst of stones at land, & those shell fish calld *Dactyli* [42] at sea. If it be reply'd that the stones wherein the Dactyli are lodg'd are full of large holes &c. I answer that though they generally are so, yet upon breaking & examining a great many of these stones, I have sometimes found of their shells though without Animals so lodg'd as that they were not any visible *meatus's* from their holes neither directly to the surface of the stones, nor to those other holes in them.[43]

To ye second, yt that's not so great a wonder as that shells should be sometimes generated, and even grow though they contain no animals, within human bodies, & within the mass of those thick shells of our large Tenby oysters which I formerly mention'd to you, as first shewn me by Mr. Wm. Cole of Bristow,[44] and have since observd my self. For we must grant that even any part of ye inland is much fitter for their reception and augmentation than humane bodies. Specially if we reflect that when the spat or seminium here supposd, meets with saline moisture in the earth, living animals are some times produced, as is before attested.

The 3d. is likewise answerd from experience. For we know that even sea shells and some stones yeild to ye growth of plants: Also that the hardest stones are impressd by the *Limpets*, though they doe but adhere to their surface, and that our hardest limestone yields to the growth of some *Echini* or sea urchins, and the *Dactyli*; or we find some of their cells much less than others; and that 'tis certain that all the holes wherein they lurk in what stones soever they are found are owing to their growth.

To the fourth I answer that this Hypothesis does not require that these marine bodies should be produced in all countreys alike. For as in vegetables we find that all seeds will not be receivd by all soils; so neither can we expect yt all earths & minerals should be equally proper for such productions.[45] And truly I thought it well worth observation, that is in all these countreys scarce any stones at land, excepting the limestone affoard marine fossils; so I never found the *Dactyli* at sea in any other though in that very common & in diverse counties of Wales.

As to ye fifth I pretend not to determin how long such bodies may continue before their dissolution; but doubt not but that according to the nature of the minerals wherein they are bedded they may last much longer in some places than others, & therefore we are not to wonder, if in such places we find a farr greater plenty of them than elsewhere.

To the sixth I answear that at *Basil's Leigh* Quarry near Oxford large specimens of the *Turbinites major* figur'd Table the 7th Num.341. may be often met with, & likewise in the same place; concreted lumps of others of the same species very minute. I have also in my collection diverse other examples of the same kind; and Steno [46] informs us that he has discoverd amongst fossils some so small as to be scarce discernable without a microscope & even minute eggs of shells.

The seventh may be in a great measure answer'd from the histories of monstrous productions.

8. As to the adhaesion of one shell to an other, that may altogether as well happen by this way of generation as at sea: And for the signs or impressions made by some that formerly adhered to them; those might have been disjoyned by the workmen in the digging, or by the sinking in of the ground where they are found or some other accident. But

as to the change of the colour of the *Plectronites* towards the root, and some of them being sharpen'd at the point, I must confess I have litle to say; but that we doe not yet know, the teeth of what fish these *Plectronitae* are; and consequently can not tell, but they may be naturally so colour'd and pointed: or else yt these and many more have been thus preserv'd in the place we find them, ever since the Deluge, which was formerly my opinion of all these marine fossils; [47] though I can not now maintain it for the reasons I have here given.

9. To the ninth may be answer'd, yt we have as yet but an imperfect knowledge of the generation of particular species of fish. For whereas you have observ'd that some of the cartilagineous are viviparous, I have noted others to be oviparous; having observd embryos in the eggs of a sort of dog fish (which were open at ye one end) cast ashore in Anglesey, Caernarvonshire, and other countreys.

10. As to the last though we acknowledge that there is an end in all the productions of Nature; yet it is no less certain that we are often but very improper judges of such final causes.[48] Who therefore can be assured but that the fertility of the earth may in great measure be owing to these marine Fossils? This much at least I have observ'd that in *Wales* they are found, for the most part in the best countreys, & that in vast quantities; and on the other hand, in those hundreds which are most barren, as the mountanous parts of Cardigan, Mongomery, Meirionydh, & Caernarvon, I could never find one of them. There is at Cleydon Field near Banbury in Oxfordshire, a place calld Hore Furlong, which is noted for plenty of the *Asteriae*, or (as there call'd) *hore-stones;*[49] and no less as some of the farmers assur'd me for its fertility. Moreover we can not be so positive, but that some minerals may from hence derive their origin, to say nothing of their physical use; the *Lapis Judaicus* & *Lyncurius*[50] having been long since well known in our shops, as perhaps some others are elswhere, & more may be hereafter. And these Sr are the notions I had to offer to your consideration, concerning the origin of marine fossils & mineral leavs. You will soon judge how frivolous they may be, or how probable: and as you find them, pass your free censure; for 'tis the truth of so important a question that's ye onely aim of Sr

Yr most obliged Humble Servant

E.L.

APPENDIX D

Hueber's Medical Corollaries

THE MEDICAL COROLLARIES appended to Beringer's *Lithographiae Wirceburgensis* by Georg Ludwig Hueber (Hueberg) were, in essence, a partial fulfillment of the requirements for the Doctorate in Medicine. The candidate composed fifty theses or propositions which, when approved, were turned over to a board of examiners. The candidate then faced the *periculum* (perilous trial)—an examination of several hours duration, in the course of which he was required to defend any or all of the theses.

In large measure his defense took the form of countering objections which, usually in syllogistic pattern, were leveled against his theses. He was obliged to answer with logical distinctions, subdistinctions, negation or distinction of *consequens* (conclusion)—all in the traditional manner of Aristotelian logic—until he had disposed of all inimical thrusts at his assertions. Thus the doctoral examination was as much a dialectical tilt as it was a test of knowledge of medicine.

Rooted deeply in the Middle Ages, this method of examination has perdured in certain circles to the present day. For example, the degree of S.T.Lr. (Lector or Reader in Sacred Theology) in the Dominican Order of the Roman Catholic Church is still obtained by the successful negotiation of such a *periculum*. It lasts three and one-half hours, five Lectors comprise the board, and the 100 theses provide a comprehensive probe of the candidate's harvest of seven years of philosophical and theological studies.

Master Hueber, therefore, earned the dignity of Doctor of Medicine by submitting not only to a searching inquiry into his medical knowledge, but to an evaluation of his acquaintance with what were considered cognate fields. It was further the custom that a candidate could only be promoted when he bore the costs of the scientific publications of his professor, whose opinions he was obliged to uphold. To meet this latter exaction, Hueber, as Beringer's student, published and championed (as his dissertation) Beringer's *Lithographiae Wirceburgensis*.

MEDICAL COROLLARIES

FOR THE

INAUGURAL DEFENSE

OF

MASTER GEORG LUDWIG HUEBER,

A.B., LL.B., PH.B.

CANDIDATE OF MEDICINE

I. The living human body, although by its very structure extremely prone to corruption, yet would grow ill more rarely were there less of moral causes and lesions.

II. The truth of this assertion is borne out by the simple observation of the fact that attacks of sickness are much more frequent in man than in brute animals.

III. This is to say that as equanimity is the font and origin of health, so perturbation of soul is the source of very many ills.

IV. Among men, this is particularly experienced by those who have greater gentleness of soul and are of a more moderate temperament.

V. Now the seat of our temperament is not the fluid parts alone nor the solid parts only, but both together.

VI. There is nothing unusual in the transition from one temperament to another.

VII. Of these, the first is designated as con-natural in origin; the other as adventitious.

VIII. Subsequently, the same temperament as the parents had is communicated to their offspring by hereditary transmission.

IX. This is abundantly demonstrated by the occasional exact likeness of the movements of children to those of their parents, as well as by the delineations of the body and by those sicknesses which are called hereditary.

X. It is a matter of daily experience that our movements correspond in many areas to the habits of our temperaments.

XI. Hence what in a sanguine personality assumes the form of alacrity in certain undertakings, by contrast, in a phlegmatic or melancholic person degenerates into languor and sluggishness.

XII. This is to say that there is an intimate communication between the movements of the soul and the essence of one's temperament.

XIII. We have intimated above that a prime requisite of sound health is tranquillity of soul; nor should this be regarded as strange, since where tranquillity of soul prevails, all things involving bodily motions are negotiated serenely and calmly.

XIV. We have stated that the directive instrument whereby the cause and effect of corruption is held in check, nothing but the good and useful is retained, and the harmful is eliminated, is the tonic movement, both general and particular.

XV. Consequently, in this function of secretion and excretion is to be found the preservation from imminent corruption, as well as health and life.

XVI. Hence it is that even in the actual state of health, Nature requires and promotes a perpetual movement and withdrawal of the humors, and elimination of harmful particles from the body.

XVII. All the soft, porous, and fleshy parts of the body are, by the strict ordering of Nature, always in a state of tension.

XVIII. However, this tension is by no means invariable, but undergoes constant slight variations.

XIX. It is altered easily and frequently by such extraordinary factors as heat and cold and other so-called unnatural conditions.

XX. And primarily there arises from a very vehement onset of heat, especially if it retains its force, a frothing of the blood, and this is very easily followed in plethorics by an overflow of vessels and an occurrence of severe hemorrhage.

XXI. From an excess of cold, the serum is arrested, the lymph is coagulated, the blood is thickened and proximately disposed to stasis.

XXII. There is said to be stasis where there is suspension of movement.

XXIII. Hence it differs from congestion which can occur even to a being existing in motion, by the mere fact of a greater dilation of channels and openings because of unusual impulsions.

XXIV. The cause of congestion is frequently the complexity of superfluous humors which tends to promote a less than satisfactory evacuation of these humors.

XXV. That veins and arteries are conjoined to the anastomoses is improbable; otherwise, how would we account for secretions and excretions?

XXVI. But the blood is pressured from the more tenuous arteries into the porous substance of other parts where it is then pressed through the pores, with an accompanying secretion of nutriments and excretion of waste, and finally is pressed back into the veins as circulation requires.

XXVII. When the flow of blood is more copiously directed to one part than to another, or is restrained, this results from a special tonic movement.

XXVIII. When, that is, a part is distended so that the blood in it is pressed out, it is afterwards relaxed and left flaccid so that the blood can more easily rush into it.

XXIX. Wherefore, in this matter it would be erroneous to blame the presence or departure of spirits, or a passive debility and subsidence of the part, all of which devices we properly reject as fabrications.

XXX. We observe that by the help and good offices of this same tonic movement, paroxysms of fevers, particularly such as are intermittent, are frequently administered and directed to a salutary end.

XXXI. For fever paroxysms, as we assume with the authorities, are nothing else than the repeated efforts of the tonic movement to control and dislodge noxious matter adhering to the primary passages or other places.

XXXII. An extraordinary and more violent exacerbation of the tonic movement is called a spasm and convulsion.

XXXIII. However, a spasmodic and a convulsive tonic movement differ from each other as genus from species.

XXXIV. These congestions and disturbances of movement are always observed to be more vehement and pertinacious if they owe their origin to moral causes and intentions.

XXXV. While, as we said, convulsion arises from an increased and excessive intensification of the tonic movement, so the suppression and deficiency of that movement is known as atony and paralysis.

XXXVI. The latter is commonly observed in two forms, one of which is called perfect or consummate, wherein the affected part, bereft of sensation and movement, grows cold and flaccid; while in the other or imperfect form there occurs at least some sensation of skin irritation or exhalation.

XXXVII. We would note in regard to this present matter that there are recorded cases of paralytics who were restored to health by a desperate movement of the soul after all medications had proved to be of no avail.

XXXVIII. Of either movement, natural as well as preternatural, no other cause is observed than the soul acting with its full vitality but often with an extraordinary effort, to the exclusion of the motion of spirits and of their influence, refluence, or passage.

XXXIX. It therefore behooves the physician to concern himself with Nature; that is, with the soul operating vitally in an organic body.

XL. For it is by the soul's energy that the body is maintained in health, and by its synergy, whereby it coöperates with medication, that health is restored to the sick.

XLI. And in this we see the origin of that axiom which in our day enjoys universal popularity, that the physician must act as the minister, spectator, and imitator of that autocratic agent, Nature, not as its master, or seducer, or opponent.

XLII. And indeed, what more prudent, what more simple, than to follow Nature and to assist its efforts, knowing as we do that left to its own devices it frequently cures ills?

XLIII. And say not that Nature sometimes succumbs; for if this occurs, it is to be attributed either to an excessive quantity of faulty matter, or to the incorrigible quality of such matter; for in this case whatever operative Nature might do and attempt, it will inevitably be unequal to the prevailing efficacy of the harmful element.

XLIV. Although it cannot be denied that Nature itself, however vigilant it may be, from time to time strays from the natural order, and is either excessive or defective in its movements.

XLV. The more grave the aberrations of Nature, and the more remote from active movements, the more serious symptoms do we see develop in the body.

XLVI. Wherefore, it is important that the attending physician know first of all how to make a mature discernment of the various movements, how to distinguish those that are autocratic from those that are erratic, how in all prudence to correct the latter by gently and calmly restoring Nature to its accustomed course, by mitigating, placating, and soothing its excessive disturbances, and by reviving, stimulating, and animating its languors.

XLVII. Let him further be skilled in distinguishing accurately between action and passion, between symptom and synergy, between ailment and that movement which Nature in its solicitude purposefully undertakes and instigates because of the sickness.

XLVIII. Let him likewise observe the routine of his patients regarding their vital movements, as well as their idiosyncracies; let him study closely the ways to which Nature has heretofore been accustomed; and let him take into account the age, sex, constitution, and character of his patients.

XLIX. As a final reminder in the interests of this function, we would point out that more delicate and sensitive persons live in greater peril of the graver disturbances and anomalous movements, than do the more robust and sturdy souls.

L. If the physician weighs all of these things intelligently, if, in dispensing his medicines, he properly discerns and observes the time, the opportuneness of the year, the quality and quantity befitting both sex and age, he will satisfy his patients and will most felicitously obtain the intended purpose which he so avidly desires.

$\mathcal{N}otes$

INTRODUCTION TO THIS EDITION

[1] James H. Fennell, *A Natural History of . . . Quadrupeds* (London, 1841), p. ix.

[2] There are several important definitions of the term virtuoso as used in the seventeenth and eighteenth centuries. The two which follow were selected for their attention to character.

"He Trafficks to all places, and has his Correspondents in every part of the World; yet his Merchandizes serve not to promote our Luxury, nor encrease our Trade, and neither enrich the Nation, nor himself. A Box or two of *Pebbles* or *Shells*, and a dozen of *Wasps, Spiders* and *Caterpillers* are his Cargoe. He values a *Camelion*, or *Salamander's* Egg, above all the Sugars and Spices of the *West* and *East-Indies*. . . . He visits Mines, Colepits, and Quarries frequently, but not for that sordid end that other Men usually do, *viz.* gain; but for the sake of the fossile Shells and Teeth that are sometimes found there. . . .

"To what purpose is it, that these Gentlemen ransack all Parts both of *Earth* and *Sea* to procure these *Triffles?* . . . I know that the desire of knowledge, and the discovery of things yet unknown is the Pretence; but what Knowledge is it? What Discoveries do we owe to their Labours? It is only the Discovery of some few unheeded Varieties of Plants, Shells, or Insects, unheeded only because useless; and the Knowledge, they boast so much of, is no more than a Register of their Names, and Marks of Distinction only." (Mary Astell, *An Essay in Defence of the Female Sex* [1696], pp. 97–98, 102–103.)

"Scholarship, physical science, the study of antiquities, the history of letters and fine arts were all within the scope of the pervasive dilettantism of the virtuoso, so long as they were approached in the proper spirit, that is, with an especial interest in the details of study and research, in the actual circumstances of their growth and life, and not as abstractions or as mere illustrations of theory and law. . . . The study of things as they are in themselves . . . is the field of virtuoso endeavour." (J. E. Spingarn, ed., *Critical Essays of the Seventeenth Century* [Oxford, 1908–1909], introduction, I, xc.)

An excellent analysis of the virtuoso, which provided the basis for the above, is Walter E. Houghton's "The English Virtuoso in the 17th Century (Pts. I and II)," *Journal of the History of Ideas*, III: 1, 2 (1942), 51–73, 190–219. See also Beringer's own plea for the virtuosi—in Chap. I.

[3] Beringer, *Lithographiae Wirceburgensis*, p. 4; p. 20 in this volume.

[4] Heinrich Kirchner, "Die Würzburger Lügensteine im Lichte neuer Archivalischer Funde," *Zeit. Deutschen Geologischen Gesellschaft*, 89:9 (November, 1935), 607–615.

[5] Carl Christoph Beringer, *Geschichte der Geologie und des Geologischen Weltbildes* (Stuttgart: Ferdinand Enke Verlag, 1954).

[6] James Parkinson, *Organic Remains of a Former World* . . . (London, 1804), I, 26.

[7] Carolus Lang, *De Origine Lapidum Figuratorum* . . . (Lucernae, 1709), p. 1.

INTRODUCTION BY BERINGER

[1] *Specifico salis, terrae, succinque petrificii glutine in lapidem transivit.* . . .

[2] Pungers: from *pagurus, paguri* (m.). Pliny ix. 51: "*Cancrorum genera carabi, astaci, maeae, paguri* [hermit crab?], *Heracleotici, leones et alia ignobiliora.*"

[3] Beringer did not figure in his plates any of the remarkable species of starfish. In the illustrations of the actual "Lügensteine" may be seen an example of what may be interpreted as representing a starfish.

[4] A discussion of the bogus nature of Beringer's figured stones and the perpetrators of the hoax will be found in Appendix B.

[5] . . . *ex Archaei subterranei, aut Panspermiae, sive aurae seminalis virtute seminali et plastica.* . . .

[6] . . . *ex fortuitis naturae ludentis erroribus.* . . .

CHAPTER I

[1] *Solem oriri indies, et occidere, et cum reliquo siderum et coelorum, quibus continentur, ambitu, ordinatissimo et nunquam perturbato cursu terrae circumvolvi* . . .

[2] This disparaging reference to Pliny does not do justice to his importance during the seventeenth and eighteenth centuries. He appears to have been the great link with the past, and is cited more frequently than either Aristotle or Theophrastus. Plot, for example, calls upon Pliny's *Natural History* sixteen times in his Chap. V ("Of Formed Stones") alone, and if allusions were to be included in the count the number would be at least doubled.

[3] The works are presented here as cited by Beringer. Complete bibliographical citations are given in Appendix A.

[4] Two authors are conspicuously absent from Beringer's list of lithographers: Jerome Cardan and Bernard Palissy. It is hard to believe that Beringer was ignorant of Cardan's *De Subtilitate* (1550), yet there is no internal evidence in the *Lithographiae Wirceburgensis* to suggest he knew it. Certainly there were abundant editions of the work—at least 19 by 1664. Bernard Palissy is another story. Again there is no internal evidence to suggest Beringer's familiarity with the work, and, unlike Cardan's *De Subtilitate*, Palissy's *Discours Admirables* existed in only the first edition (1580) until 1777, when the first of many collected editions of his works appeared.

Bernard Palissy (ca. 1510–1590), *Inventeur des rustiques figulines du Roy et de la Royne sa mere* (Catherine de Medicis), established at Paris, sometime after 1564, a cabinet of fossils—of which Sir Thomas Allbutt remarks:

"I have said that in the years 1575–1584 Palissy, having amassed a large collection of objects of natural history, of rocks and minerals, of fossils, and of various earths, and having attached to every specimen a label and description, gave formal lectures with practical demonstrations on the objects, and interpreted them with acumen and a truth of observation and argument which at that period was without parallel or compare. These lectures, as we have seen, became the fashion, and being delivered by no obscure potter but by a well-known person about court—namely, Master Bernard of the Tuileries—were attended by large audiences of the first men of the day in Paris . . . At that date Master Bernard's Museum was the first collection of the kind in modern Europe, and the scheme of its arrangement and labelling was as enlightened as that of the most recent museums of our own day . . ." (Sir Thomas C. Allbutt, "Palissy, Bacon, and the Revival of Natural Science," British Academy, London, Proceedings, 1913–1914, vol. 6, pp. 233–247.)

The labels attached to his specimens were reproduced at the end of his *Admirable Discourses*.

Palissy's thoughts on the origin of fossils are remarkable, as the following three extracts from Aurèle La Rocque's excellent translation of the *Admirable Discourses* will show:

"Therefore I maintain that shellfish, which are petrified in many quarries, have been born on the very spot, while the rocks were but water and mud, which since have been petrified together with these fishes, as you will understand more clearly later, in talking about the rocks of the Ardennes." (La Rocque, *The Admirable Discourses of Bernard Palissy* [Urbana, 1957], p. 158.)

"Some [shells] are thrown to the ground, after the fish has been eaten, and when they are in the ground, their salsitive virtue has attracted a generative salt, which when combined with that of the shell in some watery or moist place, the affinity of these matters being joined with this mixed body have hardened and petrified the main mass. That is the reason, and you need seek no other." (La Rocque, *ibid.*, p. 159.)

"In the Ardennes Mountains petrified mussels are found by the thousand, quite similar to those in the Meus River which is near these mountains. Long ago I examined the shell of the oysters of the Ocean sea: but I never saw natural oysters nor their shells in greater quantity than in many rocks of the Ardennes: the latter, though petrified, still were once alive, and this must convince us that in many places of the earth the waters are salty, not as much so as those of the sea: but they are salty enough to produce all kinds of shellfish." (La Rocque, *ibid.*, p. 162.)

Palissy is by no means a diluvialist, having emphatically denied the Deluge as the instrument responsible for fossils, thereby taking exception with the supposed teachings of Cardan: "Those who have written that the shells found in rocks date from the Flood have erred clumsily." (La Rocque, *ibid.*, p. 246. See also p. 155 ff.)

The contributions of Palissy to the fossil concept are fully treated in the introduction to La Rocque's translation, and the reader is referred to this and Palissy's chapter "On Rocks" (La Rocque, *ibid.*, pp. 146–180) for further details.

Jerome Cardan (1501–1576) is generally treated as a diluvialist, principally due to Palissy's remarks (see La Rocque, *ibid.*, pp. 155 ff.). Pierre Duhem has questioned Cardan's intention to attribute the origin of fossils to the Biblical Deluge, and believes that Palissy invented this hypothesis in order to combat it (Duhem, *Études sur Léonard de Vinci* [Paris: A. Hermann, 1906]). The passage in question is found in Book VII, p. 478 of *De Subtilitate* (in the collected edition of 1663, vol. 3 of 10). Here Cardan has examined and disagreed with Agricola's opinions on the origin of fossils (specifically *conchites*). He in turn proposes that the presence of *conchites* in a given place indicates that the region was at one time covered by the sea: "And this is certain evidence that this region was previously covered by the sea." (*De Subtilitate*, Book VII, p. 478 of collected ed.)

Palissy mentions a French edition as his source of Cardan's theory, and this we have not been able to obtain. It seems doubtful that it would contain material not found in the Latin edition, however. Duhem is evidently correct in his argument for supposition on the part of Palissy.

[5] Catalogues of personal cabinets, as well as institutional museums, became popular in the seventeenth century, and with this appeared the systematic, regional study of fossils. These works were of great general interest, being largely compilations from correspondence and the works of renowned authors. The significance of extensive correspondence during the seventeenth and eighteenth centuries, particularly as regards museum catalogues, can be partly realized by perusal of James Smith's *A Selection of the Correspondence of Linnaeus and Other Naturalists* . . . , or any of the biographical volumes in R. T. Gunther's series, *Early Science in Oxford*. The development of the museum is interesting for the debt it owes to classical antiquity and medieval natural history for its systematics. A goodly percentage of the authors to be mentioned relied on Pliny's *Natural History*, and quoted with ease from Solinus, Aelian, Aristotle, and others. Certainly the influence of medieval Bestiaries and Herbals can be seen, though more in the strictly "zoölogical" works of the period such as Edward Topsell's *The Historie of Foure-Footed Beastes* (1607), and the several works of Conrad Gesner.

An interesting source of information on cabinets, and one which gives some idea of the number which existed in seventeenth- and eighteenth-century Europe, are the contemporary accounts of continental travel. Maximilian Misson, for instance, mentions some forty-one cabinets which he visited during his travels of 1688 (*A New Voyage to Italy* . . . [London, 1695]). Misson remarks on the contents of many of the collections be examined, and this information was effectively utilized by such English collectors as Edward Lhwyd (see footnote 8, Appendix C). There is not sufficient space to permit adequate excerpts from Misson's *A New Voyage* here; the reader may wish to refer to the well-organized indices to Misson's works. The reader may also wish to refer to the works of Churchill and Harris, which are cited in the bibliography.

Following are notes on some of the most noteworthy museums and regional studies. Others will be mentioned elsewhere in the text. In some instances an author will be noted solely because cited by Beringer; such is the case with Lambeck (see Appendix A) and Behrens. However, as it is impossible to deal with more than a negligible number of museums here (and these only in a perfunctory manner) the reader is encouraged to consult for further detail the following two works, which are to date the best histories of the character and contents of early museums:

David Murray, *Museums: Their History and their Use* (3 vols.) (Glasgow: James MacLehose and Sons, 1904).

Alma S. Wittlin, *The Museum: Its History and Its Tasks in Education* (London: Routledge and Kegan Paul Ltd., 1949).

Of museums eight will be mentioned, arranged chronologically by the date of publication of the catalogue.

Johannes Baptista Oliva [Olivi, Olivus] of Cremona described the Calceolarian Museum at Verona in 1584 (*De Reconditis et Praecipuis Collectaneis ab Honestissimo, et Solertiss. Francisco Calceolario in Museo* . . . Venetiss: Apud Paulum Zanfrettum, 1584), and concluded that the oryctological specimens were "sports of nature." This same noted museum was again described in 1622, this time by Benedictus Cerutus. Cerutus relied heavily on Pliny and Dioscorides in systematizing the collection, and called upon the powers of an *occulta semina* to explain the origin of petrifactions. This same *occulta semina* was called upon by Libavius, and subsequently as the *aura seminalis* by Lhwyd and Langius, although the concepts are not entirely interchangeable—the *occulta semina* often, though not always, being a seed inherent in the earth (akin to the petrific seed described by Thomas Shirley in 1672).

In 1648, forty-three years after his death, Aldrovandi's *Musaeum Metallicum* was issued by Bartholomeus Ambrosinus. The *Musaeum Metallicum* is encyclopedic in scope, falling more under the classification of Lapidary, than of catalogue.

A catalogue of the famous collection of natural and artificial rarities belonging to Olao Worm (1588–1654), Regius Professor of Denmark, was published in 1655. The *Museum Wormianum* was, for a hundred years after its publication, one of the most frequently cited references on fossils—with Kircher's *Mundus Subterraneus* and Aldrovandi's *Musaeum Metallicum* (which it largely replaced). Worm [Wurm] deserves special mention as he is generally accepted to be the first person to have recognized "unicorn horn" as the tooth of the narwhal, in a dissertation read at Copenhagen in 1638—although a similar but tantalizingly brief pronouncement was made by Gerard Mercator in 1621. (For Worm, see also Churchill, A Collection of Voyages and Travels . . . [London, 1704] Vol. II, pp. 455–457.)

Worm's concept of fossils is set down in Book I, Section 1, Chap. I, page 1, and is perhaps more alchemical than paleontological.

"We divide the rarities which our museum contains into four classifications: Fossils, Vegetables, Animals, and those which Art has fashioned from the other three. We prefer to begin with the first kind, in order to proceed from the less noble to the more noble, from the less perfect to the more perfect.

"Fossils, so called because most of them are wrested from the earth by digging, are called Minerals by others who refer to diggings as Mines, since they are, as it were, mine deposits of fossils and metals. Still others term them Metallics, from the principal species of them, namely metal.

"Now a fossil is a perfectly mixed body, inanimate, without life, endowed by God at its creation with a peculiar form and a seminal power enabling it to procreate its like and to propagate its species. [A similar view was held by Tournefort and Camerarius.]

"By the good offices of these forms is effected the formation, disposition, propagation, and perpetuation of any body; for they are capable of multiplying, and are endowed by the Creator with a power which enables them in fact to multiply in aptly disposed matter and a favorable place. Natron provides a striking example of this. For even when all Natron is extracted from a seminal ground that has been impregnated with natronic power, if this same ground is left untouched for a time, new Natron, regenerated by this force, can be extracted from it after a brief period. This also explains why, although in these minerals there occurs a change of the external form and they are reduced to liquids or dust or glass, they can, nevertheless, without any special process, be changed back to a metallic body, because it is only the external form which has been changed, while the essential internal form remains unaffected. This can be observed in Mercury, Antimony, and Tin. Now because these fossils are themselves similar bodies, they more nearly approximate the nature of elements than do vegetables and animals, although in comparison with these they are reckoned as less complete species. Thus it happens that a fossil of one species is readily changed into another, as iron into copper. This is rarely observed in the vegetable realm, except when, by reason of a defect in the soil, there occurs a deterioration, such as wheat changing into cockle, or barley into wild oats."

The *Museo Kircheriano,* a catalogue of the collections of the celebrated author of *Mundus Subterraneus,* Athanasius Kircher, S.J. (1602–1680), was first published in 1678, and was redone in 1709. The museum is a miscellaneous collection of archeological curiosities, stuffed animals, and minerals. It is, however, in his *Mundus Subterraneus* that he extensively describes lithographs, dendrites, and fossils. In addition to a "Panspermia," to be discussed by Beringer in Chap. III (see note 28), Kircher conceived of a *Spiritus Architectonicus* or *spiritus plasticus,* which as a form-giving force worked in association with a petrifying force (*vis lapidifica*), naturally inherent is the earth. These taken together were responsible for some fossils (others falling into the realm of products of the Universal Seed, or *Panspermia*), and for all dendrites and lithographs.

Kircher describes in his *Mundus Subterraneus* (Book VIII, Chap. 4) a process by which Nature produces imitations of animal parts (particularly bones) in the earth, a process well worthy of a "frolicking nature":

"In the bowels of the earth, within the chaps of rocky mountains, there is a kind of slimy earth, which with Agricola I have before called marl, mixed with a sort of parget, which earth, meeting with a nitrous solution in the chinks of mountains, is covered over as it were with a shell of parget, which as it petrifies with time, so likewise by the luster of the nitre it resembles very much a bone in whiteness, being white, porous, and brittle. If then it meets with a round cavity in the earth, it produces a round ball, which, being broken very much, resembles a skull, or if the mold, in which it is cast, has the form of a human thighbone (or that of another animal) or of a rib, or any other bone, the marl, that is contained in it, having the nitrous liquor added to it, will resemble the human os femoris, etc.—which will be lesser, larger, very great, and almost gigantic, according to the size of the mold it happens to be cast in. And these are the bones which Nature produces, and which are sometimes called the bones of giants by the vulgar; but if you break them, there is no medullary substance to be found in them, which ought to be the case, were they the bones either of men or other animals."

Nehemiah Grew (1641–1712), an anatomist of note, in 1681 catalogued and described the "Natural and Artificial Rarities belonging to the Royal Society." He had become a Fellow of the Royal Society in 1671, and succeeded Oldenberg as its Secretary in 1677.

In Part III of the catalogue, "Animal Bodies Petrify'd; and such like," Grew is surprisingly noncommittal regarding the origin of fossils, but presents an unbalanced picture of the two opinions with which he is acquainted, his own leanings being fairly apparent.

"It hath been much disputed, and is not yet resolv'd, of many subterraneal Bodies, which have the semblance of Animals, or Parts of them, Whether they were ever such, or no. And I am not ignorant of the Arguments offer'd on both hands. If I may speak my own sense a little, Why not? Is there any thing repugnant in the matter? Why not a petrify'd Shell, as well as wood? Or is the place? [Sic] If Shells are found under ground, far from Seas, or in Hills, unchanged; as we are sure they are; then why not petrify'd? Or is the form, to which no Species of Shells doth answer? The assertion is precarious: no man can say, how many are known to some one or other; much less, how many are not known: I have reason to believe, that scarce the one half of the under Species of Shells are known to this day. And so for Artificials: if Coyns are found, every day under ground, then why not sometimes also Pictures, and other Works, in time petrify'd? And although Nature doth often imitate her self; yet to make her in any case to imitate Art, is unphilosophical and absurd: for the one, a natural reason may be given, not for the other.

"On the other side: although Nature cannot be said to imitate Art: yet it may fall out, that the effects of both may have some likeness. Those white Concretions which the Italians, from the place where they are found, call Confetti de Tibuli, are sometimes so like round Confects, and the rough kind of Sugar'd-Almonds, that by the eye they cannot be distinguish'd. To call these Petrify'd Sugar-Plums, were senseless. . . . But there can be no convincing Argument given, why the Salts of Plants, or Animal Bodies, washed down with Rains, and lodged under ground; should not there be disposed into such like figures, as well as above it? Probably, in some cases, much better, as in a colder place; and where therefore the Work not being done in a hurry, but more slowly, may be so much the more regular" (*Musaeum Regalis Societatis,* pp. 253-254).

The descriptions accompanying the catalogue are of special interest, as they reflect Grew's wide acquaintance with contemporary literature and his tendency to attribute fossils to natural processes.

The essay which is "subjoyned" to the catalogue, "The Comparative Anatomy of Stomachs and Guts," is, according to F. J. Cole, "the first attempt to deal with one system of organs only by the comparative method" (*History of Comparative Anatomy,* pp. 245-246).

James Petiver (1663[?]-1718), a London apothecary, formed, at vast personal expense, a valuable collection of petrifactions, of which he published a catalogue between 1693 and 1703, under the title *Musei Petiveriani Centuriae X., Rariora Naturae Continentes.* . . . The main part of this appeared in 1695, at which time he was elected to membership in the Royal Society of London. Petiver's cabinet and library were later incorporated into the extensive collections of Sir Hans Sloane, which became the foundation of the British Museum.

Petiver was perhaps more a learned dilettant than a professional naturalist. He published a great many works covering the full scope of natural history. He incurred the displeasure of Dr. John Woodward in 1702, by meddling with Woodward's special province (i.e., "formed stones and other fossils"). He carried on an extensive correspondence, through which he acquired specimens from regions as remote as China. Among his correspondents were Drs. Richardson and Scheuchzer (he obtained from the latter a curious collection of plants). In 1702, Petiver wrote to Richardson that he had "a great itching after the knowledge of Fossils," and in 1704 he was requesting *Entrochi* and other formed stones of Lhwyd.

While his opinions regarding fossils seem to have been ordinary, his collecting techniques had an element of freshness, for Lhwyd wrote in 1701:

"I was glad to see the letter you [the Reverend John Lloyd] enclosed from H. Jones. I think I formerly told you how Petiver and [Samuel] Doody pillaged a cargo of stones he has sent me from Maryland [and which Petiver had the further audacity to describe in a paper sent to the Royal Society: "Remarks on some animal plants, &c. sent from Maryland." *Phil. Trans.* XX, p. 393]; since which time I never could hear a syllable from him" (Gunther, *Life and Letters of Edward Lhwyd,* p. 462.)

A celebrated and much-visited collection particularly rich in antiquarian objects was that of Ludovico Moscardo, a nobleman of Verona. The collection included most of the earlier Calceolari collection (the remainder seemingly having passed into the hands of Mario Sala, an apothecary of Verona), and was visited by such worthies as John Ray (in 1663), Gilbert Burnet (in 1685), and Misson (in 1687).

Ray remarks of the Museo di Ludovico Moscardo:

"That [cabinet] of seignior Muscardo [sic], a gentleman of Verona, a civil and obliging person. He also hath a very good collection of ancient Roman medals, among which he shew'd us an Otho of gold, and told us that those of brass were all counterfeit, there having never been any found of that metal. Many sorts of lachrymal urns and lamps, great variety of shells and some fruits and parts of plants petrified. Several exotic fruits and seeds: the ores of metals and minerals: gems and precious stones in their matrices as they grew: Lapis obsidianus and a kind of stone called Adarce. But because there is a description of this Museum published in Italian [see Appendix A], I shall not descend to more particulars, but refer the reader thither" (Ray, *Travels through the Low-Countries* [London, 1738], pp. 186-187).

The descriptive catalogue of the museum mentioned by Ray was published in 1696 (see Appendix A). The catalogue is in three parts: Book I concerns artificial rarities, e.g., inscriptions, amulets, and statuary; Book II concerns minerals, rocks, earths and the like; while Book III describes living animals and plants. The marginal notations of Moscardo's sources suggest that an extensive and up-to-date library was at his disposal, although much of the classification is based upon the works of Pliny and Dioscorides. It is interesting to note that many of the specimens figured by Moscardo can be identified with the specimens figured by Cerutus in his catalogue of the Calceolarian museum.

The last museum to be discussed here is the Vatican Museum, assembled by Pope Sixtus V, and described and illustrated by Michael Mercati (1541-1593). The catalogue did not appear until 1719 (the colophon is dated 1717), at which time it was published as an "Opus Posthumum," edited by J. M. Lancisius (1654-1720, physician to Pope Clement XI), with notes by Pietro Assalti. The *Metallotheca Vaticana* was classified according to Pliny, and is exceptional only for its excellent engravings, which include figures of a *Lapis Auricularis* and *Enorchis*. The organic nature of fossils was denied, and they were placed under the providence of Heaven by attributing their present shapes to the influence of celestial bodies—much in the same manner as Galen attributed Selenites to the dew of heaven congealed by the light of the moon.

Regional catalogues were often published in the seventeenth century with a great show of chauvinism, generally by physicians who had assembled a cabinet of petrifactions sufficiently large to merit a catalogue. Some few authors were practicing naturalists, although the greater number were amateurs. But this was a century of learned dilettantes. Beringer himself was a physician of note—doubtless having gathered notes for his work on the plague (see Bibliography) during the last great European pandemic of 1710—and a largely self-styled lithographer. The following catalogues—many of which are mentioned only because they are cited by Beringer—are arranged chronologically by publication date.

Pietro Andrea Mattiolo (1500-1577), the celebrated botanist, whose commentary on Dioscorides is an encyclopedia of Renaissance pharmacology, described the fossil fishes of Monte Bolca in 1548. He adopted, however, Agricola's theory of the lapidifying juice (*succus lapidificus*), and maintained that there must be many kinds in order to satisfactorily account for the great variety of its products.

Johann Kentmann, a physician of Torgau, is said to have been the first man in Europe to make a collection of minerals, the catalogue of which appeared in 1565, bound with Gesner's *De Rerum Fossilium*. The catalogue of Kentmann's cabinet contains some 1,600 annotated entries, arranged in such classes as Earths, Efflorescences, Stones, Marbles, Petrified Wood, Pyrites, etc. To his catalogue was added a brief note "On Small Stones Generated in Man and in Human Members."

Goropius Becanus, in his *Origines Anterpianae* (1569), mentions a tooth which had been housed for some time in Antwerp and had to that time been described as "the tooth of that unmerciful Giant, whose defeat was brought about by Brabo, a son of Julius Caesar, and King of the Arcadians." Becanus recognized that it was nothing more than the molar of an elephant (p. 178). Yet he attributes the skeletons of two elephants which were found near Wielworda, while a canal was being dug from Brussels to the river Rupel, to a Roman invasion—during the reign of either the Emperor Galien or Posthumus. Becanus subscribed generally to the concept of a "lapidific current" as being responsible for the formation of figured stones, though there seems to be a confusion regarding ideas on the origin of fossils he possibly derived from Libavius.

Caspar Schwenkfeld (1563–1609), physician of Hirschberg, who studied under Caspar Bauhin, published in 1601 (colophon dated 1600), a catalogue of the fossils of Silesia. He did not, however, put forth an opinion as to their origin.

Hermann Conring (1606–1681), in analyzing the *Ancient State of Helmstadt*, defended the diluvial hypothesis—pointing to the "sea-shells, the bones of beasts and trees, or parts of trees" found both upon the tops of the highest mountains and in the deepest caverns of the earth. Conring stood firm against the then popular *lusus naturae*, remarking: "But that Nature is able of herself, without any assistance, to make bones quite perfect, such as are formed in the foetus, and afterwards completed by long nutrition in the adult, is absolutely impossible. Neither can you attribute the making of so many bones fit for a living animal, and every way perfect, only to a wanton frolic of Nature, without the greatest absurdity (p. 13)."

Agostino Scilla, the Sicilian painter, published in 1670 a work on the fossils of Calabria: *La Vana Speculazione.* . . . While he criticizes those who doubt the organic nature of fossils, he is inclined to consider them *reliquiae diluvianae*—remains of the Mosaic Deluge.

George Henning Behrens (1662–1712) published in 1703 a detailed description of the mountains, caverns, fountains, and products of nature, as well as other curiosities, from the ancient forest of Hercynia (the Hartz). The several caverns in the area (dealt with in Part I) had produced from time to time remarkable bones:

"Here [in the cavern at Scharzfeld] is also found the Fossile Unicorn, but not near in such quantity as formerly, because the Peasants, who used to dig for it, and to sell it to the *Apothecaries* and *Druggists*, have almost exhausted the place. This Fossile is of different Shapes; sometimes 'tis form'd like a streight Horn, a Scull, a Jaw-bone, a Shoulder-blade, and a Back-bone; a Rib, a Tooth, a Thigh-bone, and all other sorts of Bones both of Men and Beasts; and there is some found like an unshaped Lump or Mass of Stone, having no resemblance to any Bone at all.

"There have been great Disputes among the Learned about this Fossile: Some, considering that there are Pieces so exactly like true Bones, affirm, they must really have been part of some Animal; and, that those of an anomolous form are of the Mineral kind. But others reply, That upon Examination they cannot find that great likeness to Bones as their Adversaries are pleas'd to fancy: In particular they say, that those Bones of the Fossile Unicorn, which are call'd Jaw-bones, have such *Apophyses* as are never to be met with in the natural way; and, that some being like no Bone at all, they scruple not to conclude the whole to be a *Lusus Naturae*, or an accidental Produce of Nature. Moreover they add, that granting some to be like true Bones, it cannot be inferr'd from thence that they were really so; because else it would follow, that the Figures represented in some pieces of Slate, and the *Cornua Ammonis*, were once real; which are now allow'd on all hands to be Stones of a particular Kind" (*The Natural History of the Hartz Forest* . . . , tr. by John Andree [London, 1730], pp. 22–24).

Behrens continues:

". . . But to me it seems most probable that it is made of a Clay, or fattish Earth call'd in Latin *Marga*, or *Marl*, which is very plentiful in this Country, and serves to manure the Ground, instead of Dung. According to the figure this Earth lies in under-ground, when the petrifying Water comes to it, and causes it to grow hard, so it remains, and thus becomes sometimes a well-shapen Bone, and often a lump of Matter of no distinct Form at all. This Formation is not perfected at once; for 'tis observ'd, that some pieces lying in a place where there is room for encrease, will grow to a monstrous size.

"This Fossile hath several Names, viz. *Unicornu Minerale, Ebur Fossile, Osteites, Monoceros Vulgi, Lithomarga alba,* &c. The most common term 'tis known by, is *Unicornu Fossile;* but I can see no reason why it should rather be call'd *Unicorn* than any other Animal, since 'tis found of all sorts of Forms, and those pieces resembling the Horn of an Unicorn but very rarely to be met with" (*Ibid.*, pp. 27–28).

The unicorn was believed, however, to be indigenous to the Hercynian Forest from antiquity, for Julius Caesar remarks in the *Gallic Wars:* "Est bos cervi figura, cuius a media fronte inter aures unum cornu existit, excelsius magisque directum his quae nobis nota sunt cornibus" (*De Bello Gallico* vi. 26).

Other works which fall under these categories have been dispersed elsewhere in the text, as they deserve more extensive mention. Such others include: Plot, Lhwyd, Scheuchzer, and Leigh.

CHAPTER II

[1] Photographs of certain stones not illustrated by Beringer may be seen in the illustrations.

[2] See Appendix B.

CHAPTER III

[1] Perhaps the best example of this is the controversy aroused in Thuringia in the late seventeenth century. Wilhelm Ernest Tenzel, historiographer to the dukes of Saxony, entered into controversy with the Medical Faculty at Gotha in 1696, in a *cause célèbre* regarding the skeleton of an elephant. It was uncovered by workmen digging "pure white sand" for export, near Tonna in Thuringia, in December, 1695. The Medical Faculty decided that the bones represented either the skeleton of a fossil unicorn or a "mineral mimicking an animal production." Tenzel maintained them to be "the real bones of an Elephant, but calcined by subterraneous heat, and in a great measure petrified." (See "An Account of the Skeleton of an elephant lately dug up at Tonna," *Phil. Trans.*, XIX, no. 234, p. 757 et seq.) Tenzel did, however, consider these as having been deposited in the Universal Deluge.

[2] . . . *quia haec eorum . . . essentia est, esse occultas.* . . . Beringer gives a clue to the interpretation of this passage in his name-list in Chap. I, in which list occurs the name of Oswald Croll.

Oswald Croll (1580–1609), influential disciple of Paracelsus, about 1608–1609 wrote his famous *Basilica Chymica*. This work contains his comments, derived from Paracelsus (*ca.* 1493–1541), on the doctrine of signatures, which assumes that medicinal plants and other sources of medicine bear some symbol or sign of their value for medicine in their color, shape, or other visible sign, by which God intends that they shall become known to those expert and wise in the interpretation of the signs. The importance of the doctrine of signatures in the study of fossils is difficult to realize, save for the possibility of an occult interpretation of the signs found on certain figured stones.

The following is a brief extract from the hermetic and alchemical writings of Paracelsus which explains in concise terms the doctrine of signatures. The concept as outlined by Paracelsus is essentially that propounded by Croll nearly a century later.

"Whatever anything is useful for, to that it is assumed and adapted. So if Nature makes a man, it adapts him to its design. And here our foundation is laid. For everything that is duly signed its own place should properly be left; for Nature adapts everything to its duty.

". . . A signature, then, is that which has to do with the signs to be taken into consideration, whereby one may know another [man]—what there is in him. [Probably the best-known work on physiognomy, which attempted to estimate character by features, is Giambattista della Porta's *De Humana Physiognomonia libri IV* . . . Vico Equense: J. Cacchi, 1586.] There is nothing hidden which Nature has not revealed and put plainly forward.

"Rightly, therefore, should its proper place be given to signature, because it is a part of astronomy, for this reason, that the star builds the man up at its own pleasure, with the marks belonging to him. What is going to be tinged with black, Nature makes black, what blue, it makes blue; that which is going to sting is made a nettle, and what is to purge is made an equisetum, what is to be used for smoothing and polishing is made a smiris. In fine, to everything is assigned its own form, by which it may be known for what purpose that thing is made by Nature.

"Whatever is in anything according to its properties, quality, form, appearance, etc., is revealed in herbs, seeds, stones, roots, and the rest. All things are known by their signature. By the signature those who are instructed trace what lies hid in herbs, seeds, stones. But when the signature is obliterated and trifles are substituted for it, then it is all over with everything, even philosophy and medicine being at fault" (A. E. Waite, *The Hermetic and Alchemical Writings of . . . Paracelsus*, Vol. II. London, 1894, pp. 304–305).

[3] Robert Plot also discusses this same concept in Chap. V of his *Natural History of Oxfordshire*, pp. 80–95.

"About the origin of this matter [selenite: a stone representing the image of the moon in all its phases], Authors differ much; amongst whom Galen (*Lib. de Simp. Med. ad Patern.*) makes it the dew of Heaven, congeled, as he says, by the light of the Moon, and therefore calls it by the name of *Aphroselinum*, but restrains the performance of the feat to Egypt. Encelius (*De Lapidibus & Gemmis*, lib. 3. cap. 56) thinks it a sort of moisture of the earth, so concreted, that like Crystall it will not dissolve, but remains as it were an indissoluble Ice, whence the Germans took occasion to call it *Glacies Mariae*. But that learned and industrious investigator of Nature, Georgius Agricola, differs from them all, and makes it a product of Limestone and water, *Gignitur* (says he) *ex saxo calcis cum pauca aqua permisto* (*De Natura Fossilium*, lib. 5); and thus I find it to grow here with us at

Heddington, in a blue clay that lies over the Quarry, whose outermost crust is a hard Lime-stone."

This is a brief excerpt from Plot's discussion, and is intended only to give the reader a taste of theories which attributed the origin of certain stones to "the silent intercourse between things celestial and things terrestrial." Plot's discussion continues at some length, and we refer the reader to the pages noted above for a complete analysis.

⁴ Charles Nicolaus Lang [Langius], Doctor of Philosophy and Medicine at Lucerne and purported colleague of Scheuchzer's, proposed in Book II, Chap. 8, of his *Tractatus de Origine Lapidum Figuratorum* the hypothesis to which he subscribed, viz., that at least many figured stones originate within the earth (as distinguished from the sea) through a process of activation of animal seeds which have been deposited in the earth by any of several means (air, vapors, etc.). The activators he conceives to be subterranean heat, proper fluid matter, latent plastic power, and the seminal breeze (which Lang identifies with the lapidific current). He further insists that this process is more rapid than that of natural generation, and that it terminates at the formation of a partial body more often than occurs in natural generation.

Lang follows this discussion with a lengthy discourse on the advantages of snow water in effecting this process. The peculiar efficacy of snow water also explained, he thought, why these phenomena are found only within and upon mountains.

Lang was, in short, a supporter of a modified Lhywdian hypothesis, and took exception to the diluvial hypothesis of Woodward and Scheuchzer.

⁵ Langius, *Tractatus de Origine Lapidum Figuratorum*, Book I, Chap. 1, p. 2.

⁶ Robert Plot, *The Natural History of Oxfordshire, Being an Essay toward the Natural History of England* (Oxford, 1677).

⁷ Dr. Robert Plot [Plott], 1640–1696, first Keeper of the Ashmolean Museum, Secretary of the Royal Society, and editor of the *Philosophical Transactions* beginning in 1683, published a work in 1677 which deserves special mention, if not for its charming style or for its influence upon Elias Ashmole (which persuaded him to establish the museum bearing his name at Oxford), at least because it took firm exception to the more "progressive" views concerning the nature of fossils.

Plot recognized four classes of formed stones, of which the ". . . first treat of such formed stones as either in name, or thing, or both, relate to the Heavenly Bodies or Air [e.g., *Selenites, Asteriae* and *Ombriae*]; and next, such as belong to the Watery Kingdom [e.g., *Stalagmites*, or *Lapides stillatitii*, and *Spars*]: After them, such as resemble Plants and Animals, whether in the whole, or parts [e.g., *Conchites, Hippocephalites, Orchites*, or *Lapides testiculares* and *Bufonites*]. And lastly such stones, wherein contrary to all rule, Dame Nature seems to imitate Art" [e.g., the button-stone, a stone in the shape of the heel of an old shoo [sic] and the *Geodes*, or the pregnant stone] . . . (p. 80).

Plot undertakes, after a description of the first two classes of formed stones, a "friendly debate" without any peremptory decision on "the great Question now so much controverted in the World:"

"Whether the stones we find in the forms of Shell-fish, be *Lapides sui generis*, naturally produced by some extraordinary plastic virtue latent in the Earth or Quarries where they are found? Or whether they rather owe their form and figuration to the shells of the Fishes they represent, brought to the places where they are now found by a Deluge, Earth-quake, or some other such means, and there being filled with mud, clay, and petrifying juices, have in tract of time been turned into stones, as we now find them, still retaining the same shape in the whole, with the same lineations, sutures, eminencies, cavities, orifices, points, that they had whil'st they were shells (p. 111)?"

On the succeeding pages Plot rejects both the universality of the Noachian Deluge and the opinion that the deluge was responsible either for fossils or for their placement. He confesses that he is inclined "to the opinion of Mr. [Martin] Lister, that they are *Lapides sui generis*," and gives an account of the "plastick power [or virtue], or whatever else it is, that effects these shapes."

"That Salts are the principal Ingredients of stones, I think has so sufficiently been noted already, that to endeavor any further evidence of the thing, would be *actum agere* in me, and loss of time to the Reader: And if of stones in general much rather sure of formed ones, it being the undoubted prerogative of the Saline Principle to give Bodies their figure, as well as solidity and duration: No other principle that we yet know of naturally shooting into figures, each peculiar to their own kind, but salts; thus *Nitre* always shoots into Pyramids, *salt Marine* into Cubes, *Alum* into octo, and *Sal Armoniac* into Hexadrums, and other mixt salts into as mixt figures.

"Of these spontaneous inclinations of salts, each peculiar to its kind, we have further evidence in the Chymical Anatomy of Animals, particularly in the volatile salt of *Harts-horn*, which in the beginning of its ascent is always seen branched in the head of the *Cucurbit* like the natural Horn. And we were told the last Term by our very Ingenious and Learned Sidleyan Professor (Dr. Tho. Millington) here in Oxon, That the salt of Vipers ascends in like manner, and shoots into shapes somwhat like those Animals, placed orderly in the glass. Thus in congelations which are all wrought by adventitious salts, we frequently find curious ramifications, as on Glass-windows in the winter, and the figur'd flakes of snow; of which Mr. Hook (*Micrographia*. Observ. 14. Schem. 8) observed above an hundred several sorts, yet all of them branched as we paint stars, with six principal *Radii* of equal length, shape, and make, issuing from a center where they are all joined in angles of 60 degrees.

"What salt it should be that gives this figure, though it be hard to determin, yet certainly it must not be a much different one from that which gives form to our *Astroites* and *Asteriae*, whereof, though the latter have but five points, and therefore making angles where they are joyned at the center of 72 degrees; yet the *Astroites* both in *mezzo Rilievo* and *Intagli*, as in Tab. 2. have many more. Perhaps there may be somthing of an *Antimonial salt* that may determin Bodies to this starry figure, as no question it do's in the *Regulus*, and the *Caput mortuum* of the *Cinnabar* of *Antimony*. To such a salt may also be referr'd our *Brontiae* or *Ombriae*, and all the *Echinites*, some whereof are plainly, all in some measure stellated at the top" (pp. 122–123).

Plot was one of the last to accept the concept of a plastic power (*vis plastica*) as being responsible for the existence of certain formed stones—others coming under the special providence of the Heavens or of Water. He was succeeded on the one hand by Woodward and Scheuchzer, who argued for the Deluge, and on the other by Edward Lhwyd, who adhered to the Libavian concept of the *aura seminalis*, or spermatic principle.

[8] Helwing, *Lithographia Angerburgica, sive Lapidum et Fossilium* (Regiomonti, 1717; *Pars Secunda*, Lipsiae, 1720).

The *Lithography of Angerburg* was published by Helwing in two parts, appearing in 1717 and 1720. Helwing's position in regard to the origin of petrifactions is somewhat vague. Although he heads a chapter: "*De Lapidibus res naturales repraesentantibus*," he attributes others (specifically his lithographs) to a plastic power residing in petrificious salts, or, as Leigh might have phrased it, to a peculiar menstruum. These gentlemen spoke in generalities.

[9] . . . *nimiam salibus virtutem graphicam, plasticamque.* . . .

[10] Luidius [Lhwyd or Lhuyd], *Lithophylacii Britannici Ichnographia* (London, 1699), pp. 131–145. (In 1760 ed., pp. 131–142). Lhwyd's letter to John Ray (Raius), "Of the Origin of Marine Fossils; and of Mineral Leaves, branches, etc." is given in its entirety in Appendix C.

Edward Lhwyd (1660–1709) was the second Keeper of the Old Ashmolean Museum, succeeding Plot in 1691. He was an authority not only on fossils, but antiquities and glossography (especially Celtic philology) as well. His observations on fossils were confined to his monumental correspondence and his several papers in the *Philosophical Transactions* of the Royal Society, excepting his catalogue of the Fossils in the Ashmolean Museum: *Lithophylacii Britannici Ichnographia*.

Although Lhwyd was a student of Plot's (his Oxford tutor and seven years his superior officer at the Old Ashmolean Museum) he by no means subscribed to Plot's ideas regarding the origin of fossils. Nor did he adhere to notions regarding the Mosaic Deluge, or as far as can be discovered, the *lusus naturae* (see chap. ix, note 3). Lhwyd was, rather, a member of the animalculist faction of the preformationist movement. He was perhaps the greatest proponent of what was termed the "Spermatick Principle," or by some the *aura seminalis*. Libavius had suggested a similar idea early in the seventeenth century, but it remained for Lhwyd to formulate the theory explicitly.

In his celebrated Epistola VI, from the *Lithophylacii Britannici*, inscribed to John Ray, he sets forth the theory and arguments in its favor. The spermatic principle is a case of transposition of theories. The animalculist faction of the performationist movement thought they saw in the head of a sperm a tiny creature resembling the adult of the species. This would give the male contribution the totality of reproductive power, relegating the ovum to vegetative nutriment. Thus, for all that these eminent scholars gloried in the enlightenment of their advanced learning, they were yet proximately disposed to subscribe to this theory, inherited from the "murky ages of the scholastics," that the real generator is the male, the female being left only with the role of furnishing the generable and nutritive material:

"Among perfect animals, the active power of generation belongs to the male sex, and the passive power to the female." (See Saint Thomas Aquinas, *Summa Theologica*, I Pars, Qu. 92, art. 1, corpus.)

If this were true, and the earth contained some sort of nutrient (or developmental stimulant such as a "saline moisture" of an occult sort), then after the "spawn of animals" insinuated itself through a meatus into the earth there would be nothing preventing development.

The Spermatic Principle was short lived, being a valid hypothesis only from Libavius (1540?–1616) through Lhwyd to Lang, who modified the concept slightly. Lhwyd had a great influence in promoting this theory, which had a profound effect on such notables as John Ray and Richard Richardson.

Although he supported what we would today call a flagrantly erroneous hypothesis, Lhwyd was a more objective and scientific man than either Woodward or Scheuchzer, and in some respects even than Plot. He put into words a concept worthy of a man of his stature, and one seldom found in an age of scientific dogmatism:

"To this I must needs answer, That the frequent Observations I have made on such Bodies [fossils], have hitherto afforded little better Satisfaction, than repeated Occasions of Wonder and Amazement; forasmuch as I have often (I may almost say continually) experienc'd, that what one Day's Observations suggested, was the next called in Question, if not totally contradicted and overthrown. Nevertheless, so indefatigable is the Curiosity, and indeed so successful have been the Discoveries of this present Age, that we are daily encouraged to hope, this so important a Question will not much longer want its final Determination, to the great Advancement of that Kind of real Knowledge which relates to Minerals." (John Ray, *Three Physico-Theological Discourses* [4th ed.; London, 1732] p. 176.)

[11] Lhwyd, *op. cit.*, 1699 ed.: p. 138; 1760 ed.: p. 136.

[12] Lhwyd, *ibid.*, 1699 ed.: pp. 138–139; 1760 ed.: pp. 136–137.

[13] Scheuchzer, *Herbarium Diluvianum*, Tab. VII: 6, pp. 28–29.

[14] Dr. Johann Jacob Scheuchzer (1672–1733), a physician and naturalist of "indefatigable industry and extensive knowledge," (Knight, *English Cyclopaedia*, vol. 5, p. 435) was an adherent of the diluvial theory, and a follower of Woodward, whose *Essay towards a Natural History of the Earth* (London, 1695) he translated into Latin in 1704. Scheuchzer's name is forever coupled with *Homo diluvii testis* —a supposed antediluvial man whose parts are primarily those of a Tertiary batrachian (*Andrias scheuchzeri*), but with two vertebrae of a Mesozoic marine reptile. The remarkable fossil was uncovered at Oeningen in 1725, and described the following year by Scheuchzer in a short tract titled *Homo diluvii testis.* Scheuchzer returned to the subject of antediluvian man in his famous "Copper Bible" (the *Physica Sacra*), remarking:

"It is certain that this schist is the half, or nearly so, of the skeleton of a man: that the substance even of the bones, and, what is more, of the flesh and of parts still softer than the flesh, are there incorporated in the stone: in a word it is one of the rarest relics which we have of that cursed race which was buried under the waters. The figure shows us the contour of the frontal bone, the orbits with the openings which give passage to the great nerves of the fifth pair. We see there the remains of the brain, of the sphenoidal bone, of the roots of the nose, a notable fragment of the os maxilla, and some vestiges of the liver" (Volume I, pp. 49–50).

Among Scheuchzer's principal works are his *Itinera Alpina*, which contains the descriptions and figures of a great number of plants, as well as barometrical and mineralogical observations. His *Sciagraphia Lithologica Curiosa* was published posthumously—a work of great value for its annotated descriptions of several hundred genera of fossils.

It is interesting to note that in 1702 Scheuchzer attributed fossils to the "capricious powers" in a work entitled *Specimen Lithographiae Helvetiae Curiosae.* His succeeding three writings, neglecting the translation of 1704, were: *Piscium Querelae et Vindiciae* (Tiguri, 1708), *Herbarium Diluvianum* (Tiguri, 1709) and *Museum Diluvianum* (Tiguri, 1716)—it is said that he was so impressed with Woodward's work that he abandoned his former opinions and accepted the diluvial hypothesis.

Of his various diluvial writings, including *Homo Diluvii Testis* (Tiguri, 1726), *The Grievances and Claims of the Fishes* is probably the most remarkable—if not indeed among the whole of scientific literature. The short treatise (36 pages) is a contrived attack upon scholars who attributed fossils to any circumstance save the Universal Deluge. While much of the tract is devoted to anatomical description of the several fossil fish found in Switzerland, an equal proportion is devoted to pithy attack upon misguided scholars. The treatise deals with a trial of mankind by the fish, who were drowned in the Mosaic inundation because of man's wickedness, and indeed perished with him. Now, however, ever fickle man has denied the very organic existence of these denizens of the waters, and categorizes them as inorganic: the products of the *vis plastica*, the *aura seminalis*, or *quid vis*. Here are the first few pages of this amazing tract:

It is commonplace in our age for rights to be forcibly trespassed, appropriated or claimed, and this no less in Nature than in Polity. Everywhere Kingdoms suffer this disorder. Three of them in Nature, though many more in the sphere of Polity. To the Mineral Kingdom are consigned those things which belong to the Vegetable or Animal Realm, thus enabling the former to extend its territory beyond the bounds imposed by justice, and to threaten the rest with absorption—a penalty which the greater part of Animals and Plants did indeed once sustain in the Universal Flood. Let the Quadrupeds, the Birds and the Insects defend their rights if the fortune of each is his own concern. We, the voiceless throng of swimming creatures, here and now lay our grievances before the throne of Truth, in an effort to reclaim what is ours—which unsound philosophy, or covetousness tending to Monarchy of the Minerals, or the injustice so prevalent in our times, or that prejudicial attitude become an opprobrious by-word, respecting our dumb condition, has wrested from us. If we are ambitious, this is to our glory, not to our shame. We do not claim what is ours and what we presently enjoy, namely life and movement, which beyond any shadow of doubt place us in the ranks of the Animal Kingdom. Our contention is for a racial glory issuing from the death of our Forebears. We are concerned here, not with unearthed fishes or fossils, nor with those terrene denizens of the lower regions mentioned by Pliny, Aristotle, Theophrastus, Strabo, and others, but with that class which lived and roamed the waves before the Flood, and being submerged therein became the victim of alien vagaries. We are not concerned with that fishy structure which has survived intact in us but with those remains so mangled in the diluvial carnage that no skin clings to the bones, only a scaly figure remains, occasionally a few small bones or spines survive, though often there is no more than an impression of a skeleton on rocks. At the same time we are undertaking a cause of even greater import, which is the indomitable Testimony of the universal inundation, a testimony which, by a singular divine providence we shall thrust into the faces of unbelievers to the confusion of all brazen atheists. Let them have their say, and declaim as loudly as their throats permit; let the nectar of their Lucretian eloquence flow. Tongueless though we be and empty of all persuasive art, nor championed by any advocate, we shall yet reduce to wordlessness even the most skilled orators.

Let the Pike advance to the front ranks as the commanding officer. Let the Pike, of the class of non-spiny fishes with a single dorsal fin, surpass the rest, attacking and routing the enemy ranks with his ravenous strength. The action may begin with the drawing of the Pike in Plate I. There he will remove all doubt as to the identity of this skeleton by displaying, not a superficial likeness of just any pike, not a mere sketch, such as those found in the Eislebiana . . . This was extracted from the Oeningen Quarry, in the Diocese of Constance, at high altitude, where there has never been any fish-pond, pool, or lake. Step forth now all you sponsors of that subterranean Archaeus, Artificer and Demigod, and judge for yourselves whether this was the organic body of the Pike. Measure the parts and calculate their proportions. Study the reality, not a dim shadow, not an effigy, of whatever quality, executed by Nature in her role of artist, but the fish, the Pike, his parts here and there distorted by pressure, if you will, yet not transposed, not with his head in his stomach; nor with all his fins attached to his head, but with each fin, rib, bone and vertebra found in its proper place. Which of you will demonstrate that the origin of this machine is to be found elsewhere than in the egg? Who will deny that this body once lived and waxed? Who will dare to propose any other artificer than God? Descend to the arena all you Mechanists. Form your battlelines, you dauntless soldiers of Epicurus, brandish and hurl your spears, razor sharp in their subtlety. Summon the laws of motion and extol their testimony. The whole panoply of your armor is shattered with easy skill by our Pike, your battleline is pierced. What a spectacle! an entire army put to rout by a single fish! This is no fungus-like growth: here a fin sprouting from the earth, there a vertebra, elsewhere a head, in another spot the jaws; the conjunction of these parts is orderly, not haphazard, and such it will appear even to you who would compose Homer's *Iliad* by a random jumbling of letters, and would ascribe the origin of the Pike to an unforeseen confluence of atoms. So much, then, for the ultimate escape mechanism of your hypothesis: one which, to the very last, fails to militate against us. Hold your tongue as you gaze spellbound upon this dumb animal, you protagonists of archetypes tumbling about the world through the air, their nature quite eluding even your own grasp. Open and set forth the treasures of this new philosophy of yours, this mutation of Plantonism or Epicureanism. The moment these expressive tints become visible, they fade away. How, pray tell, was the archetype of the Pike able to expand in the fissures of stones? Where was there a place that permitted nutrition and growth? How did muddy or rocky matter yield space proportioned to the extension of each member? What was the action and reaction of the fishes upon cleft rocks? How could a fish of this size fit into strata which are parallel and contiguous throughout their length? This should be an ample consignment of knotty questions for the Ideists, though there are more, should they resolve these. And now my little band trumpeting forth the saline panspermia throughout the geocosm, what are you to us and to the Pike here present? Bring on your whole store of nitre with its power over heaven and earth, show us your pisci-carnu-cochlea-denti-luci-anguilla-percaform salts, or should I say this pantomorphic Vertumnus disguised as salts, resembling a new Archeus that expresses, moulds, and paints the likenesses of all animals and all, even the least, of their parts? Were we still groping about in the shadows of Scholastic ignorance, these cerebral meanderings of yours might be pardonable, but to cherish blindness in the clear light, shed in philosophical chambers, of so many observations, experiments and ratiocinations everywhere tempered to mathematical certitude is the behavior of owls, not of me. I appeal to your faith, not as men "whose minds Titan has fashioned from noble clay," but in whom some flicker of reason yet remains: are not these the remains of the once living animated body of the Pike? Would any other circumstances than those of an inundation or submersion favor the insinuation of fishes into the fissures of strata? On your faith we challenge you, you whose animality is possessed of reason: could we have been buried in metal mines and in the strata of towering mountains other than by that Universal Flood, fatal to men and beasts, wherein in the surface of the earth, dissolved by encircling waters, acquired its present structure? Apart from any scrutiny of its members, judge whether this Pike, which we submit for the first course of this philosophical feast, does not deserve to be designated as an authentic witness, more than equal to any objection, of that Noachic Cataclysm, obscurely intimated here and there among gentile writers, but fully chronicled, unshrouded by fables, in the writings of that Prophet, full of the Godhead, who would have fallen prey to us when the savage command of the Pharaoh exposed him to the waves, had not a special providence of God delivered him from this fate? Be not swayed from your assent by Plautus' maxim: None but a fresh fish is good, for this is a bona fide witness, having been actually present at the Catastrophe. Old indeed he is: 4,000 years, not counting his life span before the Flood. Yet he is fresh. As an eye-witness to the Cataclysm, he is fresh precisely because he is old. No tasty morsel to the gullet this, to win the plaudits of Plautus; no welcome guest to the frying pan, but welcome indeed to Museums, sating the mind with his mute utterance, fond herald to an inquiring world borne on the lips of men. Did I say fresh? Fresher indeed than animals of the same species living now, as he is more enduring in his flesh, his bones, his ribs, his whole figure. Behold this fish preserved for us from the turbulent waters lashed by the sins of men, from the mire and mud of the Deluge, to light the torch that will dispel this murky question! Behold a gentle fish, now that he has put off his native voracity and does not prey upon those who follow, as once he did, but shares his testimony with them in friendly fellowship! [pp. 3–8]

Scheuchzer carried on an extensive correspondence, and exchanged fossils with collectors in many parts of the world. He passed, in short, a life devoted "to science and useful labors, known throughout Europe by a number of learned writings, and esteemed at home for his modesty, mildness and integrity" (Knight, *op. cit.*, p. 435).

[15] The theory described here and elsewhere, that of the *occulta semina* or spermatic principle, is discussed in Appendix C and note 32 to that Appendix.

[16] See Appendix C, note 32.

[17] Langius, *Tractatus de Origine Lapidum Figuratorum*, Book II, Chap. 8, p. 64.

[18] Mercati, *Metallotheca Opus Posthumum*, Armarium Nonum, Chap. 2 (Notae by Assalti), p. 220.

[19] Dr. John Woodward (1661–1727), Professor of Physick in Gresham College and Fellow of the Royal Society of London, was a gentleman "extraordinary ingenious . . . who had ye most considerable collection of English fossils," but "of a very hot and passionat temper, and of a conversation . . . somewhat disagreeable" (Gunther, *op. cit.*, pp. 168–169). It was this same Woodward who virulently opposed Edward Lhwyd's election to the Royal Society of London in November, 1708. Gunther (p. 453) notes that "it was the last flare-up of a quarrel that had alternately blazed and smouldered for many years, and both protagonists had command of powerful vocabularies."

Woodward devoted full attention in his *Essay toward a Natural History of the Earth* (London, 1695—quotations below from second edition, 1702) to proving that fossils were laid down in the Deluge, and dismissed his opposition in a manner fitting his disposition. "I would not be thought to insinuate that the Opinion of these Gentlemen carries no shew of Truth, nor umbrage of Reason of its side. 'Tis not to be supposed, that Persons of their Learning and Abilities would ever have espoused it, were it not in some measure plausible: and had not at least a fair appearance of probability" (p. 15).

He seems not to have accepted even in the slightest degree (unlike Leigh) any accounting for fossils save that "the Sea gave Birth to these Bodies: that they are so far from being formed in the Earth, or in the Places where they are now found, that even the Belemnites, Selenites, Marchasits, Flints, and other natural Minerals, which are lodged in the Earth, together with these Shells were not formed there, but had Being before ever they came thither: and were fully formed and finished before they were reposed in that manner" (p. 19). The meaning of this seeming contradiction will soon become apparent.

Woodward introduced into his deluge theory a concept which was destined for much debate—being generally scorned by Edward Lhwyd and his followers and "refuted" by Charles Leigh—the concept of the Universal Solvent, which Woodward acknowledged to be a "Supernatural Power . . . [which] acted in this Matter with Design, and with the highest Wisdom" (pp. 164–165).

"That during the Time of the Deluge, whilst the Water was out upon, and covered the Terrestrial Globe, all the Stone and Marble of the Antediluvian Earth: all the Metalls of it: all Mineral Concretions: and, in a word, all Fossils whatever that had before obtained any Solidity, were totally dissolved, and their constituent Corpuscles all disjoyned, their Cohaesion perfectly ceasing. That the said Corpuscles of these solid Fossils, together with the Corpuscles of those which were not before solid, such as Sand, Earth, and the like: as also all Animal Bodies, and Parts of Animals, Bones, Teeth, Shells: Vegetables, and Parts of Vegetables, Trees, Shrubs, Herbs: and, to be short, all Bodies whatsoever that were either upon the Earth, or that constituted the Mass of it, if not quite down to the Abyss, yet at least to the greatest Depth we ever dig: I say all these were assumed up promiscuously into the Water, and sustained in it, in such manner that the Water, and Bodies in it, together made up one common confused Mass.

"That at length all the Mass that was thus born up in the Water, was again precipitated, and subsided towards the bottom. That this Subsidence happened generally, and as near as possibly could be expected in so great a Confusion, according to the Laws of Gravity; that Matter, Body, or Bodies, which had the greatest quantity or degree of Gravity, subsiding first in order, and falling lowest: that which had the next, or a still lesser degree of Gravity, subsiding next after, and settling upon the precedent: and so on in their several Courses; that which had the least Gravity sinking not down till last of all, settling at the Surface of the Sediment, and covering all the rest. That the Matter, subsiding thus, formed the Strata of Stone, of Marble, of Cole, of Earth, and the rest; of which Strata, lying one upon another, the Terrestrial Globe, or at least as much of it as is ever displayed to view, doth mainly consist. That the Strata being arranged in this Order meerly by the disparity of the Matter, of which each consisted, as to Gravity, that Matter which was heaviest descending first, and all that had the same degree of Gravity subsiding at the same time: and there being Bodies of quite different Kinds, Natures, and Constitutions, that are nearly of the same Specifick Gravity, it thence happened that Bodies of quite different Kinds subsided at the same instant, fell together into, and composed the same Stratum. That for this reason the Shells of those Cockles, Escalops, Perewinkles, and the rest, which have a greater degree of Gravity, were enclosed and lodged in the Strata of Stone, Marble, and the heavier kinds of Terrestrial Matter; the lighter Shells not sinking down till afterwards, and so falling amongst the lighter Matter, such as Chalk; and the like, in all such Parts of the Mass where there happened to be any considerable quantity of Chalk, or other Matter lighter than Stone; but where there was none, the said Shells fell upon, or near unto, the Surface" (pp. 73–76).

Lhwyd referred to the above when he wrote to Martin Lister: "Dr. W. holds fast to his Hypothesis in spight of all opposition. Men of his temper seldome trouble their heads to rectify their notions, or recall what they have publickly declared; but hold themselves obliged in honour to maintain their ground, and fight it out, at any hazard" (Gunther, op. cit., pp. 277–278).

Woodward did, however, distinguish between casts and molds on the one hand, and actual shells on the other.

"That the above mentioned Bodies which consist of Stone, of Spar, Flint, and the like, and yet carry a resemblance of Cockles, Muscles, and other Shells, were originally formed in the Cavities of Shells of those kinds which they so resemble; these shells having served as Matrices or Moulds to them; the Sand, Sparry and Flinty Matter being then soft, or in a state of solution, and so, susceptible of any Form, when it was thus introduced into these shelly-Moulds: and that it consolidated, or became hard afterwards" (pp. 19–20).

Woodward's concept of stratification is certainly inferior to that of Steno, and won him mention in Hill's animadversions on the Royal Society: "Woodward, and a set of Triflers like himself, have advanced some remarkable Things indeed in regard to the Disposition of Strata of this Terraqueous Globe . . ." (p. 204). His adherence to the scriptural account of the Deluge places him among Büttner, Scheuchzer, and others who, though they recognized the true nature of fossils, were more interested in reconciling fossils with theology than in correlating fossils and natural processes. Their interest, in fact, often seems to lie more in the scripture than in natural history—certainly this is true of both Scheuchzer and Woodward.

Büttner, author of two works of some note, was firmly convinced of the diluvial origin of fossils, and was strongly opposed to those who attributed these "reliquiae diluvianae" to either the "lusus naturae" (See chap. IX, note 3) or the spermatic principle. Büttner, in his Treatise on the Deposits which are Evidence of the Deluge, refers in surprisingly scurrilous terms to Lhwyd and his animalculae.

A work of remarkable insight, yet comparable to that of Fabio Columna for its yielding to dogma, was The Natural History of Northampton-shire, written by Dr. John Morton, Rector of Oxendon and Fellow of the Royal Society, in 1712. Morton recognized the organic nature of fossils, but due to his religious persuasions attributed them to the Deluge. His opening remarks in Chap. III (p. 188) are worthy of note:

"In this Third Part of my Work, I shall give an Account of the Shells of Sea Shell-Fish, that are found here bury'd in the Earth, in great Number and Variety, with their Cavities for the most part fill'd up with Clay, Sand-stone, Spar, or other Matter: As also of the Bodies consisting of Sand, Spar, etc. that were originally formed in the Cavities of the like Shells as in a Mould, and have taken the Figures of them; but are now found divested either wholly or in Part of the Shells in which they were moulded. Likewise of the Vertebrae, Teeth, and other Parts of Fishes, and of Beasts which are found in like manner lodged in the Strata of Earth, and of Stone. And lastly of the Firrs, Oaks, and other Vegetable Bodies included in the Peat-Earth, Loam, and other Terrestrial Matter. . . . In my Descriptions, I take care to note, especially those Circumstances of these Bodies that evince, they are what they appear to be, that is, real Shells: And of the same Extract and Origin with them we now find at Sea. I have also diligently noted the Form and Marks impress'd upon the Stoney and other like Matter wherewith their Cavity is generally fill'd. In describing the Stones that bear a Resemblance of Shells, but are not now found enclos'd in any Shell, I take particular Notice of those Marks of them that demonstrate, these too were originally moulded in the Cavities of Shells . . ."

He continued to compare fossil and living genera, and notably observed a correlative condition of specimens in both "states" of being:

"In one of my Samples the Convex Part of the bigger Shell, appears eroded, as it were, by Worms. Out of Oxendon Gravel-pit, I have a Fragment of another that's very full of Worm-holes. So I may fitly call them, because they are exactly like those small Holes, which we may observe in several of the Oyster-shells that are found at Sea, which have been really burrow'd thus by Worms; as Mr. Azout's Discoveries inform us (vid. *Phil. Trans.*, Vol. I, N. 12, p. 203). These Holes in some of the Fossil Oyster-Shells are found fill'd with a coarse Sort of Spar. This alone is to me a sufficient Proof that they were made when the Shell lay in the Sea, or else upon the Shores, before ever it was convey'd to Land, and thus lodged in the Earth. And hereof we have a like Confirmation from the Marks or Impressions that are sometimes seen of some of these Holes upon the Earth, Stone, and other Matter, inclosed in the Cavity of the Shell.'

The last great diluvialist to be mentioned here is by far the most representative. He is not restricted by a single opinion regarding the origin of fossils, and in this is more truly representative of the times than any of the afore-mentioned gentlemen. For this reason he is quoted at length, and it is hoped thereby to set the flavor of scholarly works of an encompassing nature.

Dr. Charles Leigh (1662-1701), Doctor of Physick and naturalist, published in 1700 *The Natural History of Lancashire, Cheshire, and the Peak in Derbyshire: with an Account of the British, Phoenician, Armenian, Gr. and Rom. Antiquities in Those Parts* (Oxford, 1700). This work is actually an enlargement of his several papers published in the *Philosophical Transactions* of the Royal Society of London, and now translated from the Latin.

Leigh's opinions on the nature of fossils are not remarkable, except for their conformity. Leigh accepted the universality of the Mosaic Deluge, but not Woodward's concept of the waters of the flood (i.e., the Universal Solvent power of these waters).

"To these [arguments for the Deluge] may be added that remarkable Mountain call'd Naphat in the Province of Conought in the Kingdom of Ireland, which is several hundred Fathom above the surface of the Sea, yet at the top of this Mountain ten Yards within it are vast Beds of all sorts of marine Shells, as *Whelks, Muscles, Cockles, Perewinkles, Torculars, Pectinites, Turbinites, Oysters*, etc. which doubtless, considering the immense height of the Mountain, could not be deposited there by any means but a Deluge, and that an universal one" (p. 62).

Leigh continues his argument, and counters on pp. 100-101 five "Opinions of the Jews," summarizing:

"The sixth and last are those that have chosen the truest Opinion, and maintain that the Deluge was universal [contra Abraham Mylius and Isaac Vossius], both in respect to the Terrestrial Globe, and its Inhabitants. . . . Hence therefore it is evident from the holy Scriptures, and from the Phaenomena in Natural History, that there was a Deluge, and that this Deluge was universal too . . ." (p. 101).

In countering Woodward's Universal Solvent, Leigh states:

"From the Phenomenon laid down we may now without great difficulty account for the those representations of Shells, Fins of Fishes, and Plants, observable in Rocks and Quarreis, and may easily be convinc'd, that to solve these there is no necessity to suppose an universal dissolution of the Globe of the Earth at the Deluge, but indeed are Arguments conclusive to the contrary; wherefore to these I shall only add one general Remark, and so close this Head. Can it be imagin'd that in that general Destruction there should be such a Menstruum, or universal Dissolvent in Nature, that should convert all the Strata of the Earth, Mines, Minerals and Metals into a liquid Form, and yet some few Shells, Bones and Plants remained undissolved, which are of a much softer texture, and as we find by repeated Experiments, far more easily dissolved? He, I say, that can averr this, cannot fairly tax a Rosicrucian with Enthusiasm, nor justly blame the Adeptist for his extravagant Notions relating to the Alchahest, that Chymical universal Dissolvent, which he himself does not believe, yet would so far impose upon the World as to have others to do so; but for this the Dr. has promis'd account in his general History of the World" (pp. 118-119).

Not all fossils were products of the Deluge to Leigh. There were two exceptions: plants and formed stones.

"My sentiment of the whole is this, (That as it is observable in Chymistry that the Salts of some Plants will divaricate themselves into the figure of the Plants) that these representations of Plants in Rocks are nothing but different Concretions of saline, bituminous and terrene Particles; and I am farther confirm'd in this Hypothesis, since they, as well as the Capsulae they are found in, seldom fail to afford us that mixture" (p. 99).

Plants were to be considered, therefore, concretions of matter or Disports of Nature, rather than the *Exuviae* of the Deluge.

In spite of his general acceptance of the Deluge, there were stones which required special treatment. These were termed, typically, formed stones. Leigh cites a fine example on pp. 119-120:

"I consider next the formed Stones, and those are the *Bufonites*, the *Belemnites*, and the *Ophites* or *Cornu Ammonis*, so denominated from the figure of a *Serpent* [see Wormius, *op. cit.*, p. 86], or the Horn of a Ram. The *Bufonites* I have seen in Marle near Preston in Lancashire; the *Belemnites* in a Free-stone Rock near Stockport in Cheshire, in which Rock likewise are observable several small Pebbles, that lie frequently in black Capsulae, and as I have been inform'd by the Masons, sometimes a living Toad has been found in Free-stone Rock, in the like *Cista* or Cavity, which doubtless must be lodg'd there in this following manner: It is to be presum'd that the Ovum of some Toad was brought thither by a Spring or Vein leading to that Cavity, for Springs are very often discern'd in Free-stone Rocks, ouzing thorow their Pores; now it cannot be imagin'd that it was lodg'd there ever since the Deluge, which must necessarily follow, unless we allow the recited Hypothesis." (See also Beringer, chap, VII and plates II and V; notes 34 and 39 to Appendix C.)

And again on page 143 he puts forth evidence of his ovist persuasion (see note 32 to Appendix C):

"The River Erke is remarkable for Eeles. . . . It may now be worth our time to make Enquiry into the manner of the Generation of this kind of Fish: I could not in these, by any Dissection I ever made, observe the distinction of Male and Female, which has given occasion to some to conjecture they came from the middle Region, since Ponds and Pits are found frequently full of them, in wch none had ever been deposited, and therefore 'tis concluded that their *Ova* being so small as not to be discern'd by ocular Inspection, they might be exhal'd with the Waters, and consequently fall down with the Rains, and when these happen'd to fall into Rivers and Ponds, they by the influence of the Sun, begin and compleat their Generation. . . . There is no doubt but the Rains are oftentimes saturated with Ova of divers Species, as may be seen by Putrifaction of the Water . . ."

Leigh's *Natural History* is certainly typical of the works of those "humble admirers of Natural History" described in Number 236 of the *Tatler*. It is one of a great quantity of treatises written by learned dilettantes in the eighteenth century, a movement which intruded into the Royal Society and led the *Tatler* to observe:

"There is no Study more becoming a rational Creature, than that of Natural Philosophy; but as several of our modern Virtuoso's manage it, their Speculations do not so much tend to open and enlarge the Mind, as to contract and fix it upon Trifles.

"This in England, is, in a great Measure, owing to the worthy Elections that are so frequently made in our Royal Society. They seem to be in a Confederacy against Men of polite Genius, noble Thought, and diffusive Learning; and chuse into their Assemblies such as have no Pretense to Wisdom, but Want of Wit; or to natural Knowledge, but Ignorance of every thing else. I have made Observations in this Matter so long, than when I meet with a young Fellow that is an humble Admirer of the Sciences, but more dull than the rest of the Company, I conclude him to be a Fellow of the Royal Society."

Leigh's *Natural History of Lancashire* runs to several hundred folio pages, with twenty-four plates, and contains many irreconcilable contradictions. It is a work of that special genre which culminated in the nineteenth century in such Plinyesque writings as the Reverend Thomas Smith's *The Naturalist's Cabinet . . .* (London, 1806–1807).

[20] Lachmundus, *Oryctographia Hildesheimensis, sive Admirandorum Fossilium* (Hildesheimii, 1669).

The fossils and "rariora" of Hildesheim were described in 1669, by Fridericus Lachmund (1635–1676) in the above-cited work. The *Oryctographia* contains many charming woodcuts similar to those found in the earlier Lapidaries. Lachmund was a physician of Osterwieck where, between 1673 and 1674, he described the hyobranchial apparatus of the swan and demonstrated that bats have tails. His position with regard to the origin of fossils was uncertain, but it was somewhere between the *succus lapidescens* of Agricola and the *spiritus plasticus* of *Kircher*.

[21] Bauhinus, *Historia Novi et Admirabilis Fontis Balneique Bollensis in Ducato Wirtembergico . . .* (Montisbeligardi, 1598). Book IV: De Lapidibus variis, tam Bituminosis quam aliis, Cornu Ammonis, Conchite, Ctenite, Myite, aliisque figuratis, Astroite, Belemnite.

Joannes Bauhin (1541–1613), a physician of Würrtemberg and brother of the noted botanist Caspar Bauhin, described in 1598 *The Extraordinary Fountain and Bath at Bollen*, including descriptions of many invertebrate fossils from the Posidonomya shales. Like Kentmann, Bauhin made no inquiry as to the nature of the fossils.

[22] Büttnerus, *Coralliographia Subterranea*, Chap. 1, paragraph 7, pp. 3–4.

[23] Baieri, *Oryktographia Norica, sive Rerum Fossilium*, Chap. 5, p. 31. Baier states, regarding the *lusus naturae:*

"When I employ the expression Jest of Nature [*lusus naturae*], and assert that certain figured stones originate therefrom, it is emphatically not to be thought that, after the manner of superstitious vulgarity, I am conjuring up some agent distinct from God, which in this universe and especially on our globe of earth and water, directs and modifies corporeal creatures, sometimes toying idly with them, often fashioning absurdities and monstrosities, something that could be regarded as a distinct feature of the formation of the stones. This only do I intend, that I be free to designate by the term Jest of Nature, what others ordinarily mean by it; that is, an ignorance of the genuine origin and cause (in this place) of the figures in certain stones. In this category, therefore, should be placed all those stones which either display a unique figure or, if they imitate the forms of other bodies, exhibit them somewhat less than perfectly, and rather fall short in bulk or extension or some other characteristics, so that they can in no way be shown to have received their origin from the things to which they are somehow likened."

Joannes Jacob Baier (1677–1735), the Altdorf Professor and defender of comparative vertebrate anatomy, described in his *Oryctography of Norica* (the area around Nuremberg) many of the invertebrate fossils of the region. Baier considered the Mosaic Deluge responsible for fossils.

[24] The *Synodus Germanica* (*Premier concile national Germanique*) was held under the direction of Caroloman, ruler of Austrasia, Allemannia (now Schwabia), and Thuringia, in the year 742. Its purpose was to improve the religious situation of Caroloman's empire.

Canon V of the Synod is directly concerned with pagan practices:

"Decrevimus ut secundum canones, unusquisque episcopus in sua parochia sollicitudinem, adjuvante gravione, qui defensor Ecclesiae est, ut populus Dei paganias non faciat, sed ut omnes spurcitias gentilitatis abjiciat et respuat, sive sacrificia mortuorum, sive sortilegos vel divinos, sive phylacteria et auguria, sive incantationes sive hostias immolatitias, quas stulti homines juxta ecclesias ritu pagano faciunt sub nomine sanctorum martyrum vel confessorum, Deum et suos sanctos ad iracundiam provocantes: sive illos sacrilegos ignes, quos neid fyr [Nied fyr, nied feor, niedfies, niedfrs, nejdfyr, nidfrs, nedfrs, nedfratres, needfire] vocant, sive omnes, quaecumque sint, paganorum observationes diligentes prohibeant."

[25] The *Synodus Liptinensis* (*Concile de Leptinnes* or *Estinnes*) was also held in the kingdom of Caroloman, in the year 743. Canon VI of the Synod prescribes the fine for pagan practices: "Decrevimus quoque, quod et pater meus ante praecipiebat, ut qui paganas observationes in aliqua re fecerit, mulctetur et damnetur XV solidis." Possibly the best source for information regarding both of the above is to be found in: Hefele, Charles-Joseph, *Histoire des Conciles d'Après Les Documents Originaux*, Vol. III, Part 2 (Paris: Letouzey et Ane, 1910).

[26] See note 3 to this chapter.

[27] *Sensus interni* or internal senses, in scholastic philosophy, are four in number: imagination (*phantasia*), sense memory (*memoria sensitiva*) synthetic sense (*sensus communis*), and instinct (*vis aestimativa*). They are called senses because their object is concrete (as opposed to abstract) beings; and they are referred to as internal because they do not have peripheral receptors, but receive their data from the findings of the five external senses.

Species impressa, or impressed species, as understood by the scholastics, is the impression made upon the sense by an object contacting it. The ensuing response of the sense, in the form of an internally produced image for the purpose of contemplating the object in a manner wholly adapted to the sense, is called the *species expressa*, or expressed species.

[28] *Panspermia*, or the Universal Seed, was one of the very popular "causative forces" of the seventeenth- and eighteenth-century savants. It was by definition "a sort of material spirit, or spirit composed of a more subtle portion either of the celestial mist [*coelestis aurae*] or of the elements." It was, more precisely, a spirituous sulphuro-salino-mercurial vapor created at the same time as the elements. While the Universal Seed did not actually consist of sulfur, mercury, and salt, its power was thought to reside especially in those chemicals.

This seed was not conceived to be alive or animate, "as is proper to vegetative and sensitive nature, but is such as inanimate bodies require for their increment and continuous propagation." Nor was it believed that metals and minerals were, strictly speaking, generated from seed, but rather in that "manner which is in keeping with the generation of fossils," which was by a "magnetic motion whereby like bodies are called to like, run together, and, by a strange consent, are united." *Panspermia* was divinely provided with two natural properties needed for the formation of things: a plastic power (*virtus plastica*) and a magnetic force (*virtus magnetica*). The first of these was thought to "confer upon its species its form, figure and color," while the second gave "to each the power to attract its like." The conception of the *Panspermia* went so far as to lead Kircher, in his *Mundus Subterraneus*, Book XII, Section i, Chap. 1, p. 349 (from which part of the above account was taken) to conclude: "Any composite body of whatever kind, if we scrutinize it accurately, will be found to be in itself nothing else than this Universal Seed which, in a particular composite has, with the remote coöperation of the elements, reduced itself to an individual of such and such a species."

CHAPTER IV

[1] See Chap. III, note 24.

[2] See Chap. III, note 25.

[3] See Chap. XI, pages 86–87.

[4] Antonii Van Dale, *Historia de Silentio Oraculorum Paganismi* ([Brunswisck]: Typis Engmannianis, 1725).
The celebrated opponent of Van Dale and Fontenelle was J. F. Balthus, who gave expression to his disdain anonymously in a work titled: *Response à L'Histoire des Oracles, de Mr. De Fontenelle, de l'Académie Française. Dans laquelle on réfute le Système de Mr. Van-Dale, sur les Auteurs des Oracles du Paganisme, sur la cause et le temps de leur silence; et où l'on établit le sentiment des Pères de l'Église sur le même sujet.* (Strasbourg: Jean Renauld Doulssecker, 1707.) For an exceptionally fine and critical analysis of these see: Fontenelle, Bernard Le Bovierde, *Histoire des Oracles*, Edition Critique, ed. Louis Maigron (Paris: Edouard Cornely et Cie., 1908).

[5] See Chap. II, pp. 35–37.

CHAPTER V

[1] Andreas Libavius, *Singularium pars Tertia Continens Octo Libros Bituminum et Affinium* (Francofurti, 1601).

CHAPTER VI

[1] Büttner, *Coralliographia Subterranea* (Lipsiae, 1714), Chap. 1, page 7: *"Viri coetera doctissimi ac laboriosissimi."*

[2] See Appendix C.

[3] Mercati, *Metallotheca Opus Posthumum* (Romae, 1717), Armarium Nonum ("Lapides Idiomorphi id est peculiari forma discreti"), Chap. 2 (Notae by Assalti), p. 220.

[4] *. . . ac varia humorum crasis. . . . crasis, -is f.* A constitution, temperature, or mixture of natural humors. (Robert Ainsworth, *Thesaurus Linguae Latinae compendiarius. . . .*)

[5] Mercati, *op cit.*, Armarium Nonum, Chap. 2 (Notae by Assalti), p. 221.

[6] A similar idea is supported by Fabio Columna, who argues for the organic nature of fossils from the axiom: *Natura nihil facit frustra*—not being able to be-

lieve that Nature ever made teeth without a jaw, or shells without an animal inhabitant. He fell prey to dogma and accepted them as *reliquiae diluvianae.*

[7] Mercati, *op. cit.,* Armarium Nonum, Chap. 2 (Notae by Assalti), p. 221.

[8] See Chap. III, note 3.

CHAPTER VII

[1] To understand the workings of the lapidifying juice one must call upon the writings of Georgius Agricola (Bauer), the first to clearly set forth the concept of a *succus lapidescens,* or *spiritu petrifico.*

Agricola (1494–1555), while not directly concerned with fossils, being occupied with geology, mining, and mineralogy, held that the *succus lapidescens* was responsible for stones, to which group fossils were admitted. In his celebrated *De Ortu et Causis Subterraneorum* he remarks:

"It is now necessary to review in a few words what I have said as to all of the material from which stones are made; there is first of all mud; next juice which is solidified by severe cold; then fragments of rock; afterward stone juice [*succus lapidescens*], which also turns to stone when it comes out into the air; and lastly, everything which has pores capable of receiving a stony juice. . . . But it is now necessary that I should explain my own view, omitting the first and antecedent causes. Thus the immediate causes are heat and cold; next in some way a stony juice. For we know that stones which water has dissolved, are solidified when dried by heat; and on the contrary, we know that stones which melt by fire, such as quartz, solidify by cold. For solidification and the conditions which are opposite thereto, namely, dissolving and liquefying, spring from causes which are the opposite to each other. Heat, driving the water out of a substance, makes it hard; and cold, by withdrawing the air, solidifies the same stone firmly. But if a stony juice, either alone or mixed with water, finds its way into the pores either of plants or animals . . . it creates stones. . . . If stony juice is obtained in certain stony places and flows through the veins, for this reason certain springs, brooks, streams, and lakes, have the power of turning things to stone." (Agricola, *De Re Metallica,* tr. by H. C. and L. H. Hoover [New York: Dover Publications, 1950], pp. 49–51. The reader is referred to the notes and appendixes of this work for detailed analysis of the thoughts of Agricola.)

Agricola's *succus lapidescens* became the heritage of Mattioli and Falloppio. It was not long-lived as an entity, being subdivided and incorporated into later hypotheses.

One of these was suggested as late as the late eighteenth century, by François Jean Marquis de Chastellux (1734–1788). The Marquis visited America between 1780 and 1782, where he found time to visit the American Museum of Pierre Eugene Du Simitiere, at Philadelphia. In Du Simitiere's cabinet he saw a number of fossils which led him to speculate: "It appears clear to me, that these petrefactions are formed by the successive accumulation of lapidific molecules conveyed by the waters, and assimilated by the assistance of fixed air" (Chastellux, *Travels in North America* [New York, 1828], p. 111).

[2] Mercati, *Metallotheca Opus Posthumum,* Armarium Nonum, Chap. 2 (Notae by Assalti), pp. 220–224.

[3] Langius, *Tractatus de Origine Lapidum Figuratorum,* Book II, Part 1, p. 42.

Lang is confusing on this point, as he appears to have been neither an animalculist, nor an ovist, *sensu strictu.* See chap. III, note 4, and Appendix C, note 32.

[4] Mercati, *op. cit.*, Armarium Nonum, Chap. 2 (Notae by Assalti), p. 221.

In this Assalti is not entirely correct. Lang would have, perhaps, allowed independent development of either spermatoza or ova, but not so Lhwyd. Lhwyd was an avowed animalculist, though he often dealt with fossils in a broad sense. The problem of the preformationist movement is briefly discussed in Appendix C, note 32.

[5] Langius, *op. cit.*, Book II, Part 1, p. 37.

The concept here described is reminiscent of the hypothesis of Pangenesis, suggested by Maupertius in the eighteenth century and developed by Samuel Butler (1879) and later by Semon (1904). Darwin himself proposed, in 1868, a "provisional hypothesis of pangenesis."

[6] The expression ". . . *a partialibus peripateticorum formis*" is a misleading allusion to the Aristotelian theory known as hylemorphism, which proposes that all material beings are ultimately reducible to two principles: prime matter (totally indeterminate, but determinable to any kind of body) and substantial form (that element which determines prime matter to a specific body). There is a snide note in Beringer's allusion here, which suggests that he was not a wholly dedicated Aristotelian.

[7] A Bufonite is described by Leigh in his *Natural History of Lancashire* . . . (see Appendix A and Chap. III, note 19), as well as by Lhwyd in his letter to Ray (see notes 34 and 39 of Appendix C). Two Bufonites are figured by Beringer on Plates II and V.

[8] Langius, *op. cit.*, Book II, Chap. 1: *De Generatione viventium in genere, eorum aura seminali* (pp. 36–45); Chap. 2: *De generatione, quae potissimum a Lapidibus Figuratis repraesentantur* (pp. 45–49); Chap. 3: *De Nutritione et accretione testaceorum, et in qua materia haec potissimum fiat* (pp. 40–56); Chap. 5: *De viventibus a substantia lapidum longe alienis et tamen intra saxa natis* (pp. 58–69); Chap. 6: *De corporibus testaceis in substantia a testa et lapide longe aliena generatis* (pp. 60–62).

[9] Mercati, *op. cit.*, Armarium Nonum, Chap. 2 (Notae by Assalti), p. 222.

CHAPTER VIII

[1] *strombus, -i* (m). Elongated conches of the sea, who purport, according to Pliny, to have a leader whom they follow as their king. Their medicinal qualities are as amazing as their social organization, for Pliny informs us in Book XXXII, Chaps. 30, 39, and 46, of the use of *strombi* as curatives for:

(1) Pains in the liver, when taken with honied wine and water, in equal quantities, or if there are signs of fever, with hydromel.

(2) Lethargy, when left to putrefy in vinegar, since they act as an excitant upon lethargic patients by their smell. They are also quite useful in the cure of cardiac diseases.

(3) Women suffering from hysterical suffocations, upon whom the odor of *strombi* putrefying in vinegar acts as an excitant.

In Part II, Class IV, page 38, of his *Methodus Nova et Facilis Testacea Marina Pleraque* . . . (Lucernae, 1722), Lang gives the following description of strombs: "Strombs are marine conches with remarkably elongated mouth and point, while the base spiral is notably narrower than in the Triton shell."

[2] Scheuchzer would this same year (1726) discover and publish on the skeleton of a human witness to the Deluge: *Homo diluvii testis*—adding to his commentary a couplet which has outlasted the work:

Betrübtes Beingerust von einem alten Sünder
Erweiche, Stein, das Herz der neuen Bosheitskinder.
which Herbert Wendt translates thus:
Afflicted skeleton of old, doomed to damnation
Soften, thou stone, the hearts of this wicked generation!

[3] Langius, *Tractatus de Origine Lapidum Figuratorum*, Book I, Chap. 9, p. 30.

[4] Mercati, *op. cit.*, Armarium Nonum, Chap. II (Notae by Assalti), pp. 222-223 [misnumbered 123].

[5] Scheuchzer, *Herbarium Diluvianum* (Tiguri, 1709). The "*Disputant inter se Chronologi, quo Mense acciderit Diluvium?*" is discussed by Scheuchzer in several sections of his *Herbarium Diluvianum*. He dissects at length the various possibilities, especially in Tab. I, pp. 8–10, and Tab. V, p. 16.

Woodward in his *Essay towards a Natural History of the Earth*, p. 164, notes that "the Deluge commenc'd in the Spring-season: the Water coming forth upon the Earth in the Month which we call May."

[6] Among the photographs of the originals of Beringer's "Lügensteine" the apricot was not found (figured on his Plate VI).

CHAPTER IX

[1] See note 3 to this chapter.

[2] Kircherus, *Mundus Subterraneus, in XII Libros digestus* (3d edition, 1678), Book VIII, Part 1, Chap. 10, pp. 40–41.

[3] Büttner, *Coralliographia Subterranea*, Chap. 1, Sections 9–12, pp. 5–13.

While Beringer refers only to Sections 9 to 12, Sections 7 and 8 have been included here to provide a suitable context for those four cited.

SECTION 7

"As though the majestic and most grave Maker would indulge in idle sport in his wholly active and actual arrangement and direction of the natural order, by at times permitting this direction to be defective. Indeed, this order, whether in all sincerity you call it *Archaeus* or the World Spirit or *Natura Naturans* or *Natura Naturata*, depends solely upon the most efficacious mind and will of the all-wise and inflexible Deity; of itself it intends nothing, nor, being mindless, can it intend, direct or effect anything. Therefore, let these bold assertors know with proper fear, especially such as glory in the Christian name, that as many idle jests as are charged to nature, so many are imputed to the most grave Orderer, while by their assertion of jests they furnish the materials for idolatry. What is more, they foster belief in Apollo and the Muses of the Pyrrhine ring and the numbering of them with these jests of crucifixes, etc., and rashly cause God himself to be reckoned as the fashioner of those idols as well as of these crucifixes.

SECTION 8

"Not for a moment do I deny that this order is disturbed and hindered when our globe of earth and water is ravaged by lethal cataclysms, or even that it is obstructed in the more proximate causes, as is shown by the numerous phenomena which even learned men, floundering on the common, unlettered level, designate erroneously as jests. Yet not even in the wake of this disturbance and confusion must the economy of nature be accused of frolicking. Strictly speaking, nature never jests, though it appears to jest to those who, with as little ingenuousness as the protagonists of occult qualities, shrink from admitting their ignorance, preferring instead to label the unobservable causes of phenomena as nature's frolics, lest they seem to be remiss in their philosophical productivity. Nature acts in earnest because it acts of necessity, even in causes which are disturbed, differently disposed, delayed, obstructed, and hence not productive of ordinary and regular effects. This is abundantly evident from what is taught of monstrosities of the animal and plant kingdoms. Indeed, there is in that refuge of pantomimists, the dendrite, a certain disposition comprising an agent acting of necessity and an apt matter, according to which, thus and not otherwise, there can be formed a chorolith or dendrite proper, quite evidently distinct from lithophytes.

Cfr. *Herbarium Diluvianum*, p. 17, et seq. by the excellent Swiss physician, Master Scheuchzer.

SECTION 9

"However, I must exercise a certain generosity of mind, lest the paegmosynophiles [frolic enthusiasts] accuse me of sweeping dissension. With the most learned philosopher and physician, Master Joann Jacob Beyer [Baier], celebrated professor of Altdorf (*Oryctograph. Noric.*, p. 31) and other philosophical notables who employ the term jest in its mere popular sense, I confess and acknowledge the existence of jest. THERE IS JEST [*LUDITUR*], I emphatically state, THERE IS JEST. But at whose feet is the fiction to be laid? Nature's? I decline. Human fancy abusing human sight? Here I take my stand. It is fancy, shorn of judgement, distrait, even gullible, not to mention farcical.

SECTION 10

"THERE IS JEST when the ordering, the course and the effect, differently predisposed, of causes, or even—and this is not uncommon—an ordinary effect, elude the frolic merchants, and these seize upon something occult which, in their simplicity, they hold up to marvel.

SECTION 11

"THERE IS JEST when the imagination is deceived and deceives by mere appearances. When the frolic merchants swear that they have seen with their own two eyes (though they have no cowitnesses) stars with long tresses, armored clouds, equestrian clouds in combat, or as coffins, clouds of brushwood, and in the midst of them, Morbona [one of the Four Horsemen of the Apocalypse, probably Pestilence] harvesting with a sickle, *den Tod mit einer Sense*, and what not?! And in great agitation they prate about these nonsenses from door to door.

SECTION 12

"THERE IS JEST when they discern in metal poured into water, in sputum on the pavement, but especially in stones of mixed matter, such as marble, agate, etc., *Orbes, urbes, cruces, duces, coronas, corinnas, lectores, lictores, Apollinem, Apellem, Moysen, Musas, Lyras, Lares, pontifices, pannifices, littora, literas, numulos, numeros* [see below]—and when they imperiously command others to see them. Particularly do they pay superstitious, not to say blasphemous, homage to the Godhead when what they seem to see bears a similarity to some religious narrative: a similarity, indeed, such as exists between *ovum* and *ovis*. This is the error of Kircher, a man otherwise of profound learning, and adopted by the author of the Disputation on Figures of Sundry Things in Stones."

Kircher. *Mund. Subterran.* Book IIX [sic], Section I, Chap 9. Autor disput . . . , Chap. II, Section 54.

In the foregoing paragraph, in which a lengthy passage is quoted in Latin, the play on words is lost in translation; in English the phrase reads: "orbs and cities, crosses and dukes, crowns and Corinnas, lectors and lictors, Apollo and Apelles, Moses and Muses, lyres and *Lares*, pontifs and clothmakers, shores and letters, coins and numbers."

[4] Kircher devotes little space to dendrites in his *Mundus Subterraneus* (Editio Tertia), and discusses them primarily in Book VIII. According to *Scheuchzer* (*Sciagraphia Lithologica Curiosa, seu Lapidum Figuratorum Nomenclator* [Ge-

dani: Thomas Johannis Schreiberi, 1740], p. 41) dendrites are stone, usually fissured and impressed with the likenesses of shrubs, leaves, and flowers, and belong properly to the class of plant fossils. Dendroides, however, are stones exhibiting various sketches of shrubs drawn on them by Nature's pencil, these shrubs having nothing in common with natural plants.

No mention could be found in Kircher of the Eichstad dendrites. See Kircher, *Mundus Subterraneus* (Editio Tertia), Book VIII, Section 1, Chap. 9, pp. 32, 42–43; Section 3, Chap. 6, pp. 84, 88.

[5] Scheuchzer, *Herbarium Diluvianum*, Tab. VI, pp. 17–25.

[6] *. . . unde Naturae, ludere aut ludendo pigere volenti, Kircheriani sales et tincturae defecerunt.*

CHAPTER X

[1] Kircher, *Mundus Subterraneus* (3d ed., 1678), Book 8; Section 1, Chap. 8, p. 23.

[2] The Tolfens Lithographs were figured thus by Kircher in Book 8, p. 23 of his *Mundus Subterraneus:*

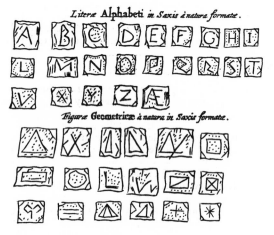

[3] Mercati, *Metallotheca Opus Posthumum*, Armarium Nonum, Loculo VIII, Chap. 12 (Notae by Assalti), p. 239.

[4] The *grammatiae* (*mono-* and *poly-grammos*) are to be found in Book 37, Chap. 37 ("The Iaspis"). The Iaspis, or meadow-green jasper, according to Pliny exists in fourteen varieties, one of which "resembles the *smaragdus* [emerald] in color, and is often found with a white line running transversely through the middle—in which case it is known as *monogrammos* [single-lined], but when streaked with several lines, is called *polygrammos* [many-lined]."

[5] The *Smaragdus* [emerald] with all its attributes is described in Pliny, Book 37, Chaps. 16–18.

[6] Langius, *Historia Lapidum Figuratorum Helvetiae ejusque viciniae*, Book II, Section 5, p. 42.

[7] Helwing, *Lithographiae Angerburgicae*, Part II (Lipsiae, 1720), Chap. 2, pp. 36–51.

[8] Helwing, *Lithographica Angerburgica*, Part I (Lipsiae, 1717), Chap. 5, paragraph 9, pp. 33–37, and Tab. XI.

[9] Helwing, *ibid.*, pp. 33–34. I.C.W.: No key to initials given by Helwing. E.A.G.V.L.: Ernst Ahasversus Graf von Lehndorff. G.E.V.L.: Gerhard Ernst von Lehndorff. L.V.R.: Ludwig von Rauter.

[10] Helwing, *op. cit.*, Part II (Lipsiae, 1720), Chap. 2, paragraph 7, pp. 46–48.

[11] Philip Ernest Christfels (Christfelss) was an eighteenth-century scholar of religion. On his conversion to Christianity in 1701, at the age of 28, he changed his name from Mardochaeus to that by which he is today solely known, Christfels. His best-known works, both published after the *Lithographiae Wirceburgensis*, are:

> *Gespräch (zweytes Gespräch, drittes Gespräch) in dem Reiche der Todten über die Bibel und Talmud, zwischen dem seeligen Herrn Doctor Luther und . . . R. Salomon Jarchi . . . zusammengetragen von einem bekandten Gerzedek P. E. C., und mit einer Vorrede versehen von Herrn J. H. Engerer . . .* (Schwabach: Roth, 1737–1739)

> *Emunah Hadashah shel Hayehudim, oder das Neue Judenthum . . . Nebst einer Vorrede . . . G. G. Zeltners* (Onolzbach, 1735).

[12] The Book of Sohar (Libri Sohar or Zohar) is a cabalistic commentary on the pentateuch, compiled or written by the Spanish cabalist Moses de Leon (d. 1305). It contains a complete cabalistic theosophy, treating of God, the cosmogony and cosmology of the universe, the soul, sin, redemption, etc.

[13] Helwing, *op. cit.* (1717), Dedication.

[14] *Schilte Hagiborim*, or *Shilte ha-Giborum (Clypei fortuim Antiquitates . . .)* by Abraham ben David de Partaleone [in Hebrew] (Mantua, 1612). [*Sacred Archeology, being a description of the Holy Temple, followed by readings in commemoration of the sacerdotal Service.*]

CHAPTER XI

[1] Beringer here is doubtless making reference to Dr. Johann Jonston's *Thaumatographia Naturalis, In Classis decem divisa: in quibus Admiranda Coeli, Elementorum, Meteororum, Fossilium, Plantarum, Avium, Quadrupedum, Exangvium, Piscium, Hominis* (Amsterdami: Apud Guilielmum Blaev, 1632).

[2] Conrad Gesner (1516–1565), author of the celebrated *De Rerum Fossilium, lapidium et gemmarum figuris* (Tiguri, 1565–1566), had no certain theory concerning the origin of fossils. Some he regarded as *sui generis*, others as the organic remains of plants and animals.

[3] Of the three mythical beasts only the *Hircocervus* is not classical. The *Hircocervus* or *hirgui Tallus* (= *hirci* + *Tallus*) was a fabulous animal compounded of goat and stag. It springs from the pages of the medieval bestiaries rather than any theology of antiquity—it appears in the years 1159 and 1365. See J. H. Baxter and Charles Johnson, *Medieval Latin Word List* (London: Humphrey Milford, 1934), p. 204.

[4] The significance of "soft soil" acting on the production of "fossil bodies" is particularly discussed in Steno's *Elementorum Myologiae Specimen . . . cui accedunt Canis Carchariae Dissectum Caput . . .* (Florentiae: sub signo Stellae, 1667). The following is taken from "Conjuncture I," as translated by Axel Garboe in *The Earliest Geological Treatise . . .* (London, 1958).

"The soil from which the bodies resembling parts of animals are dug out does not seem to produce these bodies today.

"As for the soft soil, since these bodies are the softer and withstand touching less the deeper they are hidden, there is little likelihood that the soil produces them, but rather that it destroys them. Nor should anybody believe that they are softer because they are not yet full grown; for the things that are soft while being formed keep their parts together by something glue-like (as may be seen in the soft shells of young pine seeds and almonds), but these bodies lack every sort of glue-like substance and crumble into dust, and so their softness seems to indicate decay, not growth. It cannot be argued against this that their number seems to increase in the surface of the soil; for this is due to the rain that washes away the soil between them. On the contrary, when the substance of those that are on the surface is easily rubbed to a powder, this is proof that their decay, begun in the soil, has been interrupted by the intervention of the rain" (Garboe, pp. 11–13).

[5] A figure which may be interpreted as representing a dragon may be seen among the photographs of the original "Lügensteine"; see illustrations.

[6] No attempt has been made to identify the practices listed by Beringer. The interested reader is referred to the following works:

J. G. Frazer, *The Golden Bough* (13 vols.) (3d ed.; New York, 1935).

Charles-Joseph Hefele, *Histoire des Conciles d'Après les Documents Originaux* (Paris, 1910).

[7] Tomasini (Iacobi Philippi), *De Donariis ac Tabellis votivis liber singularis* (Utini: N. Schiratti, 1639).

[8] Averrunci gods were the averting deities of antiquity.

[9] Kircher, *Oedipus Aegyptiacus. Hoc est Universalis Hieroglyphicae Veterum Doctrinae temporum iniuria abolitae Instavratio. Opus ex omni Orientalium doctrina et Sapientia Conditum, nec non viginti diuersarum linguarum authoritate stabilitum, Felicibus* . . . (Romae: Vitalis Mascardi, 1654). Vol. III, Syn. xix, pp. 518–529. Syntagma xix is divided into six chapters as follows:

Chap. 1. *De variis Aegyptorum Amuletis, et Periaptis.*
Chap. 2. *De Amuletis quae Deorum et Sacrorum animalium formam referunt.*
Chap. 3. *De mixte et monstruosae rationis Amuletis.*
Chap. 4. *De Scarabaeis prophylacticis.*
Chap. 5. *Phylacterium lapideum ex Museo Clarissimi Viri Iacobi Scaphili.*
Chap. 6. *De humani Corporis partibus in usum Periaptorum ab Aegyptiis assumptis.*

See also Vol. II: Part 2, Class XI, Chap. 4 ("De Statuis Talesmatis, et Prophylacticis Aegyptiorum; item de Execrandis, quae dictis Sacris interueniebant operationibus").

[10] Kircher, *ibid.*, pp. 523–526. One of the four scarabs was figured thus:

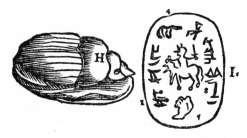

[11] Pignorius, Laurentius, *Vetusissimae Tabulae Aeneae Sacris Aegyptiorum*

Simulachris coelatae Accurata Explicatio, in qua antiquissimarum superstitionum Origines, Progressiones, Ritus ad Barbarum, Graecam, Romanamque Historiam illustrandam enarrantur, et multa Scriptorum veterum loca qua explanantur, qua emendantur . . . (Venetiis: Io. Anto. Rampazettus, 1605). The running heads read: *Mensae Isiacae Expositio.*

[12] Kircher, *Oedipus Aegypticus*, Vol. III, "Anacephaleosis Totius Operis," pp. 551–590. (Beringer refers to Chap. I, pp. 552 ff.)

[13] Kircher, *Oedipus Aegyptiacus,* Vol. I, Syn. IV (*Pantheon Hebraeorum*), Chap. 3 ("De Theraphim primis Hebraeorum Idolis"), pp. 254–262.

[14] Kircher, *ibid.,* p. 260.

[15] Kircher, *ibid.,* p. 261. Accompanying the text is a figure of the Theraphim, with only the tongue protruding and covered with mystic symbols.

[16] Langius, *Historia Lapidum Figuratorum,* Book IV, Part 1 ("Ammonis Cornua quid sint"), pp. 74–75.

[17] Langius refers to Pliny, Book 31, Chap. 10. However, this citation is incorrect, for Book 31, Chap. 10, is titled: "Waters which Color the Human Body." The correct citation is Book 37, Chap. 60.

[18] Langius says regarding the *ammonis cornua* (p. 74): "Ammonites [*Ammonis Cornua*] are coiled figured stones, convoluted after the manner of serpents, so that their circles do not have any point of inception. This is their principal characteristic.

"That this stone was known in very ancient times is testified by Pliny, Book 31 [37], Chapter 10 [60], who classifies it as a gem in these words: 'The ammonite [*Hammonis Cornu*] is one of the most sacred gems of Ethiopia, golden in color and resembling a ram's horn. It is guaranteed to inspire wholly divine dreams.' It usually has a protective outer coating of iron hue which when rubbed with liquid alum turns to a brassy or golden color, as is easily effected in the case of iron. It is called a horn because it is twisted in the manner of a ram's horn, and ammonite possibly because it abounds in the sandy soil around the majestic temple of Jupiter Ammon erected by Bacchus in thanksgiving for his having found a fountain in Libya after following a ram which he believed to be Jupiter, as we read in Polyhist. Jul. Solini, Chap. 27 [39]. There [at the Temple of Ammon] it is said of this stone that they call it the horn of Ammon for it is twisted and bent so as to resemble the horn of a ram. It is of golden color and reputed to produce quite divine dreams when placed under the head of a sleeper. On the other hand it may have been so named in order that the discoverers of this stone, which they regard as a gem, and to which heathen superstition has perhaps ascribed very many other powers, might the more effectively advertise its supposed divine qualities and recommend it to the imagination of men by gracing it with a divine name."

[19] Kircher, *Oedipus Aegyptiacus,* Vol. II, Part 1, Class V (*Cabala Saracenica.*), pp. 362–400. Class V is divided into nine chapters as follows:

Chap. 1. *De Cabale Saracenicae Origine.*

Chap. 2. *De mystico Alphabeto Arabum Saracenorum.*

Chap. 3. *De Nominibus Divinis apud Mahumedanos visitatis.*

Chap. 4. *De nominibus Dei numerorum figuris exhibitis.*

Chap. 5. *De nominum divinorum, numerorumque quibus exhibentur, ad Planetas, et duodecim signa Zodiaci appropriatione.*

Chap. 6. *De structura mysticorum nominum, eorumque significatione.*

Chap. 7. *Fabrica et usus telesmatum, una cum refutatione.*

Chap. 8. *De numeris Pronicis.*

Chap. 9. *De varia transformatione nominum et literarum, in figuras varias.*

[20] Charts occur on pages 365, 366–367, 368, 372, 373, 377, 380–381, 382, 384, 385, 386, 387, 392, 397, and 399.

[21] Kircher, *Oedipus Aegyptiacus*, Vol. II, Part 1, Class IV ("Cabala Hebraeorum"), pp. 210–360. Class IV is divided into ten chapters, beginning with a chapter entitled: *De Kabalae defintione, et diuisione,* and proceeding through a minute and scholarly examination of the cabala.

[22] The resulting figure resembles, when viewed from thumb-side, a Star of David.

CHAPTER XII

[1] Beringer probably refers to the Honorable Georg von Eckhart (Eccard), Privy Councillor and Librarian to the Court and the University of Würzburg, and J. Ignatz Roderick (Roderique), Professor of Geography, Algebra, and Analysis, who were later charged with having been responsible for the manufacture of the "Lügensteine." In Appendix B the problems of Beringer's life and career are discussed more fully.

[2] According to the Archival Transcripts of Würzburg, Roderick did the actual carving of the figures.

[3] The carvings of the pomegranate and dragon are still in existence, and are figured in the illustrations to this edition.

[4] Beringer's account here is evidently incorrect, for only two of the three diggers were brothers, Niklaus and Valentin Hehn (aged 18 and 14 respectively). The third youth in Beringer's employ was Christian Zänger (aged 17 years).

[5] Plautus, *Curculio: or, the Forgery*, Act II, scene 3. In this scene Curculio, the parasite of Phaedromus (a rich young man in love with a young woman in the possession of Cappadox, an avaricious procurer), delivers these lines as the opening of a soliloquy.

CHAPTER XIII

[1] Aldrovandi, *De Animalibus Insectis Libri Septem cum Singulorum Iconibus ad viuum expressis* . . . (Bononiensis: Clementem Ferranium, 1638), Book V, Chap. 12 ("De Araneis"), pp. 600–632. Note especially pp. 605 and 618–622 ("Cura Demorsorum ab Araneis: Phalangiis et Tarantula").

[2] *Et cui alteri quam maleficae, si e naturalium animantium classe excludas?*

[3] Helwing, *Lithographica Angerburgica* (1717), Chap. 5, p. 35.

[4] Helwing, *ibid.,* p. 36.

[5] Helwing, *ibid.,* p. 35.

[6] Helwing, *ibid.,* p. 35.

[7] Helwing, *ibid.,* p. 36.

[8] Helwing, *ibid.,* pp. 35–36.

[9] The exact location of Beringer's reference in Spener and Büttner is uncertain, but the following seem probable: Spener, "Disquisitio de Crocodilo in Lapide . . . ," p. 110; Büttner, *Coralliographia Subterranea,* pp. 2–3.

[10] Beringer could be referring here to any number of works by either Lister or Bonnano (Buonanni). The following are the works by Lister and Bonnano treating molluscs, printed prior to 1726.

Lister, Martin, *Martini Lister Conchyliorum bivalvium utriusque aquae exercitatio anatomica tertia. Huic accedit Dissertatio medicinalis de calculo humano* . . . (Londini: sumptibus authoris impressa, 1696).

———, *Martini Lister Exercitatio anatomica. In qua de cochleis, maxime terrestribus et limacibut, agitur. Omnium dissectiones tabulis aeneis, ad ipsas res affabre incisis, illustrantur* . . . (Londini: Sumptibus Sam. Smith and Benj. Walford, 1694).

——, *Martini Lister . . . Historiae animalium Angliae, tres tractatus. Unus de araneis. Alter de cochleis tum terrestribus, tum fluviatilibus. Tertius de cochleis marinis. Quibus adjectus esta quartus de lapidibus ejusdem insulae ad cochlearum quandam imaginem figuratis* . . . (London: apud Joh. Martyn Regiae societatis typographum, 1678).

——, *Historiae conchyliorum liber 1–3, Appendix ad librum 3, liber 4* Appendix ad *librum 4* (Londini: Aere inicisa, sumptibus authoris, 1685–1692).

——, *Martini Lister Historiae sive synopsis methodicae conchyliorum quorum omnium picturae, ad vivum delineatae, exhibetur. Liber I–IV* . . . (Londini: Sumptibus authoris, 1685–1692).

Buonanni, Filippo, *Musaeum Kircherianum, sive Musaeum a P. Athanasio Kirchero in Collegio Romano Societatis Jesu iam pridem incoeptum nuper restitutum, auctum, descriptum, et iconibus illustratum . . . a P. Philippo Buonanni Societatis Jesu* (Romae: Typis G. Plachi, 1709).

——, *Observationes circa viventia, quae in rebus non viventibus reperiuntur. Cum Micrographia curiosa sive Rerum minutissimarum observationibus, quae ope microscopij recognitae ad viuum exprimuntur. His accesserunt aliquot animalium testaceorum icones non antea in lucem editae. Omnia curiosorum naturae exploratorum utilitati et iucunditati expressa et oblata . . . a patre Philippo Bonanni* . . . (Romae: Typis D. A. Herculis, 1691).

——, *Recreatio mentis, et oculi in observatione animalium testaceorum curiosis naturae inspectoribus italico sermone primum proposita a. p. Philippo Bonanno . . . Nunc denuo ab eodem latine oblata, centum additis testaceorum iconibus, circa quae varia problemata proponuntur* (Romae: ex typographia Varesij, 1684).

——, *Ricreatione dell'occhio e della mente nell'osseruation' delle chiocciole, proposta a 'curiosi delle opere della natura, dal P. Filippo Buonanni . . . Con quattrocento, e cinquanta figure di testacei diversi, sopra cui si spiegano molti curiosi problemi* (Roma: Per il Varese, 1681).

[11] It is interesting that Beringer should reserve mention of Lister for the end of his text, as Lister was perhaps the most outspoken defender of the supposition that fossils were *sui generis*, as was Woodward of the diluvial hypothesis.

Dr. Martin Lister (1638–1711), conchologist, physician (House Physician to Queen Anne from 1709 until his death), and Fellow of the Royal Society, disagreed with Woodward in his views regarding fossils, thereby incurring the enmity of Scheuchzer. With Plot, who concurred with his opinion, and Lhwyd, who did not, he remained on excellent terms, being correspondent to both Plot and Lhwyd and benefactor of the Old Ashmolean, as well as sponsoring, with eight other notables, Lhwyd's *Lithophylacii Britannici.*

Lister's views are among the last to be found in the literature maintaining fossils to be *lapides sui generis.* This opinion he clearly states in a paper communicated to the Royal Society in 1671 ("Fossil Shells in Several Places of England," *Phil. Trans.* VI (No. 76): p. 2,282 et seq.):

"We will easily believe (what I have read in Steno's *Prodromus*) that all along the Shores of the Mediterranean Sea, there may all Manner of Sea-Shells be found promiscuously included in Rocks or Earth, and at good Distances too from the Sea. But for our English inland Quarries, I am apt to think, there is no such Matter as petrifying of Shells in the Business: But that these Cockle-like Stones everywhere, as they are at present, *lapides sui Generis,* and never any Part of an Animal. It is most certain that our English Quarry shells (to

continue that abusive Name) have no Parts of a different Texture from the
Rock or Quarry where they are taken, that is, that there is no such Thing
as Shell in these Resemblances of Shells, but that Iron-Stone Cockles are all
Iron-stone; Lime or Marble, all Lime-stone or Marble; Sparre or Christalline-
Shells, all Sparre, &c. and that they were never any Part of an Animal."

Lister, in supporting the *sui generis* theory, was matching wits not only with
Woodward and Scheuchzer, but with a greater if more reserved adversary: Robert
Hooke, the celebrated microscopist and first Curator of Experiments to the Royal
Society.

Hooke (1635–1703) held that fossils were a record of past life, and represented
either organisms turned to stone or impressions left by such organism. The seventeenth observation ("Of Petrify'd wood, and other Petrify'd bodies") of his
Micrographia closes with the following remark (pp. 111–112):

"From all which, and several other particulars which I observ'd, I cannot
but think, that all these, and most other kinds of stony bodies which are found
thus strangely figured, do owe their formation and figuration, not to any kind
of Plastick virtue inherent in the earth, but to the Shells of certain Shel-fishes,
which, either by some Deluge, Inundation, Earthquake, or some such other
means, came to be thrown to that place, and there to be fill'd with some kind
of Mudd or Clay, or petrifying Water, or some other substance, which in
tract of time has been settled together and hardned in those shelly moulds
into those shaped substances we now find them; that the great and thin end
of these Shells by that Earthquake, or what ever other extraordinay cause
it was that brought them thither, was broken off; and that many others were
otherwise broken, bruised and disfigured; that these Shells which are thus
spirallied and separated with Diaphragmes, were some kind of Nautili or
Porcelane shells; and that others were shells of Cockles, Muscles, Periwincles,
Scolops, &c. of various sorts; that these Shells in many, from the particular
nature of the containing or enclos'd Earth, or some other cause, have in tract
of time rotted and mouldred away, and onely left their impressions, both on
the containing and contained substances; and so left them pretty loose one
within another, so that they may be easily separated by a knock or two of
a Hammer. That others of these Shells, according to the nature of the substances adjacent to them, have, by a long continuance in that posture, been
petrify'd and turn'd into the nature of stone, just as I even now observ'd several sorts of Wood to be. That oftentimes the Shell may be found with one
kind of substance within, and quite another without, having, perhaps, been fill'd
in one place, and afterwards translated to another, which I have very frequently observ'd in Cockle, Muscle, Periwincle, and other shells, which I
have found by the Sea side. Nay, further, that some parts of the same Shell
may be fill'd in one place, and some other caverns in another, and others in
a third, or a fourth, or a fifth place, for so many differing substances have I
found in one of these petrify'd Shells, and perhaps all these differing from the
encompassing earth or stone; the means how all which varieties may be caus'd,
I think, will not be difficult to conceive, to any one that has taken notice of
those Shells, which are commonly found on the Sea shore: And he that shall
throughly examine several kinds of such curiously form'd stones, will (I am
very apt to think) find reason to suppose their generation or formation to
be ascribable to some such accidents as I have mention'd, and not to any
Plastick virtue: For it seems to me quite contrary to the infinite prudence
of Nature, which is observable in all its works and productions, to design
everything to a determinate end, and for the attaining of that end, makes use

of such ways as are (as farr as the knowledge of man has yet been able to reach) altogether consonant, and most agreeable to man's reason, and of no way or means that does contradict, or is contrary to humane Ratiocination; whence it has a long time been a general observation and maxime, that Nature does nothing in vain; It seems, I say, contrary to that great Wisdom of Nature, that these prettily shap'd bodies should have all those curious Figures and contrivances (which many of them are adorn'd and contriv'd with) generated or wrought by a Plastick virtue, for no higher end then onely to exhibite such a form; which he that shall throughly consider all the circumstances of such kind of Figur'd bodies, will, I think, have great reason to believe, though, I confess, one cannot presently be able to find out what Nature's designs are. It were therefore very desirable, that a good collection of such kind of figur'd stones were collected; and as many particulars, circumstances, and informations collected with them as could be obtained, that from such a History of Observations well rang'd, examin'd and digested, the true original or production of all those kinds of stones might be perfectly and surely known; such as are Thunder-stones, Lapides Stellares, Lapides Judaici, and multitudes of other, whereof mention is made in Aldrovandus, Wormius, and other Writers of Minerals."

CHAPTER XIV

[1] In the second edition the plates were bound together at the end of Chapter XIV, not dispersed in the text as in the original edition. The collation of the first seven plates in the first edition is as follows:

Plate I   facing page 39.
Plate II   42.
Plate III   49.
Plate IV   54.
Plate V   58.
Plate VI   63.
Plate VII   65.

[2] *Tu nec cede malis, sed contra audentior ito.*

APPENDIX B

[1] Catalogue of a Portion of the Valuable Library from Dumfries House, Ayrshire. The Property of the Most Hon. the Marquess of Bute. The First Portion: The Important Collection of Mathematical and Scientific Books. (To be sold 3rd and 4th of July, 1961.)

[2] Wilhelm Engelmann in his *Bibliotheca Historico-Naturalis* (Leipzig, 1846) cites an evidently complete copy on page 585 ("cum annexis corollariis medicis etc., litteratorum disquisitioni submittit Geo. Ludov. Hueber.") While the work is cited in the catalogues of many famous libraries, it is mentioned in neither Casey Wood's *Introduction to the Literature of Vertebrate Zoölogy* (Oxford, 1931), which notes many of Beringer's contemporaries, nor de Margerie's *Catalogue des Bibliographies Géologiques*, (Paris, 1896).

[3] Georg Sticker, "Die Entwicklung der Medizinischen Fakultät an Der Universität Würzburg," *Festschrift zum 46. Deutschen Ärztetug in Würzburg.* Vom 6. Bis 10 (September, 1927), iii–v, 3–219. See especially 89–92.

[4] Franz X. von Wegele, *Geschichte der Universität Wirzburg* (Würtzburg, 1882), I, p. 411.

[5] Erhard, *De Belemnitis Suevicis Dissertatio*, Editio Altera (Lugduni Batavorum, 1727), pp. 24–25.

[6] Johann Gesner, *Tractatus Physicus de Petrificatis* (Lugduni Batavorum, 1758), p. 36.

[7] Gesner, *ibid.*, p. 36.

[8] James Parkinson, *Organic Remains of a Former World*, v. 1, (London, 1804), p. 26.

[9] The only reference to this story known to the present authors is an anonymous article in *Littell's Living Age* (vol. X [1846], pp. 181–182):

"Some youths, desirous of amusing themselves at the expense of Father Kircher, engraved several fantastic figures upon a stone, which they afterwards buried in a place where a house was about to be built. The workmen having picked up the stone while digging the foundation, handed it over to the learned Kircher, who was quite delighted with it, and bestowed much labor and research in explaining the meaning of the extraordinary figures upon it."

[10] See illustrations in this edition.

[11] See illustrations in this edition.

[12] Many of the stones have carved figures on both sides. The transcript speaks of the right and left sides, for which back or otherside has been substituted.

[13] Materialien zur Geschichte der Universtät Würzburg 7 und 16 (Universit. Bibl. Würzburg.).

[14] *Ibid.*

APPENDIX C

[1] An abstract of his argument, presumably written by himself, was published in the Cambridge Register.

[2] †Plot (Robert), *Nat. Hist. Oxon.*, p. 111.

[3] *Entrochi* (Cuthbert Beads or Fayry Stones) are the stems of Crinoids, or Sea Lilies. See Lhwyd, *Lithophylacii Britannici* (1760). Tab. 13:1141, 1153; Tab. 22:4; Tab. 25:1140, 1146.

[4] Steno, *De Solido Intra Solidum Naturaliter Contento* (1669), pp. 15–16, 58–59.

[5] III. Tertia causa, quo minus Diluvio haec deberi existimem, in eo praecipue constat, quod raro admodum, si unquam, animalium terrestrium ossa saxis inclusa reperiuntur; cum tamen ea non minus quam piscium expectare debuissemus, modo istaec Inundatio universalis saxis credidisset.

[6] *Ichthyodontium.* See Lhwyd, *op. cit.* (1760), pp. 63–76, Tab. 15.

[7] The last five lines are deleted, the next twelve being substituted.

[8] ‡Misson's *New Voyage to Italy.* Vol. II, p. 44.

In the fifth edition (1739) of the work, the only edition available to the present authors, the citation is to be found in volume 2:1, pp. 66–67:

"The Stones of *Tivoli* put me in Mind of a memorable Accident related by Alexander Tassoni, in his *Various Thoughts.* Not many Days ago, says that Author, the Workmen that were employed to dig Stone at *Tivoli*, having cleft a great Mass, found in the Middle of it an empty Space, in which there was a living *Crayfish*, that weighed four Pounds, which they boiled and did eat. I have read in another (Alexander ab Alexandro. Bapt. Fulgosus mentions a living Worm that was found in the Middle of a Flint.) Author, That he found a wrought Diamond in the Heart of a great Piece of Marble, and a considerable Quantity of sweet and odoriferous Oil in another Piece of the like Marble; which is less incredible. Tassoni also relates, That the same Year a Cat suckled a Rat in *Tivoli;* but before I employed my Time in reasoning upon such Sort of Facts, I would be sure of the Truth of them, by undoubted Proofs."

[9] The phrase in brackets, omitted in Lhwyd's manuscript, was taken from Ray's *Three Physico-Theological Discourses.*

[10] †Insert in your margin Brands words & quote ye page. Ray appended the following:

"A gentleman in the Parish of Dunresness in Zetland, told one of the Ministers of this Country, that about five years since, a Plough in this Parish did cast up fresh Cockles, though the place where the Plough was going was three quarters of a Mile from the Sea; which Cockles the Gentleman saw made ready and eaten. Brand's *Descript. of Orkney, Zetland,* &c. p. 115." [Brand, John. A Brief Description of Orkney, Zetland, Pightland-firth, and Caithness . . . Edinburgh, George Mosman, 1701.]

[11] †Steno. *prod.* p. 87. Edit. Angl. Lhwyd is referring to: H.O. [Henry Oldenberg?], *The Prodromus to a Dissertation Concerning Solids Naturally Contained within Solids* (London, 1671).

[12] †*Append. ad Tract. de Anim. Angl. & Conch. Anat. Part. Alt.* p. 243. [Lister, Martin. *Historiae Animalium Angliae Tres Tractatus. Unus de Araneis.* Alter de Cochleis . . . Londini: Apud Joh. Martyn, 1678.]

[13] †*Lith. Brit.* p. 96. Tab. 22. N. 2.

[14] Lhwyd, *ibid.* (1760), p. 96, division 3 "Lapis niger Piscis . . ."

[15] Olao Worm, *Museum Wormianum,* Section II: Chap. 1, p. 38: "Saxum Fissile Islebianum."

[16] †Vide *Lith. Br.* p. 15.

[17] Woodward describes his collection in his work: *An Attempt Towards a Natural History of the Fossils of England; In a Catalogue of the English Fossils in the Collection of J. Woodward, M.D. . . .* (London: F. Fayram, 1729).

[18] †*Ibid.* [*Lith. Br.*] Clas. 6. p. 44.

[19] Scheuchzer in his *Sciagraphia Lithologia Curiosa* (p. 51) describes the *Judaicus Lapis* (Jew Stone) as follows: "The Jew Stone properly speaking is a stone similar in appearance to an olive, somewhat rounded and elongated, with bare spots running along its length."

[20] †Plot, *Hist. Nat. Ox.* p. 125; *Lith. Brit.* Tab. 12 p. 1002, 1008. &c.

[21] This entire section was inserted into the translation by Lhwyd, and does not appear in either of the Latin versions. The next section (X) is, therefore, Section IX in the Latin versions.

[22] . . . hujusmodi nempe testacea interdum in animalium visceribus generari. Conchylia enim, cum aliis marinis, in terra nasci non majus videtur miraculum eadem in animalibus conscrescere.

[23] Pierce, Robert. "An Abstract of a Letter from Dr. [Robert] Pierce of Bath, to one of the S[ecretaries]. of the R[oyal]. S[ociety]. giving an account of a Shell found in one of the Kidneys of a Woman." *Phil. Trans.* XV: pp. 1,018-1,019.

[24] Woodward accounted for their being found at so great a depth in the "bowels of the earth" by endowing the waters of the Noachian Deluge with an almost universal solvent power by which he supposed the rocks and mountains were melted down, and thus admitted life into their internal parts. See Chap. III, note 19.

[25] Dr. Richard Richardson (1663-1741) was a Yorkshireman educated at Bradford School and at University College, where he took the degree of M.B., and the botanical course of Dr. Paul Herman at Leyden. Retiring to Bierley, he developed an extensive medical practice, and employed his spare time in writing to numerous correspondents, going on botanical excursions, and cultivating his flower garden,

greenhouse, and hothouse, "the second oldest in England" (Gunther, *op. cit.*, p. 265).

Richardson's observations on "mineral leavs" are largely confined to his extensive correspondence with such noted men as Edward Lhwyd. Lhwyd used this correspondence in the Epistola III of his *Lithophylacii Britannici Ichnographia*, entitled: "Summarium Literarum V.C.D. Richardi Richardson M.D. De Entrocho lapide, Conchitis, & Lithophytis seu Plantis mineralibus agri Eboracensis; de Bufonibus mediis Saxis inclusis, & depictis aliquot in Schisto carbonaria Insectis." Richardson's notes on twenty-three fossil plants are recorded by R. T. Gunther in *The Life and Letters of Edward Lhwyd*, where they are accompanied by his original drawings. Several papers by Richardson appeared in the *Philosophical Transactions* of the Royal Society of London (to which he was elected Fellow October 23, 1712).

[26] †(Jac.) Hartm[anni]. Hist. Succini Prus. p. 85. [Hartmann, Philip Jacob. Succincta Succini Prussici historia et demonstratio. Berolini, 1699 (also Londini, 1699).]

[27] †*Lith Brit.* Epist. iii [see note 25].

[28] Ray, John. *Three Physico-Theological Discourses, Concerning I. The Primitive Chaos, and Creation of the World. II. The General Deluge, its Causes and Effects. III. The Dissolution of the World, and Future Conflagration. Wherein are largely discussed, The Production and Use of Mountains; the Original of Fountains, of Formed Stones, and Sea-Fishes Bones and Shells found in the Earth; the Effects of particular Floods, and Inundations of the Sea; the Eruptions of Vulcano's; the Nature and Causes of Earthquakes* . . . (Fourth ed.; London: William Innys, 1732). (First Edition, 1692.)

[29] †*Lith Brit.* Tab. 13. no. 1270.

[30] †*Ib.* Tab. 16. n. 1505.

[31] †*Ib.* Tab. 21. n. 1675 & 1740 & Scheuchz. *Lith. Helvet.* T. 1. Fig. ii. [See Appendix A.]

[32] The first of his conjectures is that of the *occulta semina*, or so-called Spermatic Principle, derived from the animalculist faction of the preformationists. The animalculists regarded all embryos as being produced from the smaller embryos provided by the male in his spermatozoa. They asserted that they had seen exceedingly minute forms of men (homunculi), with arms, heads and legs complete, inside the spermatozoa under the microscope. Gautier, in his *Zoogénésie, ou Génération de l'homme et des animaux* (Paris, 1750), went so far as to say that he had seen a microscopic horse in the semen of a horse and a similar animalcule with very large ears in the semen of a donkey; finally, he described minute cocks in the semen of a cock. (See Needham, *A History of Embryology*, pp. 205–206.)

"Sir" John Hill, signing himself Abraham Johnson, satirized this same theory in his delightful tract of 1750, addressed to the Royal Society and its Fellows: *Lucina sina Concubitu.* Hill's treatment leads one through the singular discovery of animalcula ("of every Tribe originally formed by the almighty Parent") in the air, through the story of the impregnation of Mares by the West Wind, to the invention of a machine for their capture:

"Accordingly after much Exercise of my Invention, I contrived a wonderful cylindrical, catoptrical, rotundo-concavo-convex Machine (whereof a very exact Print will speedily be published for the Satisfaction of the curious, designed by Mr. H-y-n, and engraved by Mr. V-rtu) which being hermetically sealed at one End, & electrified according to the nicest Laws of Electricity, I erected it in a convenient Attitude to the West, as a kind of Trap to intercept the floating Animalcula in that prolific Quarter of the Heavens.

The Event answered my Expectation; & when I had caught a sufficient Number of these small, original, unexpanded Minims of Existence, I spread them out carefully like Silk-worm's Eggs upon white-paper, and then applying my best Microscope, plainly discerned them to be little Men and Women, exact in their Limbs and Lineaments, & ready to offer themselves little Candidates for Life, whenever they should happen to be imbibed with Air or Nutriment, and Conveyed down into the Vessels of Generation" (p. 13).

The powers of the *occulta semina* have already been discussed in several places in the text. It is not difficult to see, however, by what means it derived its miraculous power.

[33] †Write in ye margin Sr L.H.'s Note in the *Phil. Tran.* Ray inserted the following:
‡ "In those accurate Microscopial Observations communicated to the Royal Society by Sir. C.H. ["An Extract of some Letters sent to Sir C.H. relating to some Microspocal Observations. Communicated by Sir C.H. to the Publisher." *Phil. Trans.* XXIII (March–April, 1703), pp. 1, 357–1, 372.] we find this Note: . . . Some of them also may probably be originally Water Insects, or Fish, *sui generis*, and are small enough to be rais'd in Substance or in Spawn with the Vapours, and again to fall with the Rain, and may grow and breed again in Water when kept: And this will seem less strange to you, when I assure you that I have seen; and when I am so happy as to wait on you next, will shew Fishes, some as small as Cheese-Mites of different Sorts, very wonderfully made, which are of the Crustaceous Kind shell'd with many Joints, with very long Horns, fringed Tails, and have many Legs like Shrimps, &c. *Phil. Trans.* for March and April, 1703, p. 1366."

[34] Not only these, but Lhwyd mentions in a letter to John Ray dated February 30, 1691(-2) (Gunther, *Life and Letters of Edward Lhwyd*, Letter 48, pp. 156–160; See also Letter 44, pp. 152–153) that Richard Richardson found a toad in solid stone. The toad resembled in form and color the common toad, and when released from its prison "crawled about as long as the sun shone warm upon it, but towards night died."

[35] Robert Plot, first Keeper of the Ashmolean Museum and tutor of Lhwyd, first described the *Hippocephaloides* as follows:
"After those that concern Reptils, come we next to formed stones that resemble the parts of *four footed beasts*, whereof we meet with one sort in the Quarries at *Heddington*, set in the body of the stone, the most like to the head of a Horse of any thing I can think of; having the *ears*, and *crest* of the *mane* appearing between them, the places of the *eyes* suitable *prominent*, and the rest of the *face* entire, only the *mouth* and *nostrils* are absent in them all, as in Tab. 7. Fig. 1. These are plentifully enough found, and of divers cizes, yet not mention'd that I know of by any *Author*, whereof I have taken the boldness to fit them with a mane, and in imitation of other *Authors* (in the like case) shall call them *Hippocephaloides*." (Plot, *Nat. Hist. Oxfordshire*, paragraph 142, p. 127.)

Lhwyd in a letter to Martin Lister (Gunther, *op. cit.*, pp. 100–101) corrects several of Plot's genera, and refers the above to "a very elegant sort of *Conchites rugosus* [*Curvirostra rugosa, Lith. Brit.*, Number 709]."

The Otites are also described by Plot:
"Which by reason they so well resemble the Ears of a Man, though much less, as in *Tab.* 7. Fig. 12. I have made bold to call them *Otites*, or *Auriculares:* Of which we have plenty in the rubble Quarries near *Shotover*. . . . (Plot, *ibid.*, paragraph 150, p. 130.)

Lhwyd in the same letter describes the Otites, or Auricularia as "ye Operculum of an odde sort of Conchites" [*Lith. Brit.*, Number 517].

A description of the *Bucardites* is given by Plot on p. 127 of his *Nat. Hist. Oxfordshire* (see also *Lith. Brit.*, Numbers 646 and 812): "At *Heddington* in the same Quarry there are plenty of *Cardites*, or *stones* in the forms of *hearts*, but by *Authors*, because of their bigness, generally called *Bucardites*, or stones like *Bulls hearts* . . ." (Plot, *ibid.*, paragraph 143, p. 127).

[36] ‡Ray inserted the following note, although it does not appear in the Lhwyd MS.: "V. Plot's *Hist. Oxon.* p. 87 & *Lith. Brit.* Tab. 20. Num. 1658." Astroites are equivalent to Entrochi (see footnote 3).

[37] "As earth is more dense than water, so it generates forms which are proportionately more imperfect, and which are devoid of animals."

[38] ‡Ray has inserted here his own note: "See the *Works of the Learned* for the Month of Oct. 1703." The *Works of the Learned* (*Acta Eruditorum*) for October, 1703, seems to contain nothing directly pertinent to "a certain Vegetable Growth" of shell-stones. Following are the two articles conceivably referred to by Ray.

Gregorii, Davidis, "*Astronomiae Physicae & Geometriae Elementa*," pp. 452–462.

Corte, Bartholomaei, "*Epistola de tempore, quo Anima rationalis Foetui infundi solet in Utero*," pp. 469–471.

[39] The phenomenon of animals being found whole in stones, generally alive and in some instances edible, was a seemingly common occurrence in the seventeenth and eighteenth centuries. Robert Plot's *Natural History of Oxfordshire* contains notices of many such occurrences. Most commonly, however, they are found in the journals kept during the travels made by worthy gentlemen, and are related most often second hand.

Dr. Richard Richardson, in a letter to Edward Lhwyd dated June 16, 1698, confirms to the Keeper of the Ashmolean Museum that he was "present when a stone was broken by workmen, which lay upon the top of the ground, wherein was contained a toad, in form and colour altogether resembling the common one, though something less, which, being laid upon the ground, crawled about as long as the sun shone warm upon it, but towards night died. I examined the stone, and supposed it at first to be of an extraordinary open texture, or else the hole wherein the toad lay to have some private communication with the air; but upon a more strict inquiry I found the stone of a close grit, but that place especially where she lodged to be of a much harder texture, much of the nature of the iron stone which the workmen call an iron band."

Charles Leigh likewise relates an instance of a toad found living within in his *Natural History of Lancashire* . . . :

. . . Sometimes a living *Toad* has been found in Free-stone Rock, in the like *Cista* or Cavity, which doubtless must be lodg'd there in this following manner: It is to be presum'd that the *Ovum* of some *Toad* was brought thither by a Spring or Vein leading to that Cavity, for Springs are very often discern'd in Free-stone Rocks, ouzing thorow [sic] their Pores; now it cannot be imagin'd that it was lodg'd there ever since the Deluge, which must necessarily follow unless we allow the recited Hypothesis [pp. 119-120].

There were also the instances cited by Misson (of a lobster found alive in marble) and Brand (of cockles cast up by a plough so fresh as to be edible). A multitude of such accounts exist, but we hesitate to introduce more than these few.

Many remarkable virtues were attributed to stones in the seventeenth and eighteenth centuries, not the least of which was the ability to encase an animal in a state which is best described as semi-somnescence. We have consciously avoided introducing discussion of the magical properties attributed to stones, but will take this opportunity to relate one instance of the sort of "natural magick" which surrounded peculiarly formed stones. The story is set down in Johann Eusebio Nieremberg's *Historia Naturae, Maxime Peregrinae, Libris XVI. Distincta . . .* (Antverpiae, 1635), Book II, Chap. 23: "De lapide in insula Mona."

There is here a stone almost shaped like a human thigh, which possesses this wonderful property, that being carried away to any distance, it returns, of itself, the next night: as has been frequently found, by those who reside here. Hence it happened that Count Hugh, having heard of the power which this stone possessed, had it secured, by strong iron chains to another stone, which was much larger than it, and cast at a considerable distance into the sea: but when morning dawned, to the wonder of the multitude, the stone was again found in its former situation. On this account, therefore, it was prohibited, by a public edict of the Count's, that any one should again attempt its removal. But it happened, on a time that a certain countryman, for the sake of making a fair experiment, bound the stone to his thigh—directly the thigh became mortified, and the stone escaped, and returned to its former situation [p. 430].

In the Latin version of Lhwyd's letter to Ray, this paragraph and the next were not separated.

[40] Number 3 of the series was omitted by Lhwyd in the translation. Ray either did not notice the omission, or did not bother to correct it; therefore Ray's number 3 is actually number 4, etc. The omitted paragraph reads: "*Durissima saxa eorum incremento cedere, non est verisimile.*" (It is unlikely that extremely hard rocks would yield to their increase.)

[41] Scheuchzer (*Sciagraphia Lithologia*, p. 64) defines *Plectronitae* as: "*Plectronarii dentes sunt Ichtyodontes teretes, gallinacea plectra quodammodo referentes.*" See Lhwyd, *Lith. Brit.*, Tab. 16, no. 1,318.

[42] While Lhwyd's Latin and MS translation read "Dactyli," Ray's text (evidently changed by himself) reads "Pholades." According to contemporary sources (Scheuchzer, *Sciagraphia Lithologia*) the two were distinct types: *Dactyli* being classified as Belemnites, and *Pholades* being "double-opening conches, such as are never completely closed." See Lhwyd, *Lith. Brit.*, Tab. 10, no. 877–878 (*Pholades*).

[43] ‡Ray has inserted the following note, although none appears in Lhwyd's MS: "Missum est ad me alio ex littore Saxum, in quo nullae rimae, nullae caverae, sed foramina tantum apparebant tam exigua, ut vix aciem admitterent: Eo igitur ictibus multis confracto, cavitates internae multae erant, vario situ & diversae magnitudinis in quibus conchas istas reperi. Rondel. *de Aquatilib.*"

[44] Mr. William Cole was a surveyor to the Customs in Bristol and corresponded with Robert Plot. He built up a considerable collection of "natural bodies" which Lhwyd visited in 1691. The remainder of the paragraph beginning "For we must grant . . ." has been inserted into the translation by Lhwyd.

[45] Advertendum enim, quod sicut vegetabilia non omnis fert omnia Tellus, ita neque omne genus fossilia apta nata sunt ad haec animalium semina recipienda fovenda, etc.

[46] Steno, *Prodromus* [English ed.], p. 87. [Original Edition, 1669, pp. 60–61.]

[47] †*Phil. Trans.* for the month of May 1693.

Lhwyd is probably referring to his paper "Edvardi Luidii apud Oxonienses Cimeliarchae Ashmoleani, ad Clariss. V. D. Christophorum Hemmer, Epistola; in qua agit de lapidibus aliquot perpetua figura donatis, quos nuperis annis in Oxoniensi & Vicinis agris, adinvenit." *Phil. Trans.* XVII (May, 1693), pp. 746–754.]

[48] Quod ad ultimum: agnosco verum esse, naturam nihil frustra moliri; at non minus certum est, nos esse finalium causarum minus idoneos judices.

[49] †Plot, *Hist. Oxon.* p. 85 & *Lith. Brit.* p. 57 & 112.

[50] *Lyncurius* (according to Scheuchzer, *Sciagraphia Lithologica*, p. 55) was the Lynx Stone, and referable to Belemnites. Scheuchzer continues: "Some years ago someone conceived the opinion that the belemnites known as Lyncurii owed their origin to snails, even that they were nothing more than petrified snails. He set forth this opinion with a host of supporting arguments in a letter addressed to me; but since one cannot merely indulge in idle conjecture in so singular a matter, I have simply refrained from taking any stand."

The *Lyncurius* of Lhwyd and Scheuchzer was probably originally applied to amber, rather than to Belemnites. Pliny the Elder mentions the "stone" in his *Natural History*, and the remarkable substance thereby found its way into such well known bestiaries as the *Physiologus* and *Libellus de Natura Animalium.* Pliny relates the following in Book VIII, section 42:

"The water of lynxes, voided in this way when they are born, solidifies or dries up into drops like carbuncles and of a brilliant flame-color, called lynx-water (*lyncurius*)—which is the origin of the common story that this is the way in which amber is formed. The lynxes have learnt this and know it, and they jealously cover up their urine with earth, thereby causing it to solidify more quickly."

Aelian and Solinus (Polyhistor) record similar stories. The process by which the Lyncurius became synonymous with the Belemnites of the seventeenth and eighteenth centuries must remain obscure.

Bibliography

The works cited by Beringer in Chapter I and amplified
in Appendix A, have not been relisted here.

Acta Eruditorum [Including *Nova Acta Eruditorum* and *Supplementia*]. Lipsiae:
J. Grossium et J. F. Gletitschium, 1682–1755.

Adams, Frank Dawson. *The Birth and Development of the Geological Sciences.*
New York: Dover Publications, 1954.

Adelung, Johann Christoph. *Fortsetzung und Ergänzungen zu Christian Gottlieb
Jöchers Allgemeinem Gelehrten-Lerico, worin die Schriftsteller aller Stände
nach ihren vornehmsten Lebensumständen und Schriften Beschrieven werden
. . .* Erster Band, A und B. Leipzig: Johann Friedrich Gleditschens Handlung,
1784.

Aelian, Claudius. *On the Characteristics of Animals* [*De Natura Animalium*].
Translated by A. F. Scholfield. 3 vols. London: William Heinemann Ltd., 1958.

Agassiz, Louis. *Bibliographia Zoologiae et Geologiae.* London: The Ray Society,
1848.

Agricola, Georgius. *De Re Metallica. Translated from the Latin Edition of 1556
. . . by H. C. and L. H. Hoover . . .* New York: Dover Publications, 1950.

Ainsworth, Robert. *Thesaurus Linguae Latinae compendiarius: or, A Compendious
Dictionary of the Latin Tongue: Designed for the Use of the British Nations
. . . the Third Edition, with Additions and Improvements by Samuel Patrick.*
London: C. and J. Ackers, 1751.

Anon. "Literary Impositions." *Littell's Living Age.* Vol. 10 (1846), pp. 181–182.

Baxter, J. H. and Charles Johnson. *Medieval Latin Word List.* London: Humphrey
Milford, 1934.

Beringer, Carl Christoph. *Geschichte der Geologie und des Geologischen Weltbildes.* Stuttgart: Ferdinand Enke Verlag, 1954.

Beringer, Johann Bartholomew Adam. *Connubium Galenico-Hippocraticum, sive
Idaea Institutionum Medicinae Rationalium, Secundum Veterum et Recentiorum
Sententias Compendiose Contractarum, in qua Et prima Rudimenta, et solidiora
Fundamenta totius Medicinae distincte et perspicue ostenduntur . . .* Herbipoli:
Martini Francisci Hertz, 1708.

——. *De Therapia Hippocratis, respondente Jo. Fr. Seiz.* Herbipoli, 1730.

——. *Dissertatio Prima De Peste in genere et Lue Epidemica modo grassante in
specie.* Norimbergae: Joannem Fridericum Rüdigerum, 1714.

——. *Gründlich und Richtigste Untersuchung Deren kissinger Heyl- und
Gesundheits-Brunnen, Welche aus Gnädigster Verordnung Des Hochwürdig-
sten, des Heil . . .* Wirtzburg: Joh. Jacob Christoph Kleyer, 1738.

Boehmers, George Rudolph. *Bibliotheca Scriptorum Historiae Naturalis Oecono-*

BIBLIOGRAPHY
204

miae Aliarumque Artium Ac Scientiarum . . . 9 vols. Lipsiae: Johann Friedrich Junius, 1785–1789.

Brunet, Jacques-Charles. *Manuel du Libraire et De l'Amateur de Livres.* Paris: Librairie de Firmin Didot Frères, 1860.

Buckland, Reverend William. *Reliquiae Diluvianae; or, Observations on the Organic Remains Contained in Caves, Fissures, and Diluvial Gravel, and on other Geological Phenomena, Attesting the Action of an Universal Deluge.* London: John Murray, 1823.

Carus, J. Victor and Wilhelm Engelmann. *Bibliotheca Zoologica* . . . 2 vols. Leipzig: Verlag von Wilhelm Engelmann, 1861.

Cerutus, Benedictus. *Musaeum Franc [-isci]. Calceolari. Ivn. Veronensis a Benedicto Ceruto Medico Incaeptum, et ab Andrea Chiocco* . . . *Luculenter Descriptum, et Perfectum, In quo multa ad naturalem, moralemq. Philosophia Spectantia, non pauca ad rem Medicam pertinentia erudite proponuntur, et explicantur, Non sine magna rerum exoticarum supellectile, quae artifici plane manu in aes incisae, studiosis exhibentur.* Veronae: Angelum Tamum, 1622.

Chastellux, François Jean Marquis de. *Travels in North-America, in the Years 1780–81–82. Translated from the French, by an English Gentleman, who Resided in America at that Period. With Notes by the Translator* . . . New York: [no publisher given], 1828.

Churchill, John. *A Collection of Voyages and Travels, some Now first Printed from the Original Manuscripts. Others Translated out of Foreign Languages, and now first Publish'd in English. To which are added some few that have formerly appear'd in English, but do now for their Excellency and Scarceness deserve to be Re-printed* . . . 4 vols. London: Printed for Awnsham and John Churchill, at the Black Swan in Pater-Noster-Row, 1704.

Cole, F. J. *A History of Comparative Anatomy from Aristotle to the Eighteenth Century.* London: Macmillan and Co. Ltd., 1949.

Cuvier, Georges. *Essay on the Theory of the Earth* . . . New York: Kirk and Mercein, 1818.

Davis, J. I. *Libellus de Natura Animalium. A Fifteenth Century Bestiary, Reproduced in Facsimile.* London: Dawson's of Pall Mall, 1958.

Douglas, Reverend James. *A Dissertation on the Antiquity of the Earth, Read at the Royal Society, 12th May, 1785.* London: Logographic Press, 1785.

E. [sic]. "Die Würzburger Fossilienfälschungen." *Zeitschrift für Angewandte Geologie.* Band 5, Heft 10 (October, 1959), 507–508.

Earl of Crawford. *Bibliotheca Lindesiana: Catalogue of the Printed books Preserved at Haigh Hall, Wigan.* Aberdeen University Press, 1910.

Engelmann, Wilhelm. *Bibliotheca Historico-Naturalis* . . . Leipzig: Verlag von Wilhelm Engelmann, 1846.

Fantuzzi, Giovanni. *Memorie della vita di Ulisse Aldrovandi* . . . *Con alcune Lettere scelte d'Uomini eruditi a lui scritte, e coll'Indice delle sue Opere Mss., che si conservano nella Biblioteca dell'Instituto* . . . Bologna: Lelio dalla Volpe, 1774.

Fennell, James H. *A Natural History of British and Foreign Quadrupeds; Containing Many Modern Discoveries, Original Observations, and Numerous Anecdotes.* London: Joseph Thomas, 1841.

Flower, Sir William Henry. *Essays on Museums and other Subjects Connected with Natural History.* London: Macmillan and Co., Ltd., 1898.

Frati, Lodovico. *Catalogo dei Manoscritti di Ulisse Aldrovandi.* Bologna: Nicola Zanichelli, 1907.

Garboe, Axel. *The Earliest Geological Treatise (1667) by Nicolaus Steno,*

Translated from Canis Carchariae Dissectum Caput. London: Macmillan and Co. Ltd., 1958.

————. "Nicolaus Steno (Niels Stensen) and Erasmus Bartholinus: Two 17th Century Danish Scientists and the Foundation of exact Geology and Crystallography." *Danmarks Geologiske Undersøgelse*. 4th series, vol. 3:9 (1954), 1–48.

Gesner, Johann. *Tractatus Physicus de Petrificatis in duas partes distinctus, quarum Prior agit de Petrificatorum differentiis, et eorum varia origine; Altero vero de Petrificatorum variis originibus, praecipuarumque Telluris mutationum testibus*. Lugduni Batavorum: Theodorum Haak, 1758.

Gimma, D. Giacinto. *Della Storia Naturale delle Gemme, delle Pietre, e di Tutti i Minerali, ovvero della Fisica Sotteranea . . .* 2 vols. Napoli: A Spese dello Stesso Muzio, e di Felice Mosca, 1730.

Grässe, Johann Georg Theodor. *Orbis Latinus . . .* New York: Steiger, 1909.

Grew, Nehemiah. *Musaeum Regalis Societatis. Or a Catalogue and Description of the Natural and Artificial Rarities Belonging to the Royal Society And preserved at Gresham College . . . Whereunto is Subjoyned the Comparative Anatomy of Stomachs and Guts*. London: W. Rawlins, for the Author, 1681.

Gunther, R. T. *Early Science In Oxford, Volume XII: Dr. Plot and the Correspondence of the Philosophical Society of Oxford*. Oxford: Oxford University Press, 1939.

————. *Early Science in Oxford, Volume XIV: Life and Letters of Edward Lhwyd*. Oxford: Oxford University Press, 1945.

Harris, John. *Navigantium atque Itinerantium Bibliotheca, or, A Complete Collection of Voyages and Travels. Consisting of Above Six Hundred of the most Authentic Writers . . .* London: Printed for T. Woodward, S. Birt . . . , 1744–1748.

Hefele, Charles-Joseph. *Histoire des Conciles d'Après les Documents Originaux*. Volume III:2. Paris: Letouzey et Ané, 1910.

Hill, "Sir" John [signing himself Abraham Johnson]. *Lucina sine Concubitu. A Letter Humbly address'd to the Royal Society; In Which Is proved by most Incontestable Evidence, drawn from Reason and Practice, that a Woman may conceive and be brought to Bed without any Commerce with Man*. London: Printed and Sold by M. Cooper, at the Globe, in Pater-Noster-Row, 1750.

————. *A Review of the Works of the Royal Society of London; containing Animadversions on such of the Papers as deserve Particular Observation. In Eight Parts*. London: R. Griffiths, 1751.

————. *Theophrastus's History of Stones. With an English Version, and Critical and Philosophical Notes, Including the Modern History of the Gems, etc. described by that Author, and of many other of the Native Fossils . . .* London: C. Davis, Printer to the Royal Society, 1746.

Hooke, R[obert]. *Micrographia: or Some Physiological Descriptions of Minute Bodies made by Magnifying Glasses. With Observations and Inquiries thereupon*. London: Jo. Martyn and Ja. Allestry, 1665.

Houghton, Walter E. (Jr.) "The English Virtuoso in the 17th Century. (Pts. I and II)." *Journal of the History of Ideas*. vol. III: 1, 2 (1942), pp. 51–73, 190–219.

Jonston, Johannis. *Thaumatographia Naturalis, In Classis decem divisa: in quibus Admiranda Coeli, Elementorum, Meteoroum, Fossilium, Plantarum, Avium, Quadrupedum, Exanguium, Piscium, Hominis*. Amsterdami: Apud Guilielmum Blaev, 1632.

Jugler, Johannes Fridericus. *Bibliotheca Historiae Litterariae Selecta . . .* Jenae: Christiani Henr. Cunonis, 1754.

Kircher, Athanasius, *Oedipus Aegyptiacus. Hoc est Universalis Hieroglyphicae*

Veterum Doctrinae temporum iniuria abolitae Instavratio. Opus ex omni Orientalium doctrina et Sapientia Conditum, nec non viginti diuersarum linguarum Authoritate stabilitum, felicibus . . . Romae: Vitalis Mascardi, 1654.

Kirchner, Heinrich. "Die Würzburger Lügensteine im Lichte neuer Archivalischer Funde." *Zeit. Deutschen Geologischen Gesellschaft.* Vol. 87:9, (November, 1935), 607–615.

———. "Neues über die Beringer 'schen Lügensteine." *Forschungen und Fortschritte.* Jahrg. 12:5, (February 10, 1936), 67–68.

Knight, Charles. *The English Cyclopedia.* 6 vols. London: Bradbury and Evans, 1856.

Knorr, George Wolfgang and Jean Ernest Emanuel Walsch. *Recueil de Monumens des Catastrophes que le Globe de la terre a Éssuiées, contenant des Pétrifications dessinées, Gravées et Enluminées, d'après les originaux.* Nuremberg, 1775–1778.

Langius, Carolus N. *Methodus Nova et Facilis Testacea Marina Plearque, quae huc usque nobis nota sunt, in suas debitas et distinctas Classes, genera, et species distribuendi* . . . Lucernae: Henrici Rennwardi Wyssing, 1722.

Leonard, Camilli. *Speculum Lapidum* . . . *Cui Accessit Sympathia Septem Metallorum ac septem selectorum Lapidum ad Planetas.* Parisiis: Apud Carolum Senestre et Davidem Gilliu, 1610.

Leschevin, Ph. X. "Notice sur l'ouvrage singulier intitulé: *Lithographia Wirceburgensis*, et sur la mystification qui y a donné lieu." *Magasin Encyclopédiqué, ou Journal des Sciences, des Lettres et des Arts* (Paris), (Nov., 1808), 116–128.

Libavius, Andreas. *Singularium pars Tertia Continens Octo Libros Bituminum et Affinium.* Francofurti, 1601.

[Lowe, John Jr.]. *A Treatise on the Solar Creation and Universal Deluge of the Earth; by which is Illustrated many of the most curious Points in Natural Philosophy. By a Native of Manchester.* London: Printed for the Author, no date [seventeenth century].

Lyell, Charles. *Principles of Geology; or, The Modern Changes of the Earth and Its Inhabitants Considered as Illustrative of Geology.* (7th edition.) London: John Murray, 1847.

MacDougall, Curtis D. *Hoaxes.* New York: Dover Publications, 1958.

[Maillet, Benoit de]. *Telliamed ou Entretiens d'un Philosophe Indien avec un Missionaire Francois sur la Diminution de la Mer, la Formation de la Terre, l'origine de l'Homme* . . . Amsterdam [Paris]: L'Honore, 1748.

Marsh, O. C. "History and Methods of Palaeontological Discovery." President's Address, American Association for the Advancement of Science, Saratoga Meeting, August 28, 1879, pp. 1–44.

Martius, Ernst Wilhelm. *Wanderungen durch einen Theil von Franken und Thüringen. In Briefen an einen Freund* . . . Erlangen: Waltherschen Buchhandlung, 1795.

Misson, Maximilian. *A New Voyage to Italy. With Curious Observations on several other Countries* . . . (5th edition). London: Printed for J. and J. Bonwick, 1739.

Morton, John. *The Natural History of Northampton-shire; with Some Account of the Antiquities. To which is Annex'd a Transcription of Doomsday-Book, so far as it relates to That Country.* London: R. Knaplock at the Bishop's-Head, and R. Wilkin at the King's-Head, 1712.

Murray, David. *Museums: Their History and their Use.* 3 vols. Glasgow: James MacLehose and Sons, 1904.

Needham, Joseph and Arthur Hughes. *A History of Embryology*. Cambridge: Cambridge University Press, 1959.

Neuer Zeitungen von Gelehrten Sachen auf das Jahr 1725, October 4, 1725, pp. 774–776.

Neuer Zeitungen von Gelehrten Sachen auf das Jahr 1728, February, pp. 106–111.

Otto, H. "Nochmals zu 'Beringers Lügensteinen.'" *Zeitschrift für Angewandte Geologie*. Band 6, Heft 3 (March, 1960), p. 137.

Padtberg, August. "Die Geschichte einer vielberufenen paläontologischen Fälschung. (Beringers *Lithographia Wirceburgensis*)." *Stimmen der Zeit: Monatschrift für das Geistesleben der Gegenwart*. Band 104 (1923), pp. 32–48.

Palissy, Bernard. *The Admirable Discourses . . . translated by Aurèle La Rocque*. Urbana: University of Illinois Press, 1957.

Parkinson, James. *Organic Remains of a Former World. An Examination of the Mineralized Remains of the Vegetables and Animals of the Antediluvian World; generally termed Extraneous Fossils*. 3 vols. London: Sherwood, Neely and Jones, 1804–1811.

Pauly, Alphonse. *Bibliographie des Sciences Médicales . . .* London: Derek Verschoyle, 1954.

Peyer, Bernard. "Johann Jakob Scheuchzer im Europäischen Geistesleben seiner Zeit." *Gesnerus*. Jahr. I, Heft 2 (1945), 23–45.

————. "Johann Jakob Scheuchzer's *Herbarium Diluvianum*." *Eclogae Geol. Helvetiae*. Vol. 37:2 (1944), 457–459.

Pignorius, Laurentius. *Vetustissimae Tabulae Aeneae Sacris Aegyptiorum Simulachris coelatae Accurata Explicatio, in qua antiquissimarum superstitionum Origines, Progressiones, Ritus ad Barbarum, Graecam, Romanamque Historiam illustrandam enarrantur, et multa Scriptorum veterum loca qua explanantur, qua emendantur . . .* Venetiis: Io. Anto. Rampazettus, 1605.

Pliny, Gaius Secundi. *Natural History*. Translated by H. Rackham. London: William Heinemann Ltd., 1940.

————. *Naturalis Historiae*, ed. Ludovicus Ianus. Lipsiae: B. G. Teubneri, 1865.

P[lot], R[obert]. *The Natural History of Oxford-shire, Being an Essay toward the Natural History of England*. Oxford: Printed at the Theater in Oxford, and are to be had there: And in London at Mr. S. Millers . . . , 1677.

Quirini, Joannis and Jacobi Grandii. [Quirini] *De Testaceis Fossilibus Musaei Septalliani. et* [Grandi] *De Veritate Diluvii Universalis, et Testaceorum, quae procul a Mari reperiuntur Generatione. Epistolae*. Venetiis: Typis Valuasensis, 1671.

Ray, John. *Travels through the Low-Countries, Germany, Italy, France, with curious Observations, Natural, Topographical, Moral, Physiological . . .* London, 1738.

————. *Three Physico-Theological Discourses, Concerning I. The Primitive Chaos, and Creation of the World. II. The General Deluge, its Causes and Effects. III. The Dissolution of the World, and Future Conflagration . . .* (4th edition.) London: William Innys, 1732.

Ritter, Alberti (Albrecht). *Epistolica Historico-Physica Oryctographia Goslariensis . . . Editio Altera priore multo auctior et correctior*. Sondershusae, 1738.

————. *Specimen II. Oryctographiae Calenbergicae sive Rerum Fossilium quae . . . in Ducatu Electorali Brunsvico-Luneburgico Calenberg eruuntur historico-physicae delineationis . . .* Sondershusae, 1743.

Rosinus, Michaele Reinholdus. *Tentaminis de Lithozois ac Lithophytis olim marinis jam vero subterraneis, Prodromus sive, De Stellis Marinis quondam nunc Fossilibus Disquisitio . . .* Hamburgi: Nicolai Sauer, 1719.

Scaligeri, Julii Caesaris. *Exotericarum Exercitationum Liber XV. De Subtilitate, ad Hieronymum Cardanum* . . . Francofurti: Claudii Marnii, 1612.

Scherz, Gustav, ed. *Nicolaus Steno and His Indice.* (Acta Historica Scientiarum Naturalium et Medicinalium. Edidit Bibliotheca Universitatis Hauniensis.) Vol. 15. Copenhagen, 1958.

Sanders, John E. "The Beringer Case." *Geotimes. V* (September, 1960), 28–29.

Scheuchzer, Johann Jacob. *Homo Diluvii Testis et* θεόσωπος *Publicae* συζητήοει *expositus* . . . Tiguri: Joh. Henrici Byrgklini, 1726.

———. *Sciagraphia Lithologica Curiosa, seu Lapidum Figuratorum Nomenclator.* Gedani: Thomas Johannis Schreiberi, 1740.

Schwenckfeld, Caspar. *Stirpium et Fossilium Silesiae Catalogus. In quo praeter etymon natales, tempus; Natura et vires cum varijs experimentis assignantur: Concinnatus* . . . Lipsiae: Impensis Davidis Alberti, 1601 [colophon reads: 1600].

Seguier, Joanne-Francisco. *Bibliotheca Botanica, sive Catalogus Auctorum et Librorum omnium qui de Re Botanica, de Medicamentis ex Vegetabilibus paratis, de Re Rustica,* [and] *de Horticultura tractant . . . Accessit Bibliotheca Botanica Jo. Ant. Bumaldi* . . . Hagae-Comitum: Joannem Neaulme, 1740.

Shepard, Odell. *The Lore of the Unicorn.* Boston and New York: Houghton Mifflin Co., 1930.

Smith, James Edward. *A Selection of the Correspondence of Linnaeus and Other Naturalists, from the Original Manuscripts.* 2 vols. London: Longman, Hurst, Rees, Orme, and Brown, 1821.

———. *Tracts Relating to Natural History.* [Tract II: "Discourse on the Rise and Progress of Natural History."] London: Printed for the Author by J. Davis, 1798.

Smith, Reverend Thomas. *The Naturalist's Cabinet: Containing Interesting Sketches of Animal History; Illustrative of the Natures, Dispositions, Manners, and Habits of all the Most Remarkable Quadrupeds, Birds, Fishes, Amphibia, Reptiles, etc. in the Known World.* 6 vols. London: James Cundee, 1806–1807.

Solinus, Caius Julius. *The Excellent and Pleasant Worke Collectanea Rerum Memorabilium . . . Translatde from the Latin* [1587] *by Arthur Golding.* Gainesville, Florida: Scholars' Facsimiles and Reprints, 1955.

Steno, Nicolaus. *Opera Philosophica.* Edited by Vilhelm Maar, at the Expense of the Carlsbergfond. 2 vols. Copenhagen: Vilhelm Tryde, 1910.

Sticker, Georg. "Die Entwicklung der Medizinischen Fakultät an der Universität Würzburg." *Festschrift zum 46. Deutschen Ärztetag in Würzburg.* Vom. 6. Bis 10. (September, 1927), iii-v, 3–219.

Tomasini, Jacobi Philippi. *De Donariis ac Tabellis Votivis liber Singularis.* Utini: N. Schiratti, 1639.

Thomasius, Gottofredus. *Bibliothecae Thomasianae sive Locupletissimi Thesauri ex Omni Scientia Librorum Praestantissimorum Rarissimorumque* . . . 3 vols. Norimbergae: Apud Wolfg. Schwarzkopfium, 1765–1770.

Topsell, Edward. *The Historie of Foure-Footed Beastes. Describing the true and lively figure of every Beast, with a discourse of their severall Names, Conditions, Kindes, Vertues (both naturall and medicall) Countries of their breed, their love and hate to Mankinde, and the wonderfull worke of God in their Creation, Preservation, and Destruction. Necessary for all Divines and Students, because the story of every Beast is amplified with Narrations out of Scriptures, Fathers, Phylosophers, Physitians, and Poets: Wherein are declared divers Hyeroglyphicks, Emblems, Epigrams, and other good Histories, Collected out of all the volumes of Conradus Gesner, and all the other Writers to this present day.* London: Printed by William Iaggard, 1607.

———. *The Historie of Serpents. Or, The Second Book of living Creatures* . . . London: Printed by William Jaggard, 1608.

Vallisneri, Antonio. *De Corpi Marini, Che su'Monti si Trovano; della loro origine; e dello stato del Mondo avanti L'Diluvio, nel Diluvio, e dopo il Diluvio* . . . Venezia: Domenico Lovisa, 1721.

Waite, Arthur Edward. *The Hermetic and Alchemical Writings of Aureolus Philippus Theophrastus Bombast, of Hohenheim, called Paracelsus the Great* . . . London: James Elliott and Co., 1894.

Warren, Erasmus. *Geologia: or, a Discourse Concerning the Earth before the Deluge. Wherein The Form and Properties ascribed to it, In a book intituled The Theory of the Earth, Are Excepted against: And it is made appear, That the Dissolution of that Earth was not the Cause of the Universal Flood. Also A New Explanation of that Flood is attempted.* London: R. Chiswell, 1690.

Wegele, Franz X. von. *Geschichte der Universität Wirzburg.* 2 vols. Wirzburg: Stahel'sehen Buch- und Kunsthandlung, 1882.

Winter, G. "Lüge und Irrtum: Zur Geschichte wissenschaftlicher Fälschungen." *Kosmos, Hanweiser für Naturfreunde.* 49:6 (June, 1953), 243–247.

Winter, John Garrett. *The Prodromus of Nicolaus Steno's Dissertation concerning a Solid Body Enclosed by Process of Nature within a Solid.* New York: Macmillan Co., 1916.

Wittlin, Alma S. *The Museum: Its History and Its Tasks in Education.* London: Routledge & Kegan Paul Ltd., 1949.

Wotton, William. *Reflections upon Ancient and Modern Learning to which is now added a Defense Thereof, In Answer to the Objections of Sir. W. Temple, and others.* London: Tim. Goodwin, 1705.

Index

Acta Eruditorum, 112, 200; reviews cited, 114, 115, 117, 118, 119, 120, 121, 122, 123, 124

Aelian (c. 170–c. 236), 162, 202

Agricola [Bauer], Georgius (1494–1555), 4, 29, 112–113, 151, 161, 164, 166, 169, 181, 184; quoted, 184
  Ortu et Causis Subterraneorum, De, 29, 113, 169, 184; quoted, 184
  Re Metallica, De, 29, 112–113

Aldrovandus [Aldrovandi], Ulysses (1522–1605), 29, 84, 103, 113, 163, 195; his museum, 163
  Animalibus Insectis, De, 103, 192
  Musaeum Metallicum, 163
  Quadrupedibus Digitatis Viviparis, De, 113
  Simia in Lapide, De, 29, 113

American Museum of Pierre Eugene Du Simitiere, 184

animalculist faction of the preformationist movement, 172, 184, 185, 198. See also aura seminalis

Animalibus Insectis. See Aldrovandus, Ulysses

animals found alive in stone: crayfish, 196; lobster, 145, 200; toad, 180, 199, 200; worm, 196

Antiquissimo Statu Helmstadii, De. See Conring, Hermann

Aquinas, St. Thomas (1225 [?]–1274), 172; quoted, 172
  Summa Theologica, 172

Archaeists, 42

Archaeus, 22, 42, 72, 174, 175, 186

Aristotelian philosophers, 39, 40, 185. See also Peripatetics

Aristotle (384–322 B.C.), 160, 162, 174

Ashmole, Elias (1617–1692), 170

Ashmolean Museum, 170, 172, 193, 199, 200

Assalti, Pietro, 29, 41, 59, 63, 64, 66, 68, 76, 85, 112, 113, 166, 185; quoted, 59, 60, 64, 66, 68
  Notes to Mercati's Metallotheca Vaticana, 29, 63, 76; quoted, 59, 60, 64, 66, 68

Attempt Towards a Natural History of the Fossils of England, An. See Woodward, John

aura seminalis, 2, 22, 40, 41, 45, 56, 58–62, 63, 64, 65, 66, 68, 148, 162, 170, 171, 172, 174, 176, 178, 198, 199; attacked by Beringer, 58–62; defended by Lhwyd, 149–150; difficulties found by Lhwyd, 151; difficulties answered by Lhwyd, 151–153

Avicenna (980 [?]–1037), 162

Baier, Joannes Jacob (1677–1735), 29, 43, 113, 181–182, 187; quoted, 181–182
  Oryctographia Norica, 29, 43, 113, 181–182, 187; quoted, 181–182

Balbinus, Boheslaus [Bohuslai Aloysius] (1621–1688), 29, 114
  Miscellanea Historia Regni Bohemiae, 29, 114

Balthus, Jean François (1667–1743), 183; opponent of Van Dale and Fontenelle, 48
  Response à l'Histoire des Oracles, 48, 183

Basilica Chymica. See Croll, Oswald

Bauhin, Caspar (1560–1624), 167, 181

Bauhin, Joannes (1541–1613), 29, 42, 114, 181
  Historia Novi et Admirabilis Fontis balneique Bollensis, 29, 42, 114, 181